California Street

A Novel
by
NIVEN BUSCH

Simon and Schuster   New York

I

The Waiting Room

"Some generations are close to those that suc-
ceed them; between others the gulf is infinite
and unbridgeable."

—F. SCOTT FITZGERALD

1   "All right, dear," the pretty pinklipped nurse said, "now we'll just slip off our clothes and tumble into bed," and Jessica said, "I presume from your use of the plural, nurse, that you intend slipping out of your clothes too," and the nurse thought that was priceless. She repeated the remark to all the other nurses.

It was a fine sunny morning and beyond the high hospital window the city lay sumptuous on its eleven hills and the traffic flickered over the red bridge and the silver bridge, the gulls circled over the harbor and the salt crystals splintered in the air like bullets. It was a fine sunny morning in the city of San Francisco and they came and got her out of the house she had lived in so long and wheeled her up the ramp, down the corridors and taped the intravenous feeder to her vein and turned the gadget on the door to no visitors. "Are you more comfortable now, Mrs. Saxe?" they asked and she said, "Oh, yes, I am much more comfortable," hating the nurse for no reason at all. And Dr. French came and Dr. Whatshisname, the San Diego man, and the stiff sullen little prod of the needle in her flesh because a little sedation was indicated. "Take me," she said to the shadows standing in

3

the corners of the room, the furies with their secret faces blurred a little now because of the needle, "take me then if that is what you want but get it over with." It would have been so much better in the house than in this alien place, smelling of unknown smells, better in the great sleighbed with the smooth, brown mahogany coil of the footboard carved like benign twin serpents, so much better there in the great house which Gertrude Atherton said looked as if it had been designed by a number of competent architects in violent disagreement. But the release had to be signed first, the pinklipped nurse holding it apologetically, extending the ballpoint pen at the same time. Ridiculous really. Just a hospital rule she had to give them permission to operate, and Jessica wrote her name with a wobbly hand, looking at them with her blazing captive eyes. "I'll tell you one thing," she'd said in the old days, "I'll go to my end with black hair. I can't stand gray, and there's no reason to as long as they manufacture dye." So every other day after the first operation a man came from Mister Louie's and once she'd even had a wax job. She'd gotten to like wax jobs, they were so frivolous, the sweet soothing little torments one suffered for beauty like the throes of love itself. So much better the following week and on the last night of all such a good sleep although not a sleep at all really just an elevator dropping, and The Thing they wheeled in level with the bed and a nurse, not the pinklipped one but a new one, young and strong and soapy with straight serious eyes. She wouldn't fool you, not this one, honesty was her form of kindness. She said, "I'm afraid it's time," and they wheeled Jessica Saxe out into the hall.

2 ANY ATTORNEY worthy of the name had to foresee the long-range consequences of his work—the more so if, in addition to his professional position, he happened to be a personal friend of the client involved. All his life George Dudley had been aware of this tenet of his trade and he had tried to adhere to it. Frequently—and it seemed more and more as he grew older—people came to him requesting some procedure which appealed to them but of which he disapproved, and in such cases he not only refused to do what they wanted but often talked them into adopting quite a different course of action.

He had tried to do this very thing with Jessica Saxe. He had tried and he had failed. Jessica could be a very stubborn person in some

4

ways, just as she was also a very proud and independent person. She had not been able to see his point of view at all.

Dudley regretted his failure with Jessica. He would have liked to use in her behalf the skill he had acquired in a lifetime spent in law practice; he could, he felt, if given the chance, have set up her estate so that the Will would have done for the family after her death what she had always done for it in person while she was alive.

There was, of course, the question of whether his devices would have proved successful. The essence of Jessica's achievement—its true greatness—lay in the fragility of its structure. That kind of fragility made a lawyer's job more difficult, just as it made a banker's job more complicated. To use law or money effectively you had to be dealing with a pattern based on law and money, and the house which Jessica had built depended, for its strength, on neither; it was upheld by the lift of Jessica's spirit and the fire in her slender, desiccated bones. There was a good chance that when she was no longer there to look out for it, the whole affair would fly apart at the touch of the first angry hand.

Dudley hoped this wouldn't happen. Experience told him that the prognosis wasn't good but he hoped for Jessica's sake. Both because he was so deeply fond of her and because, even after she had fallen ill, there might still be an opportunity of reopening the matter of the estate, he called regularly at the California Street house and continued his visits after she was taken to the hospital. He undertook small errands and assumed responsibility for little chores which she would have ordinarily done herself and which she worried about, as sick people will, while she lay in bed. Getting a Revere cream pitcher to Shreve's to have a dent taken out of it. Making a trip to Bekins for a cherrywood desk Jessica had promised Sharon, her youngest daughter, for the house in Burlingame. Trifling jobs like that, assignments for a friend rather than a lawyer, easily falling into the compass of one who was both, trifling only to him, not to Jessica, on whose narrowed horizons, through the empty wastes of the past and present and conjoined night and day along which her mind now moved, they had a greatly exaggerated importance. Also, since there was no one else to do it—it hardly seemed worth while putting them through her husband's office—he handled the household and medical bills and had his secretary prepare checks for Jessica's signature.

Being thus in almost daily touch with her, he was asked to undertake a final, less agreeable piece of work when Jessica's condition suddenly turned critical. What happened was that Sister Dominica, the Sister in charge of the fifth floor at St. Ann's, where Jessica had her room, asked Dr. French as he was on his way to surgery whether the family should be called. Dr. French, stepping into the elevator, merely nodded—or possibly he did not nod. Sister Dominica wasn't sure. From what had developed that morning she, personally, felt that the family should be called, but just in case the doctor hadn't nodded, and what had seemed to be a nod had simply been an unintentional wobble of his head—if, perhaps, he hadn't even heard her question—it would be well to have somebody else take responsibility for making the calls. She thought of Mr. Dudley, whom she had come to know during his visits to the patient, and after looking up his number in the telephone book she called his office and told him what had happened. She did not, of course, make any suggestion about what should be done. The fact that she was making the call, she felt, would be enough. She could leave the next step up to Mr. Dudley. "I wasn't sure from what Doctor said," Sister Dominica stated—it seemed better to suggest a conversation with Dr. French rather than go into the matter of the nodding—"just what he wished me to do. I thought you would know best."

She was pleased when Mr. Dudley indicated that she'd done the right thing in calling him.

"Thank you very much, Sister Dominica," he'd said. "I'm very grateful that you called me. Please let me know immediately, when anything further develops."

3 WHILE SPEAKING to Sister Dominica, Mr. Dudley had, from force of habit, made some notations on his desk pad. From the outset of his career, more than forty years earlier, he had held and practiced the belief that every business conversation, no matter how inconsequential, should leave behind some written record. When he had been engaged in full-time practice, his memorandum pad, by the end of an ordinary day, had been covered with notations in his diminutive but legible hand—names, figures and little notes to himself, many of these to be expanded later by dictation to his secretary, Ann Siegel, or simply copied from the memorandum pad itself for entry in the client files. Lately he had been relegating some of his duties to Milton Klein and Harlon Worthington Devore. Dudley was getting near retirement age—near enough to be talking about it, at least, though he knew that his associates didn't take him very seriously. Still, he had slacked off somewhat, and the memo pad at this early hour in the morning had been as yet bare of other

6

scribblings when, still listening to Sister Dominica's information, he jotted down the names of the three women who, he felt, should be contacted just as soon as Sister had rung off. The memorandum pad itself was a handsome one, having a solid bronze base and a bent brass spindle on which the leaves, as they were filled, could be slipped over and passed to the rear without becoming detached; on each leaf was printed the name of the firm—Dudley, Klein, Devore and Winterhalter—and the current date, in this case November 14, 1949.

Mr. Dudley placed his telephone back in its cradle. He studied the memo pad and then, to the names which he had written there, he appended—as a means of bringing them to mind—three addresses. Thus he had before him the names and addresses of Mr. and Mrs. Anchylus Saxe's three daughters and these he examined again for a second or two, checking his memory about the addresses and wondering whether he had the related telephone numbers in his private book or whether he would have to ask Miss Siegel for them.

> *Mrs. Bradley Iverson   Floribunda Avenue   Burlingame*
> *Baroness Nicholas Alexis Drobny   RFD#1   Sonoma, Calif.*
> *Mrs.   (?)   Harper   ?   ?*

George Dudley took a metal-covered telephone book out of his top right-hand drawer and checked. The Iverson number was there all right, but under the Burlingame address Miss Siegel, who was always efficient in keeping the book up to date, had written *Mark Hopkins Hotel*. He remembered now—some trouble there, or rumored to be: Bradley Iverson, the columnist or commentator or whatever you wanted to call him, living back in Washington, D.C., where he did most of his work, Sharon keeping a suite at the Mark. That would be EXbrook 2-3434.

George Dudley couldn't have said why he'd jotted down Mrs. Iverson's name first. Possibly it had come to mind most easily because, of the three, it was the best known. He wrote the hotel telephone number on his pad, then examined the next name on the short list—the name of the Baroness Drobny. Odd how all three of the girls, though born and raised as San Franciscans, now lived outside the city limits—Alexandra Drobny actually in the country, where she had a ranch. Since the call to her would have to go through the long-distance operator, little or no delay would be entailed in simply asking for the ranch without waiting to find out the number in advance. That left only Pamela to check off.

Mr. Dudley buzzed Miss Siegel. "Ann, see if we have a number for Mrs. Harper. Pamela Saxe Harper? I never can remember the name of that chap she's married to, Kingsford or Coleman or something. Or that place they live in. I believe it's one of those GI developments, out in the sticks somewhere."

"We have the number, Mr. Dudley," Miss Siegel said.

They had, of course, all numbers. Miss Siegel saw to that. Either in Mr. Dudley's private book or in the larger extended index in her own desk they had all the numbers of the people with whom Dudley, Klein, Devore and Winterhalter did business in any fashion, and some with whom they had long ceased to do business. Even as she spoke, her fleshy, rather attractively shaped hand, the nails of which were enameled in a color called Orchard Orange, had the index open and was moving through the *h*'s. Dudley, however, had left the intercom.

He gave himself an outside line and placed the long-distance call to Sonoma. It was, he realized, inevitable to call Alexandra first, even though he had written her name in second position. Alexandra had the sort of personality that made you pay attention to her first, in any situation, whether you liked her or not. Dudley was not—had never been—sure that he liked Alexandra; in fact, he was rather inclined to think he didn't like her. As a little girl she had been too sharp and self-interested and as a young woman too arrogant and beautiful for anyone to get along with her very easily. Dudley had had his own rather memorable set-to with her; he felt a chill even now as he recalled the day she had come into the office, with Sharon in tow, and demanded that he, George Dudley, should forthwith supply a legal breakdown on the status of the adopted daughter, Pamela, in the Saxe family.

That had been a day, all right. It had opened his eyes to the truth of some of the things people were saying even then about the younger generation. It must have been in 1933 since Alexandra and Pamela also, by a unique arrangement, made a joint debut in 1934—the former's visit to his office having taken place almost a year before the famous party that had brought them out.

A long time ago. Anyway, rightly or wrongly, he'd told Alexandra what she wanted to know. He had even let her read the law on it. Looking back on that occasion, he didn't see what else he could have done but he remembered there had been the devil of a stink about it. Hiram Galt had him on the carpet as if he'd been an apprentice fresh out of law school instead of a partner with a partner's rights

8

and privileges; Hiram had been terrified that if Anchylus ever found out, the firm—Galt, Winterhalter & Dudley, as it was known then, Harry Winterhalter still being alive and his son, young Harry, the present partner, not yet out of boarding school—would lose not only the family trust estate but the right to represent the San Francisco Day Publishing Company, a California corporation, and *The San Francisco Day*, a newspaper. None of these eventualities had come to pass and the whole thing was water under the bridge now; still, it had been the sort of incident that one did not forget.

Buzz—buzz-buzz-buzz. In terms of farm-line telephone code George Dudley, having himself lived in the country, could tell that the operator was ringing one-three; he made a notation of this number opposite Alexandra Drobny's name, wondering as he did so how many phones were on that line. If it was controlled by the Bell system, probably not more than six; if it was one of those community companies, then God only knew. He was quite sure he'd heard at least one receiver lifted; whatever he said to Alexandra would be all over the neighborhood in an hour or less. He rather doubted whether Alexandra minded. She must, he thought, have developed through the years a reasonable indifference to gossip of all kinds, she herself having been the source of so much of it. Why, only a few weeks ago he had seen something about her in Letty Meeker's column; he tried without success to remember what it had been; something intimate and, as was so often the case with regard to news about Alexandra, rather scandalous. Dudley was sorry it had slipped his mind. There was nothing scandalous of course about his present call, nor could information concerning an imminent death in the family be termed as secret; however, with a lawyer's sharpened sense of discretion he would have felt better if he hadn't had to discuss this or any other personal matter on a rural party line.

"Hello."

The voice was pitched so low that for a minute he wasn't sure whether it was a man's or a woman's.

"May I speak to the Baroness Drobny?"

"This is she."

"Hello, Alexandra. This is George Dudley."

"Why, hello, George," the voice replied. "How are you?"

"I'm very well, thanks. But I'm afraid I'm not the bearer of very good news."

"Oh?" The husky voice changed its tone though not its pitch. "You mean Mother is—"

9

"No," George Dudley said quickly. "She's—well, they haven't lost hope. But there has been a crisis and a consultation. The doctors felt a second operation was necessary immediately."

"Oh, my God."

"She went to surgery a few minutes ago. The hospital called me. I felt you should know."

There was a momentary silence in which he could hear, at Alexandra's end, nothing at all.

"I'll come right down," Alexandra said. "She's still at St. Ann's, of course."

"Yes."

"I'll leave now," Alexandra said. "I'll be driving. It will take me at least an hour and forty-five minutes to get there."

"I believe that, even if the worst happens, you will be in time. I'm terribly sorry about this."

"I'll leave right away," Alexandra repeated. She had already, George Dudley could tell, started in her mind the long, pressured trip which could terminate only beside a deathbed.

"Have they really any hope at all?"

"I believe that's contingent entirely on the operation. I'm afraid there's nothing more that I can say."

"I understand. And I know how you feel too. I will have to hurry now. Thank you for calling, George."

"Goodbye, Alexandra."

"Goodbye, George."

4 GEORGE DUDLEY broke off the connection. Keeping his outside line, he dialed the number of the Mark Hopkins.

"Is Mrs. Bradley Iverson registered?"

There was still in his mind the possibility that Miss Siegel's notation in the book might have been outdated.

"Yes, sir. Do you wish me to ring her suite?"

"Yes, please."

The next voice, answering even before it seemed possible that a ring could have been given, was obviously a maid's; it had just the proper maid's tone although fogged a little with a European accent. French, probably.

"May I speak to Mrs. Iverson?"

"Mrs. Ivairson is not here, sir."

"Do you know where she is?"

"She went to the hospital, sir."

"You're sure she went to the hospital?" Dudley asked, surprised. If this were truly where Sharon had gone she did not, certainly, need further notification; he merely wondered how she had received the news. He doubted whether Sister Dominica would have telephoned her before speaking to him, and there would have been little point in her doing so afterward. Could Hugo French have called her? From what Sister had said he would not have had time to.

"She say she is going there, sir."

"I see. Well, if she comes in, or you hear from her, and she has *not* been there, will you please tell her to call Mr. George Dudley at his office?"

"Yes, sir. What is the number, please?"

George Dudley gave the number and rang off. Still wondering how Sharon had heard of the medical crisis, he picked up the slip of paper which, while he spoke to the maid, Miss Siegel had laid at his elbow. It was a leaf from a scratch pad on which was written:

Pamela Saxe (Mrs. Clifford) Harper
65 La Canada Drive, Cypress Gardens   CY 7-2333

5   A CHILD'S VOICE answered the second ring—a voice supplemented by the screech caused in a two-piece instrument when the receiver is held too close to the mouthpiece.

"Hello."

"Hello," Dudley said firmly. He repeated the salutation twice, hoping some older person would answer, but this maneuver bore no results.

"Is your mother there, dear?" George Dudley said.

"Yes," the voice said. Since this statement seemed all that was required at the moment, a silence ensued while the owner of the voice awaited further developments.

Just as he had experienced trouble in remembering the name of Pamela's husband, Dudley never could quite recall the names of her children, although, in connection with his work, he had probably encountered them at one time or another. Under the circumstances, as a form of address, it seemed safer to stick to *dear*.

"Could I speak to her, please, dear?"

"Yes," the voice said. Evidently the mouth of the person speaking was not removed from actual contact with the mouthpiece; a wild mixture of sounds, issuing from a sizable area, now entered the wire: a baby screaming, a household appliance of some sort chunking, and a radio playing.

"Mummy," the voice said, pitting itself effortlessly against the racket, "it's for you." Then into the telephone, "Hold your horses, she's coming."

"Thank you," George Dudley said. There was a giggle, then a thud as the receiver was put down. Dudley held his own instrument a safe distance from his ear as the broadcast of the American household noises continued (now amplified, unless he was becoming confused, by the yelps of a puppy). He could not help remembering the days when, if you called the Anchylus Saxe residence, the upstairs maid answered in the mornings, the second man (downstairs) in the afternoons, whichever it was immediately and politely transferring the call to the member of the family being called or, if this person were not available, to the butler, Temple, who took messages in his office next to the pantry, writing them down with a gold pencil.

"I'm so sorry," Pamela said at length. "All hell seems to be breaking loose here."

She sounded so unruffled that Dudley had a moment of regret for the upsetting information he was forced to give her. He heard her take in her breath sharply.

"—at St. Ann's," she repeated. "I'll go up there as soon as I can. I'll have to get a sitter first."

The last sentence appeared to Dudley, at that moment, a fantastic understatement. The baby's howls had changed in character; they now had a subhuman intensity, punctuated with silences which seemed to be due to some type of strangulation, possibly self-inflicted.

"Excuse me," Pamela said. "Margot, go see what happened."

"He fell off his toytoy."

"Well, *see if he's hurt.*"

"I shall be in touch with Dr. French later," Dudley said. "I'd suggest that if it's inconvenient for you to leave home at the moment I could telephone you again when more is known—"

"Oh, could you? I mean, it wouldn't . . . be too late?"

The change in personality from the harried suburban mother and housewife to the deeply agitated, almost agonized human being, somehow coming over the wire, brought Pamela quite vividly before George Dudley's eyes. A lonely sort of person, he had always thought her. Lonely and somehow appealing. When she had been younger he had guessed, from the direction in which her life had headed, that

12

she would turn out to be an old maid. On which score she had certainly fooled him and anyone else—and he happened to know that there had been several—holding a similar opinion. In some ways it seemed agreeable that she was the only one of the three who had made a solid marriage, this also a rather odd fact when you came to think about it—Pamela's marriage having once been considered so unfortunate, such a comedown. George Dudley felt sorry that he'd never met her husband; he felt almost as if he should apologize to her for his inability, a few minutes earlier, even to remember his name. Fellow who'd been in the Marine Corps, he recalled now, and had some sort of house-moving or trucking business in the suburbs. Dudley had wondered about the husband and even, to a limited extent, his own bachelor instincts to the contrary, envied him, having run into Pamela several times during her mother's illness, once standing to chat with her for several minutes in the big stone forecourt of the California Street house. She had turned out, he'd noticed, to be a rather good-looking woman. The lonely quality was still there, the habit of stiffening, as if out of shyness, before she spoke, and of wrapping herself in a kind of protective shell. But if she lacked the high styling which made her two sisters in their respective ways so striking, she seemed—though actually somewhat older—younger than either of them, and stronger, as if the children she had borne and the work she had done (she had, he recalled, left home to be a nurse or secretary or something) had added to her stature and resources rather than draining them away, as happened with so many women. Even in purely physical terms she had confronted him with an impression of young, warm sexuality brought out in curves which Dudley had noted in the course of their chat, short as it was—noted, actually, with an old man's appreciation of a good-looking woman which was none the less, and perhaps more, exacting now that, as he told his friends with a small gleeful chuckle which seemed hopefully to suggest otherwise, all he could do was look. Pamela Saxe Harper also had a quality which Dudley felt to be unusual in the young women he met these days; she looked, not smug but content, and her contentment (dull as that might be to some) was expressed in her friendly way of looking out of her gray eyes and in something relaxed and ready to laugh or smile in the set of her soft, full mouth. She had driven in, from wherever it was she lived, in a three-year-old Chevy station wagon in which, as they stood talking beside it, Dudley had noticed a clutter of household objects, including the sort of small canvas chair in which, by clipping them onto the seats of automobiles, babies can be transported.

13

"I can't tell you that," Dudley said, "but I think we've grounds for hoping it won't be."

He felt compelled to comfort her and groped, rather to his own surprise, for a means of doing so.

"Sometimes the words of great writers help us. 'For the heart's deepest feelings no words are.' I've said those words to myself many times."

"They are beautiful words."

"I think I realize your feeling. That was why I quoted them."

"Thank you, Mr. Dudley. Margot, please be quiet. And thank you for calling. If I'm not here when you call again, you'll understand that I'm on my way to the hospital."

"Yes, of course. And I am sincerely sorry to be the bearer of such sad news. I hope the next word we have will be better."

"I hope so, Mr. Dudley. And thank you for calling."

"Goodbye, Mrs. Harper."

"Goodbye, Mr. Dudley."

6 GEORGE DUDLEY rested for a moment. There was always a certain amount of strain in having to announce to anyone a situation which would affect that person emotionally. By making the announcement you shared the emotional tax; however, he was gratified to feel that on the whole the conversation had gone very well. He sat quietly at his desk for several minutes, thinking about Pamela and smoking a cigarette. Dr. Hugo French, who was his physician as well as Jessica's, allowed him five cigarettes a day, but he felt that under the circumstances he could indulge in an extra one. He seldom exceeded his allowance in this or in the rigidly limited amounts of daily exercise and alcohol to which Hugo restricted him. Not that he had ever been addicted to excesses in any form. Far from it. However, at his age even a very small indulgence immediately forced the recognition that it must be classified as an excess.

Dudley did not think he was afraid of death. He had never examined himself deeply on this subject, the fear of the time when he would stop being Mr. George Dudley, attorney at law, and be nothing, but he knew very definitely that he wanted to live as long as he could. He enjoyed life. There was no reason, he had found, why you could not enjoy it as much at sixty-eight as at any other age. Your taste in what was enjoyable changed through the years only as your capacities for enjoyment changed. He did not grieve, for instance, because he now needed to take a rest after lunch, with his feet up, or because he no longer felt the impulse to drink a bottle of Pinot Noir, as had once been his habit, with his dinner. Five cigarettes a day and one cocktail, the continued practice of his profession, and two or at the most three games of bridge a week with players of his own level of proficiency (carefully chosen, also, because he found their personalities agreeable) could constitute an enjoyable life.

It was all a matter of your point of view.

Dudley had never—except once, with one particular person—visualized marriage as a desirable state or one for which he was particularly suited. At his death he would leave no issue, and this, possibly, was regrettable in one sense, since it meant that an important experience had been denied him—the experience of begetting offspring. However, in another sense, this deprivation might not be as regrettable as those persons seemed to feel who had gone whole hog the other way. In place of a wife, he had substituted the companionship of a number of agreeable women: the fact that later they had all gone on to other destinies neither impaired his memory of the pleasure they had given him nor inspired the wish that such pleasures should have been continued indefinitely—it was not conceivable that they could have been. In place of children he had his work, a good deal of which was occupied in drawing documents protecting clients against the mistakes they had made by becoming parents. He felt solaced. The only woman he had ever seriously thought of marrying had been Jessica Saxe (then Jessica Rupke), and judging by the stresses which her marriage had involved—and which her death, if that were imminent, by no means promised to remove—he knew he could account himself well off.

George Dudley put out his cigarette. Still looking back over the years of his life, arranged in serried rows, uniform and dusted and orderly, he rubbed the top of his head, where he had a bald spot. He performed this action several times each hour, in moments of reflection, and it always afforded him a measure of reassurance. His head was more round than elliptical and, except for the bald spot, covered with coarse white hair so thick and short that it made him look as if he were wearing a small woolly cap. Rising now, he covered both hair cap and bald spot with a black Homburg which he took from a coat tree in the corner of his office. Though it was at least an hour too early even to think about lunch, he had decided to go to his club and read the papers until the time when he could decently order a cocktail. This was a Saturday and on Saturdays he lunched

15

early and had a martini, sometimes a double martini, before lunch instead of saving it to have before his dinner. After lunch on Saturdays he liked to play three rubbers of bridge, no more and no less, with three old friends, all of them about his age—Bunny Folsom, one of the first Stanford men to make Walter Camp's All-American Football Team, Jackson Pugh, a retired Federal Court judge, and Hans Munzer, like himself the senior partner in a law firm.

Bridge in the afternoon had an adventurous and even rakish flavor about it which made it more enjoyable than evening bridge. Dudley realized that if he had been younger, it would not have looked well to be seen playing bridge in the afternoon, but at his age nobody cared, and he, in his own right, felt entitled to the relaxation. He felt especially entitled to it today, after his trying morning. He would definitely have a martini, and it would be a double with a stick of lemon peel in it instead of the damn big olive the club bartender liked to put in, the kind of olive that sank straight to the bottom of the glass and used up a quarter of an ounce of liquor space. The martini and the bridge would keep his mind off what he did not want to think about, namely, the operating table where, under a bonfire of lights, the doctors would be operating on Jessica Saxe.

"I'll be at the Pacific Union, Ann," he said as he passed his secretary's desk. He added, although he knew the admonition was unnecessary, "Call me at once if there is any word from the hospital."

"Yes, Mr. Dudley," Miss Siegel said. "Oh, Mr. Dudley—"

"Yes?"

"Did you by any chance notify Mr. Saxe?"

Mr. Dudley looked at her rather stupidly. His mind had been so occupied with the daughters that it had not occurred to him to make the call which, beyond doubt, he should have begun with— the call to Anchylus Saxe himself. Perhaps because Anchylus was located at the nerve center from which most news emanated you presumed, in most situations, that he didn't need to be told. The present situation was obviously different. When Sister Dominica had spoken of notifying the family, she had meant everyone, not just the girls.

"Why, no. I didn't, Ann."

Mr. Dudley's expression reflected recognition of his oversight. "Shall I get him for you?"

"Yes . . . that is, well, no." George Dudley felt that he had had enough for one morning. He had prepared himself inwardly for the healing beneficence of the martini rather than the explosive irritability of a man who, like an emperor who strikes down the battlefield messenger bringing news of defeat, had been known to take the incidence of even the slightest misfortune as a personal, calculated insult.

"Why don't you just call his office, Ann—speak to Miss Wilke and ask her to tell him, if he doesn't know already? And thank you for reminding me."

"Yes, sir," Miss Siegel said.

Waiting for the elevator, George Dudley realized why the idea of calling Anchylus had eluded him. Actually it had crossed his mind during the conversation with Sister Dominica—a good thing that Ann had been listening on the extension, a habit she had when the call had come in from someone she didn't know—but he had not made a note of his intention on his pad just so that, guided by the platitudes of the defunct Hiram Galt, he would not *have* to remember this part of his duty. Smothering to the best of his ability the jealousy of an unsuccessful suitor for the man who has beaten him out, he had served Anchylus' interests for many years and he would, he knew, continue to serve them; yet if he had any dissatisfaction about the manner in which Jessica's Trust Estate had been set up, that dissatisfaction was offset to some extent by the knowledge that if the conflicts which he sensed in the family broke out into open warfare the sufferer would not be Jessica herself or even the girls but none other than Anchylus himself. No, let them praise his accomplishments—and you couldn't gainsay some of them —let them say he was a goer (and he was), there was one thing George Dudley had always felt about Anchylus Saxe and still felt about him: he should have worn leather breeches. A man like that might have been all right back in the forty-niner days, there might have been a place for him then; but when you added him up in terms of the modern city, there was just one conclusion you could come to: a man like that didn't belong in San Francisco.

7 MATT BRODY, Managing Editor of *The San Francisco Day*, sat at his desk, his feet braced on an iron bar beneath it. He sat watching the clock and waiting for the News Editor, Pete Zorach, to finish *The Chronicle* crossword puzzle so that they could go out and have coffee together. It was a source of minor but daily

irritation to him that Pete always did the crossword puzzle in *The Chronicle* in view of the fact that *The Day* also published a crossword puzzle, generally at the bottom of the children's page. Once or twice he had asked Pete about this and Pete's answer had been that the children's page was just where *The Day's* crossword puzzle belonged. Pete held the opinion that the readers of *The Day* were on a lower level intellectually than the readers of the other San Francisco morning newspapers, which was why they had to have kiddy-level crossword puzzles.

"They're the kind," Pete said, "who buy sexology mags and compete in circulation premium contests. Gum-chewers! That's what we called them in New York."

Matt Brody did not share this opinion. In Matt's opinion *The San Francisco Day* was the best newspaper in San Francisco and one of the best in the world. He was conscious of its importance and as Managing Editor he gave the news that passed under his scrutiny a city slant as opposed to a California or even a United States slant. He had also, in part unconsciously, altered his personality to go with his job. He wanted to be truly, although not conspicuously, representative of *The Day* in his manner of dressing, walking and talking and in the organizations to which he belonged. Just as he had constructed in his mind a concept, different from everyone else's, of what *The Day* was, so he had also created a picture of what a *Day* man, socially and professionally speaking, ought to be. A *Day* man was a middle-of-the-roader. He was intelligent, but intelligent without the consciously intellectual slanting that had characterized *PM* or, earlier, the *New York World*. He belonged to his own era and his own city and he had freed himself of the piratical past. Under its founders, Jacob Rupke and his son, Fabian, and later under Anchylus Saxe, *The Day* had been the first newspaper on the Pacific Coast to print sports stories and cartoons on the front page and to give full quotation to the question-and-answer testimony in murder trials and divorce cases. Competition of the period, possibly, has justified such expedients; Matt Brody wanted no part of them. In its present styling the paper adhered to a line between the rather literary, highly streamlined *Chronicle* and the hard-boiled, professional *Examiner*—and your true *Day* man walked the same line socially: he neither set styles nor rebelled against them; he did not try to join exclusive clubs or desire to be seen at first nights—other than opera first nights, where he could be seen because the boss had a box; his political allegiance didn't have to be, as the paper's was, Republican, but neither should it be too deeply committed. It

18

was a good idea not to accept membership in national fraternal organizations, which might pressure you to sponsor their pet projects, or in veterans' organizations, even if you happened to be a veteran of some war.

You had a place to fill and a duty to perform. Both place and duty were well defined. If your employer had turned out to be a ferocious individualist, that was all the more reason, as Matt Brody saw it, why you, as a *Day* person, should not be; it was high time, he also felt, that the principle of the company-directed, collectivistic man, long the norm in other businesses, should be accepted in the newspaper field. Thus, if anyone accused you of conforming, you didn't hit him on the chin; you accepted his statement as a compliment. What he was saying, in effect, was that you were a useful member of your culture and a successful practitioner of your trade.

There had been only one period in his life—a period which he now looked back upon with some embarrassment—when Matt Brody had exposed himself to norm-departure. Starting out as a cub in the late twenties, he had cultivated the conversational style, and some of the other crudities, of the character of Hildy Johnson in the play *Front Page*, which he had seen in a road-company production in 1931. Even then it could not be said with much truth that he had been a social rebel—or, if it could, then only with the quickly added footnote that his chosen form of rebellion, like his later conformity, had worn the hallmark of popular acceptance. Half the men who started in the newspaper business when he did made up like *Front Page* characters if by that you mean wearing beat-up clothes, with your tie pulled around to one side, knotted below the place where your shirt buttoned, also shaving only occasionally, seldom getting a shoeshine, mumbling when you talked, cussing in front of women, not caring how you lived but caring a hell of a lot, though you never admitted how much, about the paper and the people on it, carrying loyalty to them and it deep in your bones.

"It wasn't necessarily an affectation," Matt said, discussing this with Pete Zorach during one of their morning coffee sessions. "Most of us follow a tradition-type during our formative years. That's how we find a style. We may drop it later for some other style, but it helps at the time. It gets us over the rough places."

Whatever elements of personality Matt had borrowed from fictional people had rubbed off, all except his habit of talking out of the side of his mouth in a rapid, low, uneven voice the way Hildy Johnson had talked in the play. In the city room Matt was known as The Mumbler. He was aware of this and rather liked it. In the newspaper business any nickname, flattering or not, is a kind of knighthood, and Matt, like all true conformists, had enough frustrated yearning for recognition to make him enjoy knighthood.

He dropped his feet off the metal brace and stared out over the long, cluttered room. Gray, cloud-filtered sunlight from the tall windows churned around in the whitish metal pour from the neons which—not recently but nevertheless more recently than in any other San Francisco newspaper—had replaced hanging single-cord reflector bulbs as a means of illumination. The mixture of lights, hopefully contending with the basic dimness of the walls and the linoleum-covered floor and the ceiling of time-dark unknown coloring, gave the people in the room the grayness and authority of figures in a steel engraving.

In front of Matt and slightly to his left, presented in a rear view, were the sloping shoulders and brown bullethead of Delph Hensom, the City Editor. Delph was flanked by two assistants—Johnny Varney, a rat-nosed little fellow, not long out of Stanford but fantastically brilliant and forever on the prod, and Alex Whicher, a stolid, red, bald man who had been assistant to a couple of other city editors and would someday, if his blood pressure didn't prevent, be assistant to Johnny. Facing Delph—a solid rectangle—were the desks of the Cityside reporters and across from these, divided from them by an aisle, the news writers on general assignment working under Pete. Neither on the Newsside nor on the Cityside were the desks occupied during any given hour, even the busiest, nor were there on *The Day*'s payroll enough writers to occupy them. *The Day* was somewhat understaffed at the moment since, due to reasons familiar to the Board of Directors but not publicized by them, it was currently undergoing an economy wave.

Matt knew the reasons. He knew them not only because he had daily opportunity to observe them, firsthand, but also because he himself happened to be a member of the Board—its youngest, as a matter of fact. He had been urged, and urged in terms which brooked no contradiction, to buy the stock which made him eligible (ten shares), then personally placed on the Board by Anchylus Saxe himself, nor did his position thereon, however modestly he carried it off, seem less important to him for his realization that it was a strategy in the old man's war against his minority stockholders.

"Why, that's an impudent lie!" Mr. Saxe had said when challenged by a stockholder who had declared that Mr. Saxe ran the paper, as he did the Board, to suit his own whims. "Even my editors are directors of this outfit. Yes, by God, the men who get out *The Day* with their hands, like Brody here, sit on this Board and tell us what to do."

Actually, neither the economies effected so far nor the motives which had impelled them had been too drastic. Many papers had suffered drops in circulation, and consequently in advertising volume, when the war ended. It was not a permanent situation. *The Day* was basically rich; stockholders could complain as they liked about the dividend rate, they still enjoyed the protection of a solid cash surplus. No business nervous system was as jittery as a newspaper's: all you had to do was let out a few people—no matter how incompetent, alcoholic or unpleasant (or all three) the severed ones had happened to be—and nobody felt secure any more. Every day Pete Zorach, to give an example, pestered him with importunities about the company's condition, and so forth, who was going to be axed—Pete, the worrier, whose job was as solid as the Ferry Building. He'd probably start the same line this morning, if he ever got through his stinking puzzle.

Matt Brody snorted. Although separated by only a few yards, he and Pete were out of earshot except at very quiet times or if you wanted to shout. Matt Brody decided that he did.

"Pete," he yelled, "if we don't leave now, we won't have time."

Pete Zorach pushed up his right hand in the manner of an umpire throwing a runner out. He brushed the puzzle page into a desk drawer, then leaned forward and hoisted himself to his feet: he gave you the feeling that he was afflicted with some vicious ailment which made all his movement agony—an agony to which now injustice was added since he had been engaged in a rewarding occupation and should not have been disturbed. He stood tall in the gray light looking down at Matt with the weary and betrayed dignity habitual to him, his eyes clear and friendly above their hypochondriacal circles.

"Let's go," he said.

Matt took his coat off the hook behind his head and the two walked out into the hall. There was no use ringing for the elevator. At this hour it was full both ways, up and down, hauling back the first shift of Circulation girls from their own coffee break and hauling down the second shift for theirs. The operator, Harry Black, seeing the two editors waiting, would close his doors and make a special trip to get them.

"Do you know what I saw them doing yesterday," Pete Zorach said as they waited, "on the fourth floor? Putting in a machine. An automatic vending machine for coffee. What are we coming to?"

"I heard about that," Matt said.

"Three spouts it had, mind you," Pete said, "with writing over each one. Cream and sugar. Sugar only. Black. I'm planning to switch to tea and make it on a burner on my desk."

"It's just part of the economy kick. It doesn't mean anything," Matt said.

Pete took a large yellow pill out of his pocket and swallowed it, his Adam's apple swelling up enormously in his long, thin neck. Matt stared at him uncertainly. He half expected to see the pill, in the form of a descending bulge, wiggle downward toward Pete's stomach as is the case with pythons when, in the movies, they are given a rabbit to eat.

"Sure," he said when he was able to speak again, "I know. Only, are you talking now as a pal or as a Board member of a company that puts in coffee vending machines?"

"I'm talking for your own benefit, Pete, and I'm telling you the truth. Quit fretting."

Pete Zorach wasn't paying attention. "Another thing," he said. "What about taking the paper towels out of the john? God, I remember when they had real linen ones. How do you like that gadget that belches hot air on your hands to dry them?"

"You scare too easy, Pete," Matt Brody said. "I don't know just exactly what the Old Party is up to, but you know as well as I do that these gadgets won't save him eleven cents. Confidentially, we passed a motion, the Board did, at least, to hire an industrial management team; these toys are part of the team's recommendation. Ditto a few possible payroll cuts. If you ask me, the whole program is window dressing for the annual stockholders' meeting. Once that's over we'll bounce right back to normal."

Pete Zorach seemed slightly heartened. "I never thought of that," he said.

"Well, start thinking about it," Matt Brody said, "and pass the word down the line; there's nothing to worry about."

"When is the stockholders' meeting?"

"Next Friday," Matt said. "That's almost a week away. Why don't you buy some stock so you can be there? Then you'll get the whole poop."

"What, invest my money in this filthy sheet?" Pete said with horror. "Not me, boy. This year I'm going in for blue-chip investments only, like classic automobiles. There's a nineteen twenty-seven Buick down in Pebble Beach I'd give my eyeteeth for. If you say everything is all right, I think I'll go down there Sunday and buy it."

"Good idea," Matt said. "You know, Pete, we've had you cast all wrong around here. You should be writing the financial page."

Pete Zorach took this gibe in stride. "I could do it, and do a damn sight better job than the phonies they've got back there now."

Harry Black had brought the elevator back for them. He was smiling through the glass panel as he opened the door. Matt motioned Pete to precede him and then pulled him back; the executive call bell had just tolled out Matt's call, a washed-out, genteel sound like the door jangler of a country store. The call-bell system was another item of *The Day*'s equipment which the managerial experts had tried to get rid of, but Dan Winkler, the production manager, had argued to keep. A loud-speaker system, he'd insisted, might be more efficient, but it would not be in the tradition of *The Day*.

The editorial receptionist, who had picked up the call, leaned across her desk to hand Matt the telephone.

"Brody speaking."

"Oh, Mr. Brody. I'm so glad I caught you." The speaker didn't have to identify herself. It was Miss Wilke, senior secretary in Mr. Saxe's office.

"Yes, Angela."

"Mr. Saxe was wondering if you could ride uptown with him."

"Sure. When?"

"Immediately."

"I'll be right up."

"Oh, no, Mr. Brody," Miss Wilke said. "Mr. Saxe has already gone down to the car. He'll be waiting for you on the Sixth Street side."

"Okay, I'll go down then."

"Thank you, Mr. Brody," Miss Wilke said.

Matt hung up. He handed the phone back to the receptionist and turned to Pete. "I've got to go someplace with the Old Party."

The elevator was waiting again, the operator holding it for them this time. As they got in, Pete pulled a strip of wire copy out of his pocket. "Then you better tell me what to do about this."

It had been wordlessly understood between them, after Matt's last statement, that Zorach would handle the editorial meeting at eleven o'clock.

Matt looked at the copy. It was Bradley Iverson's daily column— a syndicated piece which came in with the last of the Overnight. Pete had marked a paragraph stating—as an Iverson exclusive—that one of J. Robert Oppenheimer's men had asked to be strapped to the A bomb, the first time it was dropped on human beings, as a penalty for having participated in making it.

"I thought," Pete said, explaining why he'd pulled the copy to discuss at coffee break, "the Old Party might like it. He likes anything that's anti-administration. Don't forget—the Demos dropped the bomb, a cruel and unnecessary act."

Matt Brody frowned at the flimsy and handed it back. They got out of the elevator.

"Maybe so, maybe so," he said.

"You don't want to do anything with it?"

Matt shrugged. "Try to get a confirmation or a denial out of Oppenheimer. And the name of the guy that wanted to be strapped on. If you get any part of that, we could run a box or a Section Two lead with a picture of Oppenheimer. That's about all it's worth."

"It would be worth more than that," Pete Zorach said sourly, "if it weren't an Iverson exclusive."

He knew that Matt Brody disliked Brad Iverson and his column if only on the ground (or at least so Pete's thinking went) that Brad had married Sharon Saxe. Matt had known the Saxe girls slightly in his younger days and even boasted that he had attended the joint debut party given for the older two in 1934.

"Winchell and Pegler get their facts right," Matt said. "Not that I give a damn. Forget the box. Write an editorial comment and run it right beside the column. Write it yourself—when you get through with the finance page."

"And it better be brilliant and coherent, I suppose," Pete Zorach said, using Matt's favorite editorial adjectives. "And punchy," he added.

"Brilliant will be good enough," Matt Brody said.

They reached the Sixth Street door. Beyond, parked at the curb, Anchylus Saxe's blue Cadillac limousine could be seen, the first new Fleetwood, as far as anybody knew, that had been delivered in San Francisco when the War Production Board permitted General Motors to resume the manufacturing of passenger automobiles. It was clear that the economies planned for *The Day* hadn't yet affected, if they were ever indeed to affect, the personal life of its editor-publisher. Anchylus' broad, sawed-off shape, bisected by a chinchilla lap robe, could be seen inside the car.

"Only brilliant," Pete Zorach said. "That's perfect. And me with a leaky ventricle and blood pressure of one sixty over ninety-five."

"Is that good or bad?" Matt said. He smiled buoyantly at his friend but instantly regretted the remark and wanted to say something nice. Pete never took kidding too well, and his health, in spite of his exaggerated concern for it, was not the best. He would have to put in a number of difficult hours handling his own work plus the editorial meeting and the comment on the A-bomb thing. Matt had an impulse to tell him he could go to Pebble Beach tomorrow and make sure the 1927 Buick didn't slip through his fingers. The thought came into his mind, but it was never uttered. The discipline of keeping for *The Day* what was *The Day*'s was too strong—of not only keeping it but squeezing just a little extra out of it. He still wanted to say something nice, but all he could come up with, in his characteristic mumble, was: "Try some of that coffee out of the machine. I hear it's good and strong."

He smiled once more, encouragingly. Then he was gone, out across the pavement and into the big blue car as Dino, the chauffeur, pulled the door open for him and then closed it after him, firmly but without slamming it, and went around to his own seat and the car edged out slowly into the midmorning traffic.

Pete Zorach stood looking dourly into the street. He felt in his pocket for another pill.

8 ANCHYLUS SAXE acknowledged the presence of his managing editor with a nod. Matt Brody said, "Good morning, sir." That was the extent of their communication during the first ten minutes of the trip, which lasted approximately fifteen. By the terms of their relationship there was no need to search for conversational topics and no pressure upon either man to do so. Each knew exactly where he stood with the other and was familiar with his associate's opinions on almost all subjects except the current problems of their working days, these problems being what they ordinarily talked about when together. Matt had not been surprised, nor was he flattered, by the summons from Anchylus to take a drive with him. Anchylus did not like to go anywhere alone. His sense of his own importance made it desirable to travel with one or more male companions just as a medieval lord when riding to the hunt equipped himself with an appropriate retinue. He volunteered no information on where they were going, nor did Matt Brody see fit to question him.

It was cool in the car, Anchylus preferring it that way. The air smelled of cigars and the heavy doubled-distilled bay rum which Anchylus used and the slightly metallic, luxurious and acid smell of automobile upholstery. After a block or two the old man picked up an attaché case lying on the seat and began going through his morning mail.

Matt looked out the window. He enjoyed the trips he took with Anchylus—whether to New York, Chicago or Washington, or just down to the Palace to get Anchylus a haircut; the trips were part of his job, and his job pleased and satisfied him; he would not have changed it for another no matter what inducement had been offered. He had not been lying when he affirmed his faith in *The San Francisco Day*. He knew all about its current difficulties (and far more about them than he had been willing to indicate to Pete Zorach); he also knew what steps—some of them far removed from staff reduction, pay slashes and the installation of time-saving mechanisms—Anchylus had been taking to meet them. Matt Brody's belief that, no matter what happened, *The San Francisco Day* would continue to be a living newspaper and a good one grew out of his personal and somewhat hero-worshiping attitude toward Anchylus himself, though he knew all about him too.

Anchylus Saxe had been seasoned in the wars. He had emerged, apparently unimpaired, from the era when a newspaperman had frequently needed and employed an armed bodyguard and had sometimes found it expedient to answer by advertisement, rather than through personal communication, the letters challenging him to single combat. He was an old man, rich, mischievous, life-loving and arrogant. He was a robber. He had plotted and connived desperately to make a success of his newspaper, often at fearful costs to himself and others. He had few friends. Matt sometimes felt he was the only person whom Anchylus trusted. Whether this was true or not, he relished thinking that it was, seeing that for the most part Anchylus showed immediate understanding but no liking for the men he dealt with, even those in his employ, and they in their turn always stood on their guard with him as if in the presence of an enemy.

Anchylus had a bad reputation. Unlike some of his contemporaries, who had conferred on their depredations the air of public services, he had plundered openly. His misdeeds were well known. A courageous governor of California had publicly referred to him as a "monster"; at the next election the governor, though popular and able, had been defeated. When an enemy had fallen, Anchylus showed no magnanimity but followed the beaten man's trail like a bloodhound, watching for an opportunity to tear out of him whatever life might remain.

During his long and eventful life he had cared nothing for any of the arts except for music and in this only opera and particularly those operas in which predominated soaring female voices. The soprano arias of these operas could often make tears come to his eyes. His taste for both the sounds themselves and the women who produced them had diminished little with the onset of age—and in truth, though it would have been hard to find anywhere a person less deserving of immortality, he seemed designed to endure forever, like the armchair in which he sat in Room 100 in the Day Building, when presiding over *The Day*'s annual stockholders' meetings and the occasional formal conclaves of its Board. The chair was famous. Made in a design he had thought up, it was sort of a throne conceived to represent in its elements the natural resources responsible for the growth of San Francisco. Its base was constructed of a dark, volcanic-looking substance which was high-assay gold and silver ore; its frame was made of wood taken from a clipper ship's mast, its footrest out of two chunks of railroad steel. Seated in it, during those sessions when conformity to law made a directors' meeting necessary, he rode herd on his fellow board members, whom he called "The Bellhops." At such times, with cigar smoke sifting oily halos around him and the overhead light bouncing on his long iron curls, brushed sidewise across his skull to hide their thinness and fluffing up curiously above his ears and the back of his collar, he had the stern, garlanded air of some figure of mythology, dangerous and indestructible, like a primitive idol.

He took on something of this same air in the car. Matt could not help popping occasional sidelong looks at him. Anchylus was wearing one of the heavy darkish suits he liked and always wore except when some festivity induced him to put on a clawhammer and silk topper. These everyday suits—Anchylus probably had two dozen of them—always seemed to be brand new, were somewhere between brown and dark gray in color and cut in the fashion of an older time, suits with squarish lapels, corded pockets and cloth-covered buttons. Anchylus wore his sideburns a little long—he was pretty hard on Nick LaBrasca, his regular barber at the Palace, if Nick took off a quarter of an inch too much—and the angle of his sideburns matched the angle of the lapels. His upper lip, soft and thin, tender and fine as a woman's, was clean-shaven; his thick, gross lower lip, as if to compensate the mismatched upper, stuck out like a mastiff's snout. His head was massive, tapering toward the top like a gorilla's, his nose large, ruddy, veined and knobbed—a monstrosity of a nose; his

27

hands, though very deft and agile (he never fumbled with the letters he was signing or spilled the ash from his cigar) were broad, corded and muscular. The right hand was curiously mashed. His body was thick and powerful and except for occasional attacks of arthritis he was always healthy. When the car made a turn on Divisadero, and the pale concrete towers of St. Ann's Hospital reared up ahead, Matt felt quite sure their visit there—if the hospital was where they were going —involved no medical crisis for Anchylus.

His companion presently confirmed this thought. Putting the attaché case down and screwing the cap back on his thick gold fountain pen, he turned and looked at Matt for the first time.

"She went to surgery today."

The statement had a boding, heavy tone—but so did many things Anchylus said. Matt did not know who was being referred to or what, exactly, was expected from him by way of reply. To be on the safe side he assumed a reflective expression.

"I'm sorry to hear that."

"Went up at nine o'clock," Anchylus said. "Got the word from George Dudley's office, so I called the nurse. This will hand you a laugh! They tried to make her have the operation at seven A.M. but she refused. Said she'd never got up before nine in her life, and she wasn't going to start now."

The old man made a sniffing sound. It seemed to come from the sinuses, though whether it indicated approbation or postnasal drip Matt couldn't tell. However, the fact that Anchylus was taking this much interest in the case, and the fact that the person under discussion was a woman, brought him to the conclusion that the patient they were on their way to see or inquire about at St. Ann's might be Mr. Saxe's wife, Jessica.

"Was the surgery expected?"

"She'd had one go at it. They'd been trying to avoid another."

The car made a right, then a left turn and slowed down, pulling into the narrow fenced forecourt of the hospital. "Round to the side, Dino—the side!" Anchylus shouted to the chauffeur.

The driver swerved down a ramp, pulling up at a door lettered, EMERGENCY—AMBULANCES ONLY.

Anchylus hunched forward. Without waiting for Dino to open the door, he jumped out and led the way into the hospital, Matt following. From time to time in the past Matt had accompanied his boss on hospital visits to sick staffers or important personages on whom Anchylus felt it was his duty or to his advantage to call. The procedure had always been the same. Anchylus would locate some obscure or

28

forbidden entrance to the building, dash in, head down and lower lip protruding, looking for an elevator. He always seemed to have inquired in advance the floor on which was bedded the person he wished to see, and once in the elevator he moved unerringly to his goal, bypassing receptionists, admittance clerks and warning signs of all sorts. Once in the sickroom, he would move around uneasily, growl a few questions, and scowl at the medical chart, if one were, as sometimes happened, fixed to the foot of the bed, as if he felt the treatment undertaken had been badly chosen and would lead to no good. After a few moments—when it became clear that he had thoroughly upset the patient and would soon, if he did not leave of his own account, be asked to go—he would abruptly say goodbye and dash back to the car, his steps ringing sharply on the hard floors.

Matt had expected the same pattern to be followed now, and at first his expectation was fulfilled. Anchylus quickly found an elevator. He pressed the automatic control, raising himself and Matt to the fourth floor. Here, with an air of urgency which precluded questions, he tramped in his usual rampaging style past the floor administration office, soon arriving at a waiting room placed at the junction of two corridors. A young nun with a clipboard in front of her was seated at a desk outside the waiting-room door. This was Sister Margaret, who, at eleven, had replaced Sister Dominica.

"Was there someone you wished to visit, sir?" she asked gently.

"My wife, Sister," Anchylus said.

"May I see your pass?"

"You may not, my dear young lady," Anchylus said.

Sister Margaret showed no surprise. "You'll have to have a pass, sir," she said, "or you cannot visit one of the patients. Our visiting hours are between two and four except on Wednesdays, when they are between twelve and two."

"My dear girl," Anchylus said, "I'm afraid you are mistaken."

Putting his hand on Matt's shoulder, he propelled him gently toward the waiting room. "You'd better go in there," he said, "until I find out what's what."

He turned and made off down the hall.

The waiting room had a gaily colored rubber-tile floor and flowered slipcovers on the divans and chairs. The frames of the furniture were made of rattan and there were side tables and a center table of Philippine mahogany and some rubber plants in pots. Compared to most hospital waiting rooms, it was a cheerful place.

Matt sat down on one of the chintz-covered divans and started reading a two-week-old copy of *Look*. The fact that St. Ann's Hospital had in its waiting room a copy of a magazine only two weeks old was proof to him that it was a good hospital. When his children, Doodie and Elly, had been born, he had spent a number of hours, successively, in two different downtown hospitals, and in the waiting rooms of each of them he had found copies of magazines more than six months old and in the case of one of the hospitals more than a year old. The age of the magazines had suggested to him that the hospitals were not well run, and he had been worried about the children and his wife's care in giving birth to them and had been somewhat surprised to find that the process of lying-in had, in both cases, been conducted without mishap. He started reading an article in the magazine about the new look in women's clothes. The article included some photographs of models wearing clothes which made them appear to be very flat-chested. He was studying the photographs, trying to decide whether the models were really built that way or whether the strange clothes, designed by a couturier named Christian Dior, merely made them look so, when Letty Meeker, *The Day*'s society editor, came into the waiting room and sat down opposite him.

Matt glanced up and nodded but he did not smile. He didn't care for Letty. Though she was a venerable part of *The Day*'s organization, he would have liked to replace her. He felt she gave *The Day*'s society column a creepy breath of secrets stored in family vaults and names that had faded from the scene. Such an atmosphere, in his opinion, had no place in pages which reported the diversions of rich and pleasure-loving people. Such people enjoyed reading about one another's current doings. They cared very little who had married whose grandmother and what musty, horrible old scandal, decked in cerements, scented of the grave, leered behind the hickory smoke of a contemporary barbecue.

Letty seldom personally attended the frivolities which she reported. Indeed, she was seldom asked to. When she did appear somewhere, it was because the event in progress had the rating of something more than news: a milestone. By converse reasoning her presence conferred this rating on any affair she attended. There was, in addition, a suggestion of augury—and not a suggestion which made anybody happy—in her appearances. She could not only detect the historic significance of what was happening but also perceive, by sibylline gifts, what was about to happen. If a man and wife contemplated divorce it was Letty who called, while the troubled pair were still at each other's throats, to ask them when the complaint would be filed. If a bridegroom failed to show up for a wedding, Letty waited with the bride; if an important man or woman died in mysterious or discreditable circumstances, Letty arrived at the scene along with the deadwagon, if not actually in it, and her story, ill-written and ill-spelled, full of words italicized according to some weird system of emphasizing only the unimportant words, appeared in the next edition of *The Day*.

Letty loved Saxe with a fanatic old maid's love. He, in turn, seldom reproached her no matter what she said or did. Matt Brody remembered that Letty had never been on good terms with Jessica Saxe. There had been some difficulty involving the reportage of the famous Saxe debut party—a party which was supposed to have been one of Letty's exclusives. The trouble had never been patched up and, in view of the ill feeling it had engendered, Letty's presence in the waiting room could not be attributed to concern. Matt didn't feel it presaged any good for Jessica Saxe. He watched Letty with ill-hidden resentment as she sat down in one of the uncomfortable rattan chairs. She was a soft-moving, dumpy little woman with a cottony skin blotched with age freckles. Here and there in her dress and her complicatedly wound scarf and small blue-straw hat shone little dabs of jewels once fashionable but seldom worn or even remembered any more: carbuncles and chip rubies, topazes and garnets and tourmalines and jet. Her eyes, of a blackish-brown color, quick and glazy, looked like further samples of this type of stone.

"She went to surgery at nine o'clock," Letty said.

"I know," Matt said.

"She'd been a great deal better," Letty said. "They had hoped to avoid an operation." She waited for a beat or two, then added as her *pièce de résistance*, "The daughters have been called."

She paused again, but still Matt Brody made no reply. He was not playing fair and he knew this. Letty had offered her small, morbid wares as barter for whatever news he might have to exchange. This was her method of making collections, adding through the years, item by item, to the immense, petty and sinister doomsday book accumulated in her files and memory. When she submitted any of this treasure to the users of barter, she solicited, in fact demanded, a return in kind. By refusing this he forced her into direct questions—a course she took only when all else failed.

"I suppose," she said, "you're here with Mr. Saxe?"

"Yes, Letty, I am," Matt said.

Letty smoothed her skirt. "I only hope," she said, "he hasn't come too late."

She suddenly broke off, then—with a change of expression—stood up. Anchylus had come into the waiting room.

"Good morning, Mr. Saxe," she said.

"Hello, Letty," Anchylus said. He dropped onto the divan beside Matt. "She hasn't come down yet," he said. "It must be a long operation." He took a cigar out of his pocket and lighted it. Matt Brody returned to his magazine. Letty resettled herself, studying the patches on her hand—these too having disaster shapes, like charts of ship-sinkings, mine cave-ins, or some such catastrophes.

So they waited. All three, from time to time, separately or together, consulted their watches, for all—though their thoughts were otherwise divergent—had in common the strange sense that time itself had slowed down. The atmosphere in the waiting room altered. Many anxious people had sat in this same crisp and merry room, and the bygone worries crawled out of the cheerful flowered prints and varnished sticks of furniture and beset those who sat there now and whose waiting had gradually and harshly taken on the feeling of a death watch.

"Have they got any coffee in this place?" Anchylus asked after awhile.

Before Matt could answer, Letty said sharply, "All the nurses have it, Mr. Saxe, but they won't give it to you."

She shook her head, condemning the nurses' niggardliness with regard to the coffee. Her eyes invited conversation, but once more none was volunteered.

"Well, I suppose there's a place downstairs, a commissary or something," Anchylus said.

"There is, sir," Matt Brody said.

"I could go down and get you a cup, Mr. Saxe," Letty offered.

"Well, no, thanks, Letty. I'll go down myself. Want to join me, Matt?"

Anchylus made clear with a turn of his head that the invitation applied to Matt alone and not to Letty. This exclusion, however, Letty did not take as an insult as she would had it come from anyone except Anchylus. She sat down again. Into the folds of her queer, ornamental clothes and her flabby, patient person she gathered the interrupted mood of the death watch. If the men, by going, had proved they dreaded it—were unable to sustain it—then she herself would, unassisted, see that the watch was observed.

She sat quietly, sometimes tapping a little with her foot on the rubber tile. She turned the moonstone ring on her pudgy finger.

9 MATT BRODY and Anchylus walked slowly down the hall. They were proceeding toward the elevator which had brought them up and which was located in the center of the long, L-shaped corridor. Behind them, almost at the end of the corridor and just around a corner from the waiting room was another elevator, one with the words SURGERY ONLY printed in light-gray paint on the darker-gray steel panel of the door. This door now opened and two men emerged—a plump one and a taller, thin one. Both had on surgical tunics and both wore surgical masks which they had pushed down from their mouths so that the masks lay slumped in front of their throats like small monk's cowls reversed. At first it seemed that they intended to enter the waiting room, but almost in the doorway of this room the plump man, who had seen Anchylus and Matt Brody from a distance, checked the taller man from going in and called out in a low but somehow penetrating and commanding voice, "Mr. Saxe, Mr. Saxe."

Anchylus paused and turned, Matt Brody doing likewise. They stood waiting while the two men in their surgical accouterments walked up to them. Anchylus, because of his nearsightedness, did not recognize the shorter until both the man and his companion were close up to him.

"Oh, hello, Hugo," he said. "I believe you know Mr. Matthew L. Brody, our managing editor? Dr. French."

"How do you do, sir," Matt said.

Dr. French, turning from him, was presenting his colleague. "Dr. Immelman—Mr. Saxe, Mr. Brody."

"How is she?" Anchylus asked. His eyes switched from Dr. Immelman to Dr. French. Neither, in that moment, answered—their silence being unintentional to the extent that it was unplanned but at the same time constituting a sufficient indication of what they had come to say. This, however, remained to be said and must be said, although two of the men present already knew and the other two felt sure what it was to be.

"Could we step to one side for a moment, Anchylus?" Dr. French said.

"Anything you have to say to me, Hugo, you can say in front of Matt," Anchylus said. He added in a low voice, "I gather that the news is bad."

Dr. Immelman cleared his throat. He had a bony, intellectual face which at that moment was filled with genuine suffering.

"Everything that could possibly be done for your wife, Mr. Saxe, was done."

His long jaw wobbled slightly as he spoke. He had a deep, actorish voice and sounded terribly sincere. At the same time he made you feel he was a good doctor and if he said everything possible had been done it had surely been done.

"She suffered no pain, old man," Hugo French said. He put his hand lightly on Anchylus' arm.

"What happened?" Anchylus asked. He glared at a point in the air midway between the two doctors.

"The surgery, you understand, was exploratory," Dr. French said. "Quite a wide area was affected. Both Dr. Immelman and I feel that she would have had a good, perhaps an excellent chance of recovery if circulatory conditions had been satisfactory. It was the circulatory emergency that caused death. A coronary embolism."

"She died on the table, is that it?"

Dr. Immelman's jaw stopped in a mid-wobble, but Hugo French, having known Anchylus through the years, was unperturbed.

"Alone like that," Anchylus said as if to himself.

"She was not alone, old man," Dr. French said. "Sharon was with her."

"Eh?"

"She arrived," Dr. French said, "just as the patient was on her way to surgery. In fact, she requested permission to remain through the operation. This, of course, I could not allow."

"Where is she now?"

"I'm sorry, old man," Dr. French said, "I haven't seen her. I suppose she's returned to her hotel."

"Not Sharon," Anchylus said heavily. "Jessica . . . Jessica, where's Jessica?"

"You mean where has the body been—"

"I mean, *where is she?*"

"In our Hospital Repository."

"Where's the Repository?"

"In the Pathology Building."

"Thanks," Anchylus said. "And thanks to you, Doctor." He jerked his head in the direction of Dr. Immelman, then turned on his heel.

"I hope you will accept, as coming from both Dr. Immelman and myself, our deepest sympathy in your loss," Hugo French said. An-

34

chylus never heard the last part of this speech, having already resumed his walk toward the elevator. Matt followed him, a step or two behind.

They had to inquire their way to the Pathology Building—a two-story annex of the east wing, lying directly across the forecourt. The Repository was on the ground floor. It was a narrow, neon-lighted, white-tile room with a gray asphalt-tile floor. An attendant opened the door at once. He had evidently been expecting them.

"Mr. Saxe?" he said. "Dr. French just telephoned."

He held the door farther open, standing politely to one side.

The attendant was an internish fellow with something both fleshy and effeminate about him. Anchylus didn't look at him. He merely raised his right fist, thumb up, motioning with the thumb toward the door through which he had just passed. The attendant went out and Matt closed the door behind him, watching Anchylus, who was moving solidly and slowly forward down the center of the room. On each side of the center passageway or aisle were a number of shelves the same width and height as a hospital bed. Some of these contained sheeted cadavers identified by cards slotted into the foot of each shelf. Anchylus quickly found the one that he was looking for. He stood beside it a moment thoughtfully. Then, with great care, he drew back that portion of the sheet which covered the face.

"Jessica," he said.

Matt was not sure for a second or two if he had heard right. However, after a pause, Anchylus repeated his wife's name again, this time more loudly—in an almost irritated tone.

"Jessica!"

Matt was appalled. He had always had a feeling that a dead person should be left alone until those who professionalized in death had attended to him. The silent walk to this withdrawn and terrible place, the ejection of the attendant, and now Anchylus' summons to his wife had shocked him deeply. The whole procedure had in his eyes an air of morbid eccentricity. Yet . . . yet in the appeal of the living man to the dead woman there was something more than this, a desperation, as if—had Jessica only been alive to hear—some wrong could have been righted which would have made her going easier or a piece of business finished which was now left hanging in the air.

Anchylus didn't speak again. With the same stubborn care with which he had first uncovered her he put the sheet back again and left the room. The attendant, who had been smoking in the hallway, gave them both a look of puzzlement combined with frank dislike as he went back to his duties. Anchylus stood with his back to the door, his lower lip stuck out, rubbing his cheekbone with his mashed knuckles.

"Too bad, too bad," he said.

"It is, indeed," Matt said inadequately. The words and phrases of sympathy learned at many a wake had all deserted him. With this man and in this situation they seemed to have no application.

"Those god-damn doctors," Anchylus said. "I knew it was no good."

Matt shook his head sympathetically. "Still," he said, "I'm sure they did their best."

Anchylus was lost in thought. "Now I want you to make all the arrangements. Should be Grace Cathedral, next Wednesday or Thursday."

"Yes, sir," Matt Brody said.

"Call Dudley. He'll be at the PU Club; this is his day for bridge. Have him call the girls. Tell him I'd rather he did it. I suppose Zorach handled the editorial meeting? What broke in the Overnight?"

Matt mentioned briefly the Iverson item about the A-bomb man and his instructions to Pete with regard to it. He wondered, in a somewhat chilled fashion, how Anchylus could show intense, strangely explosive sorrow one minute—if his outburst in the Repository could be so interpreted—and the next instant, without stopping to draw breath, turn to a routine discussion of business.

Once more the old man seemed lost in abstraction. "Well, I leave it all in your hands," he said, leaving Matt to guess whether he was referring to the funeral arrangements or the make-up of the next day's newspaper or both. For response Matt compromised with what he felt was a look of over-all understanding. He stood watching Anchylus' thick figure, in the heavy, unseasonable clothes, cross the courtyard toward the long car.

He's hit pretty hard, he thought. I don't think he understands she's dead yet. Maybe it's better that way.

10 LETTY, as it happened, could have told Matt Brody a good deal about the probable effect of Jessica's death on Anchylus.

Letty knew about every family in San Francisco, but the family she knew most about was the Saxes. They were not a typical San Francisco family but they had prestige—the basic requisite for interest on Letty's part. Prestige and something more. Vitality might be a better term for what had made the Saxes—father, mother and daughters—noteworthy even in a city where status often called for an output of vitality which would have seemed extraordinary anywhere else. The Saxes had made an impression on their era out of proportion to their fortune or their social placement. All of them, in spite of the ups and downs of their personal lives, had always seemed to have a wonderful time, whereas Letty, whose family had gone broke when she was ten years old, had never had a wonderful time, but had been all her life a timid, shy person, neglected by men, a wallflower at dances, and—worst of all—so poor that she had had to begin earning her own living at a time when a woman who earned her own living was looked down upon.

Snobmanship is a subtle science. Letty's success with it had been due to a grasp of its fundamentals. She knew that its essence consisted in the feelings which people harbored about their ancestors and she had been quick to see that in San Francisco these feelings were the reverse of those accepted as proper in most other parts of the world. Whereas in Europe, and also in the eastern and southern portions of the United States, the respect for ancestors was such that it amounted to a religion, ancestors in San Francisco served their descendants better when forgotten than when brought to mind. As a candidate for, and later, in a limited sense, a member of, the aristocracy, Anchylus had been in the ideal position of having no ancestors at all. He was a Johnny-Come-Lately of the worst sort and had had some trouble getting eating money after his arrival in the city. Fabian Rupke had given him his first job, and Letty had appeared at *The Day* soon afterward—at first as a writer of fillers and small gossip items, later as a full-time reporter. She soon proved she had a nose for news and—much rarer—the ability to build an organization for newsgathering. She had created, through the years, a private gestapo. She had stringers in clubs, cabarets, steamship lines and domestic employment agencies. She also employed a number of debutantes and married women, who, faced with the task of keeping up appearances on slender means, would convey to her the secrets of their own or anybody else's home, boudoir or countinghouse—for pay. By no means neglected in her information network were the city's hospitals—a type of coverage most necessary to Letty. In hospitals, including the best regulated, many happenings occur that a gazetteer must know about even if she cannot print what she knows: the emergency appendectomies which, when more closely examined, turn out to be terminations of unwanted pregnancies; the "periodic check-ups" which so often presage the death throes of some prominent individual; the odd little household accidents like bathtub falls and fainting fits on stairways which, when bad enough to call for hospitalization, can—although it is not always true that they do—indicate a homicidal quarrel between married folk or kissing cousins.

One of the most interesting aspects of hospital coverage, to Letty, was the visiting that went on. She was always careful to get full reports on visiting, feeling that you could often tell more about a person by his hospital callers than from the list of those who might later attend his funeral. The nature of hospital visiting was different when the patient was a woman. In the case of a man there would always be callers who hoped for future favors, if the fellow recovered, but let a woman take to her bed and no one would bring flowers but her friends.

It had been easy to get a list of those who called on Jessica Saxe. Although officially denied callers (an instruction to this effect had been placed on her door) the rule had been relaxed during the early part of her stay because she had been showing such improvement. People who came to see her, however, were required—like all visitors at St. Ann's—to procure passes from the admitting office on the main floor. A carbon copy of each pass was kept in the office. Letty Meeker's contact in St. Ann's was a clerk, a certain Mrs. Hazel Ryerson, who worked in the admitting office. Some of Jessica's callers could have been predicted: the Timothy Wilkinses, Sr., of the Pacific Midland Bank, the Hiram Winterhalters and Mr. George Dudley were friends of long standing and also business connections; the Oakleigh Donovans had been original stockholders in the paper; the Hyman Bregsteins' relationship went back to the time of Fabian Rupke, as did that of the Mortimer Dibbles, the Liam G. O'Connells, the Webster Nashes, Milton Kahns, Elbridge Howells and Judge Benjamin Weis. Thus many top-level Protestant, Catholic and Jewish names were mingled, making the visitors' list a true reflection of a hierarchy which in addition to rejecting ancestors had also rejected racial and religious partitions. This unification was an inheritance from pioneer times—a feature of the city's pride, and a necessary element in its development. People faced with the job of turning a gold-rush town into a world metropolis had made friends and enemies quickly and without recourse to prejudice, forced by the pressures on them to accept one another for what they were.

No politicians had called on Jessica. A former governor and a former U.S. president had sent flowers but again—as Letty knew—only because they were old friends. Letty's theory that a woman's

38

callers came because they wanted to rather than to see what they could get did not hold true for politicians. They would come—or would have come in the old days, and not so long ago either—because the call on Anchylus' wife might please Anchylus; lack of politicians indicated some lessening of *The Day*'s power, possibly attributable to the recent circulation drop. Along with politicians, Letty noted the absence of social climbers, experts in investments, recent arrivals, heavy drinkers and theatrical people. The new rich were also without representation, with one exception. Prince and Princess L. C. Shimenko, she a wellborn San Francisco girl, he an émigré whose title, once presumed to be bogus, had turned out to be genuine. Prince Shimenko, who had once made his way by cadging invitations to parties where free food and drink could be obtained, had shown a knack with arithmetic quite exceptional in a person of high lineage, whether bogus or not, and had turned up as partner of Old Man Wilkins' son, Tim III, in a new brokerage firm. Had he been seeing Jessica on business? If so, what business? Letty made a mental note to find out.

For some minutes after Anchylus and Matt had left the waiting room Letty sat as she was, humped over in her chair. She looked almost asleep. Her dumpy body relaxed against the bright upholstery and her breathing was regular but her shoe-button eyes, folded in the creases of her flesh, were open and her faculties were busy; suspicion wriggled its antennae in her nerves. She sat up straighter, and her eyes came open wider. Something was happening—or had already happened. Something she ought to know about. Anchylus and Matt Brody had gone out for coffee, but a trip for coffee at a time like this should have been quick, and this trip hadn't been quick; the two of them weren't even back yet. Letty Meeker didn't like it. She got up and went with little trotting steps to Sister Margaret's desk.

She didn't ask Sister Margaret if she could use her telephone. She just took the receiver off the hook and spoke.

"Mrs. Ryerson, please," she said. When Hazel Ryerson answered, Letty turned her back toward Sister Margaret and cupped her hand around the instrument.

"Hazel?"

"Where are you, Letty?"

"Still up in the waiting room. Has she—"

"*Yes* . . ."

"Then she did. You mean she *did*."

"Yes. I was trying to get hold of you."

"Then why didn't you? I was right here."

"I thought you must have gone back. I telephoned your office."

"What time?"

"Just now."

"No, I mean what time did *she*—"

"Oh, well, I'm not sure, Letty. We just got word. But it was—"

"There? In surgery?"

"Yes."

"My God!"

"I tried to get hold of you, dear. Ask your office. They'll tell you I called."

"I'm coming right down."

"Well, look, Letty. There's someone at the desk. I'm afraid that I—"

"Wait a minute."

"Yes?"

"Did the Baroness Drobny—has she been at the hospital?"

"Not this morning. Or if she was, I didn't see her."

"She'd have to check with your office, wouldn't she?"

"Not *have* to. Not if the patient is—"

"But normally she *would*."

"Yes, she would. Letty, I really have to hang up."

"And you haven't been away from your desk?"

"Only once or twice. Not for long. Goodbye, Letty."

This time Hazel Ryerson hung up. Letty did the same. She smiled at Sister Margaret, who had been fiddling with small objects on the desk as if she were contemplating hitting Letty over the head with one of them.

Letty Meeker didn't mind having people glare at her; she meant to see her self-appointed task through to the end. Her column had a 12:30 P.M. deadline—the earliest on the paper except the editorials and three hours before the next earliest, which was Sports. However, Letty's assistant, Dot Fraser, was competent to put the copy through and had standing orders to do so if for any reason Letty was not back on time.

Nothing to worry about there. Jessica's obit would not be carried on the society page; it would be a general news story. Letty knew that Matt did not like her, and she suspected he had tried to get her fired, but she also knew that he respected her as a newspaperwoman and that there was not, anywhere, anyone so well qualified to write Jessica's obituary as she, and she was glad that Jessica, though a well-known person, hadn't fallen into the category of celebrities whose obits are written in advance. She was already composing it in her head as she went down to the main floor and took up her vigil at a new station—the admitting office waiting room just off the front door. This room was dim and conventional, suited for its use for office transactions, quite unlike the strongly colored, merry waiting room upstairs, which was designed for sorrow, anguish, tedium and deadly apprehension.

Letty sat on a bird's-eye maple bench—a rather high, straight bench which almost lifted her short legs off the floor. She sat facing the two front windows, both of which gave onto the motor court, one covering the east ramp and one the west.

She had been waiting only a short time when a black foreign car, of prewar manufacture, drove up the east ramp and parked in the area marked DOCTORS ONLY. The car had no medical identification on its license nor did the person at the wheel look like a doctor. This person was a good-looking woman with bright blond hair. She was about thirty years old, quite tanned, and stylishly though rather sloppily dressed—wool suit, no hat, excellent jewelry. She got out of the car and started toward the door of the hospital, walking as if she knew that no good fate or happy news awaited her inside but yet couldn't check the joy and strength which she felt in her body. In her walk and her rough-looking, small-featured good looks and full figure she had a certain distinction but it was a distinction without poise and without place. She looked like a person used to living with stresses and strains, surviving in spite of them, tailor-made by them, as it were. Letty was familiar with this look and with every other matter pertaining to this young woman, a person whom she had been studying wonderingly and enviously, and at length destructively, through much of her life.

The woman entered the hospital. She went straight to the admitting office. The clerks in charge, who would have attended to her, happened to be busy at that moment—Hazel Ryerson looking for a chart in the files and the other girl, Ruth Tanner, Hazel's assistant, talking on the telephone.

Letty Meeker came out of the waiting room. She came up quickly on the woman with her little trotting walk.

"Baroness," she said.

The woman stiffened her neck a little—but warily. The shape of her back showed that she knew who was speaking to her.

"Please leave me alone," she said.

Letty hesitated. Then she put out her hand. She plucked the beautiful woman slightly by the sleeve.

"May I speak to you a moment, Baroness?"

"No," the Baroness Drobny said. "I have to go upstairs."

"That's what I want to tell you," Letty said. "The . . . the need for that has passed." Ruth Tanner, the clerk, had ended her telephone conversation and was coming toward the desk, but Alexandra Drobny had now turned the other way, toward Letty.

"You're lying," she said.

"I'm sorry, Baroness, to be the bearer of such sad—" Letty said in a low, hurried voice.

She went on, as Alexandra's tilted eyes turned square to hers, blank, not hating or yet accepting the sorrow which her brain was trying to reject. "It happened on the operating table. I just got the news. I felt possibly you'd rather hear it from me than a stranger."

Alexandra Drobny made a quick, rejecting gesture. She was terrified—and this made her seem younger. She turned toward the door, the main door, as if to escape Letty and her news at the same time. She stood there and pressed her hands to her face.

"My dear," Letty said in a voice of great sympathy, "I know what a shock this must be to you—how you must feel not to have *been* here."

"Go away, you bitch," Alexandra said.

"You must pull yourself together, dear, before you talk to Dr. French."

"Must I?" Alexandra said.

"Why don't you sit down for a moment?"

"You horrible dirty bitch," Alexandra said, "you *would* be the one to tell me. You couldn't wait, could you?"

"I shall go now," Letty said with dignity.

"You may as well. You've had your hour. I hope you enjoyed it. How long have you waited for it?"

"I forgive you for what you are saying. I understand the agony you must be feeling."

"I understand too. Why don't you just go away and leave me be, the way I asked you? Do you think I want to see your horrible old bitchy face at a time like this?"

People passing in the busy hallway looked curiously at the young blond woman in her country suit and her good jewels standing there, her eyes full of hate fixed on Letty.

"It is the nature of these sad occasions; we get upset, as you are now, and we say things we do not mean."

"Who doesn't mean what? You'll find out."

"Are you threatening me, Baroness?" Letty said.

"Yes, I'm threatening you. You've waited for things to hurt me, and I've been waiting too. Don't think I haven't been. You'll find out. I promise you. So will you please go away and leave me alone?"

Letty squeezed her hands together and the freckle patches stood out red on them instead of brown.

"Goodbye, Baroness," she said gently. "I pity you in your bereavement."

11 THE SLAM of the door was an announcement. The young man who had just come into the house waited for a moment, expectant and quiet. Then he called out firmly, "Hey! Anybody home?"

There was a scuffle in another room, followed by whispers. A child's feet could be heard running, and another child saying, "Sssh." From a remote corner where the small living room, which also served as an entrance hall, opened into some sort of hallway, a girl of three entered with an impish, sorrowful face, dragging after her a chubby, bullet-headed boy perhaps a year younger. Both stood gazing seriously at their father.

The man said, "What's going on around here? And don't I get anything when I come home?"

The little girl giggled. She puckered up her mouth, raising herself on tiptoes to deliver a dry, wild little kiss like the brush of a secret wing tip.

"Mummy's in her room," she said. "She doesn't want no noise."

The boy let out a wail.

"She said we could cook dinner, Daddy," the girl said. "Can we?"

"We'll see," the man said. "Now you quit hollering, Georgie. If Mummy doesn't want any noise that's no way to do. You guys wait here—"

It was only three steps to the bedroom, but the climate was different. Here twilight had come early—perhaps some time ago; Pamela sat with her back to the window.

"Hello, darling," she said.

Now the man's eyes found her in the soft, brownish gloom. "What gives? You sick?"

His wife shook her head. "Mother Saxe died," she said. "She died this morning, but I heard only a little while ago."

"Why didn't you call me?"

"I did, but you were out. Mr. Dudley telephoned. You know, the lawyer. That was earlier. He said she'd had an operation. I was trying

43

to get a sitter, but I couldn't, and then I had to go to the store, and I suppose he called again while I was out, because when he finally got me he told me it was all over. . . ."

"That's a tough break."

"I feel just terrible about it."

"I guess so," the man said slowly.

"She was always so wonderful to me," Pamela said. "After I was old enough to figure out the score, I started to realize how wonderful. And then this winter when she was so sick I meant to go, of course, but I just never seemed to get up there to see her."

"You got there," her husband said; "you got there plenty."

"Not as much as I should have."

"Well, you got there," he said, "so don't start blaming yourself about that. Do you want me to bring you a drink or something?"

"No, honey, I don't want anything. I'll come out and start dinner. Margot wanted you three to cook it, like when I had the flu, but I think we can skip that."

"It might be an angle, though."

"No, I'm feeling a lot better now. I'll be out in a minute. I haven't cried about anything for so long, I think I can stop now."

"We could do it, though," the man said.

"No, I'm all right," Pamela said.

She was silent for a moment and neither moved.

"Cliff," she said, "she died all alone. She died that way, and she'd had such a hard life. I mean really hard, with Dad and all. You know how I love him, but that's how it was. She had a hard life, and I was one of the reasons for it. I didn't want to be, but I was. But I hope I don't die like that."

"You won't," the man said.

"If I died like that I couldn't stand it, and yet I've had everything, and she hardly had anything, compared to me."

"Some people might figure she had a lot," the man said. "I guess maybe she didn't want the same things. People were figuring it different when she started out."

"Everybody wants the same things, when you come down to it."

She stood up. Throwing off her terry cloth robe, she began dressing hurriedly, guiltily, as if ashamed of the hour she had given up to death thoughts, sorrow thoughts—to the flight and terror that had been, once, so much a part of life for her, a part which the woman who was dead had done so much to put an end to. When she had first received the news, she had taken down a book and read some words in it—words which she had often read before.

44

And he said unto them, take me up and cast me
forth into the sea; so shall the sea be
calm unto you; for I know that for my
sake this great tempest is upon you.

She did not feel that she was praying, but nevertheless the solemn, self-accusing words, as she said them over, grew into a prayer in her mind, and she brought her stepmother before her and dedicated the words to her, hoping they would be of some comfort in that place where the dead learn that they have been separated from humankind just as human beings must at times learn, gropingly and unbelieving, in a room of darkness, that they have been separated from the dead.

This was the only prayer said that day for Jessica Saxe.

II

The Courtship

"*Careful now,*
We're dealing here with a Myth.
This city is a point upon a map of fog;
Lemuria in a sea-unknown; like us
It doesn't quite exist. . . ."
                                    —AMBROSE BIERCE

1 ANCHYLUS COULD never have told what he had been trying to say to his wife when she lay dead in the hospital morgue. He puzzled about it himself, going back to his office, sitting there and looking at the hole in the world left by Jessica. He didn't understand.

People ought to have a chance to finish, and they'd never finished. They'd started something so great, different from what other people had, something their own. They had come together unerringly long ago through all the million circumstances that could have kept them apart. Each then had been a person of capacities, perhaps, but no great sureness. Once he'd had her in his arms, though, breath to breath, heart on fire and the legal papers all made out, sureness had started; whatever each could be, at the fullest extension of power, they had each become.

Now she was gone. This was the awfulest mystery of all, that the spirit could vacate, could leave nothing but the death-delivered souvenir on the labeled cot. It was a doomful, unrealizable thing. Anchylus grappled with it, the dread feelings once more of having his back to the wall coming back on him in spite of the protection of the fine office, the money in the bank, the rhythm of the presses stirring in the walls, and all the inky, oily, sweaty and familiar climate of presstime in the air he breathed and loved. He was going to have to live in it.

Not that he hadn't been a wheeler and dealer before he met Jessica, but the wheeling and dealing and the plain, dull succession of rather hopeless jobs he'd had for a long time seemed headed no place at all. He had been worming along toward San Francisco, working for little newspapers on the way, pulled along by the thought of a dream and a city in a dream, spread out on hills, magical there at the continent's end, a city where something would happen. Finally in the spring of 1913 he'd made it, empty as a starving coyote, thirty years old, dressed in a pawnshop suit and the bones of his burned-out youth. He'd made it only to find the city full of printers thrown out of work by the bad business of the year before. War looming up in Europe had helped business, but it was always the other man's business; and after making certain arrangements which provided him with a place to sleep, Anchylus had gone to stand every day in the fall fogs with the fog-colored men who waited in Clay Street at a place, Docker's Warehouse, where by a custom the city people sometimes went to hire them. On this day, arriving late, he'd picked up a buzz of talk about a man who'd been there, inquiring for a linotype operator. A man with a gold-headed cane. Everyone came running to tell him about this man and his own misfortune in missing him by only a few minutes. Several of the printers knew the man, a publisher named Rupke. A millionaire! All assured him of that.

Anchylus hadn't waited to hear more. He'd experienced a powerful feeling right then that he must find this Rupke. He'd started out in the fog to do so, though not having the least idea which way to go.

2   There was a saloon on the corner of Clay and Battery, a place known as Harpoon Harry's. The door stood open as it always did each day, winter and summer, until dark. Two prostitutes sat at a small table to one side of the bar. They were drinking gin and feeding bits of cheese to Harry's dog, Nipper, who begged in front of them. Harpoon Harry himself stood serving the bar. His long yellow face with its crooked nose and slablike jaw shone greasily in the glow of the kerosene lamps behind the bar. He would not talk to the prostitutes, whose trade he discouraged; he was wait-

ing for someone to come in whom he could tell about his fight with Paddy Ryan twenty years earlier. Ryan, later defeated for the championship by John L. Sullivan, had won the fight in the seventeenth round after breaking Harpoon Harry's nose and six of his ribs and giving him a hemorrhage of the spleen, but the fight, nevertheless, was the only event in Harry's life with which he was completely satisfied and which was clear in his mind in all its details. He had spent many years at sea in whaling ships, but of these years he never spoke and did not seem to remember anything about them.

Outside Harpoon Harry's Anchylus hesitated. He looked up and down Battery Street and then spoke into the saloon.

"Harry, did you see a man go by just now?"

"I did," Harpoon Harry said.

"A feller with a stick, he had a gold head to it?"

"That's the one," Harpoon Harry said.

"Which way did he go?"

"He went along toward Market, lickety cut," Harpoon Harry said. He reached under the bar for his glass of soda water and wet his lips.

"Thanks, Harry," Anchylus said.

He turned south, walking faster than before. He held his head up, sniffing the wet, salty air. It was as if he felt the air itself would bring him a scent of this unknown man for whom he was searching, and his confidence gave him the air of a winner—one of those confident, exceptional people for whom life provides unusual and lucky experiences.

So! So if nothing happened and the man didn't hear him—what about that? So then the movement of his legs was enough, striding along lean and limber like a man in the woods. So then the gulps he took of the foggy air would be enough and the blood passing through him and his head up above the other people and this movement and this day in the city, all of this would be enough and perfect and yet no better than any other quest or any other evening, since all were good.

He stopped. He did not know why he stopped, but suddenly it seemed the right thing to do. He stood quiet for a moment, looking for some sense to what he had done. He was on the corner of Battery and Sacramento, heading south. To reach Market Street he should have kept straight ahead. Instead he turned west on Sacramento. A wary look came into his eyes. He no longer swung his arms but took smaller steps, peering all around him. Something made him feel that he was drawing near his quarry.

Where did he go, I wonder? he said to himself.

51

He kept on, walking slowly. He felt suddenly weak in the knees. There before him, on the corner of Leidesdorff Street, was the man he had been looking for: it could be no other. Rupke! The gold-headed stick was what had caught his eye. The man on the corner of Leidesdorff was twirling it, holding it negligently in his left hand. The cane was very beautiful. That much could be seen even at a distance. The gold knob at the end of it made flashing spirals as the man spun it around.

Anchylus came on faster now, closely looking at the man who twirled the cane. This man was small and dandified. He was perhaps sixty or sixty-five years old, with a swarthy face and very bright black eyes. He was most elegantly dressed, although not quite in fashion. He had on a felt hat, for instance, instead of a bowler, which would have been more fashionable, and instead of a sack coat he wore a silk-faced long coat of dark cloth, like a preacher or an undertaker. His black shoes were highly polished; they had cloth button tops. His pants were striped—creased at the sides instead of in the middle. He waited quietly and negligently as the young printer came up to him—he waited, in fact, not quite approvingly, as if the two of them had had an appointment for which the younger man was late.

"Were you looking for a printer just now over in front of Docker's on Clay?" Anchylus asked.

The dandified man smiled. His teeth gleamed. He looked less lackadaisical when he smiled—meaner.

"I asked for a man who could run a linotype machine. Can you run one?"

"No, sir," Anchylus said, "but I'm a printer."

Rupke nodded. He turned the answer over in his mind and nodded again, as if it had been what he wanted to hear.

"You're a printer," he said. "Farm boy, eh? What's your home state?"

"Michigan," Anchylus said; "my name is Anchylus Saxe."

Fabian Rupke laughed. "That would have to be your real name. No one in his senses would *make up* an appellation like that. A printer! What else can you do?"

"Write news. And I can sell advertising."

"Rot," Rupke snapped. "How fast can you set type?"

"Not fast. But I've been foreman of a shop."

"How old are you?"

"Thirty, sir."

"You've never been a foreman."

"I've been one, sir," Anchylus said. For some reason, he had

52

never wanted to work for anyone as much as for this nervous, mercurial little fellow with the stick, who spoke to him so commandingly.

"How did you get your hand banged up?"

"I disremember."

"Like hell you do."

Anchylus had mashed the hand himself. One night working in a small-town paper, in a fit of discouragement, he had let that hand slide between the tympan and the form of an old-fashioned press. Letters had printed themselves onto his bones. What had they said? His fate had been sealed there—a fast typesetter with two good hands would never be anything else. Anchylus didn't want to be a typesetter. He wanted to be an editor. He stood towering in the foggy air above Fabian Rupke, waiting to be hired or else sent away. He waited with a massive and ironic patience, as if either outcome were the same to him—his own future being assured in any event.

"Come on then," Rupke said impatiently, leading the way up Leidesdorff. "I'm tired of messing around. The linotype hasn't even been unpacked yet—just arrived from R. H. Hoeg in New York. It's the latest thing, though we have others; we're not unequipped. The main problem is tomorrow's paper. You can grasp the simple logic of that, can't you?"

"Yes, sir," Anchylus said.

"Love of God, man, don't *sir* me," Fabian Rupke said. "Not that I subscribe to any principle of social equality. Voltaire popularized all that junk. He was a fraud anyway—stole everything from Descartes." He twirled his cane. Anchylus had to step back to avoid being hit by the spinning gold knob.

"What I dislike with the passion of my soul is loose ink, whether in thought or in speech. Unnecessary verbiage. Do you know what I mean? When there's a job to be done, get to it I say and never mind the foot-scraping and kowtowing. Have you eaten anything today?"

"Yes, sir," Anchylus lied. "I took something." Modifying his great stride to Rupke's smaller, bouncier step, he followed the latter down the small, ill-smelling street.

3   SITTING ALONE, in the zero hole, in the cold and puzzlement the day his wife died, Anchylus could see before his mind's eye the words painted on the strips between the steps of the stairway he had climbed that day with Fabian Rupke:

Gleets
Prostatorea and
of Rheumatism
CURED
You Can Be
Despair
Do Not
Men

The sign ran backward up the flight of stairs, painted on the runnels between each step. Rupke tucked his cane under his arm and bounded up the stairs two at a time. From a hallway made of splintered wood, the *slitherwhap-teboom* of a folder could be heard and the smell of ink, melting lead and human-foul air stood caged. Rupke opened one side of a span of double doors. He motioned Anchylus into a large room furnished with small gilt tables and an immense, soft, soiled golden-yellow carpet. There were large smeary mirrors on the walls and, at one side of the door, an alabaster statue of a man and woman embracing. Rupke hung his hat on an extended portion of the statue. He leaned the gold-headed stick against the bottom of it. Then he took his place at a large, ornate gilt desk.

Two chairs, one made of mahogany and the other improvised out of a packing box, had been placed beside the desk. Anchylus sat down in the mahogany one, looking wonderingly around the room. More than a dozen people sat working at the two banks of desks and tables facing Rupke. Some of the men were talking on telephones, others writing, and still others chatting idly or reading newspapers which they sometimes sliced up with shears; copyboys passed among them picking up what they had written and taking it to a bald man whose desk, on the opposite side of the room, architecturally balanced Rupke's. Brass tubes ran overhead, and through these, with a hiss like steam, the copy traveled to the pressroom after being slugged and edited.

Anchylus Saxe felt goose pimples rise on his skin. He knew the sort of room this was. In spite of its strange furniture and trappings and the harassed and indifferent faces of the men working here, it was the sort of place which he had dreamed about through years of squalid work in country papers and printshops. This was the newsroom of a big-city daily.

Directly in front of Rupke was a small desk with a human skull on it. The skull was used as a paperweight. Next to it was a metal sign, screwed onto the desk: EDITORIAL. A gray-haired man sat bent over this desk, writing rapidly on yellow copy paper. He broke off his writing, looking anxiously at Rupke; then he raised his hand and shook it like a schoolchild trying to gain the attention of the teacher. Rupke ignored him. He lighted a cigar and leaned back in his chair, speaking to Anchylus with an indulgent, fatherly air.

"The office of my paper, *The San Francisco Day*," Rupke said, "owned and published solely by myself. The only honest newspaper in California, perhaps in the United States, its circulation in this city surpassed only by *The Chronicle*. The salary to start will not be large—twelve a week, nothing found. All right with you?"

"Yes, sir," Anchylus said.

He had made twenty-five on his last job, but when Rupke said twelve he made it sound like a raise.

"Good. I don't know why I hired you, but we need— Never mind. I hope you're handy with tools. I, regrettably, am not. We must keep going. *Ora et labora*. Pray and work. That was the motto of the monks who founded California, and they did a whiz-bang job of it until our good friend General Frémont and the whisky-sodden rabble he called an army frigged everything up, let alone the glorious gold-seekers—but let's leave them out of it. An honest newspaper! That's the ticket! Worth more to a city than a division of troops . . . as much as a university or a good climate. Just a minute—can't you see I'm busy?" He yelled at the gray-haired man, who had come over and stood warily beside the desk holding his scribbled sheet and breathing wheezily through his mouth. The gray-haired man made a despairing gesture, rolling his eyes and looking for sympathy toward Anchylus, who ignored him also.

Rupke walked up and down the rich-looking, filthy carpet, talking about *The Day*. It had been founded, he said, by his father in the eighteen eighties and had occupied its own building until this was destroyed in the Fire and Earthquake. *The Day*'s present quarters, he explained, were temporary, though the newspaper had occupied them close on ten years. "Who wants fancy trimmings? You?" he demanded, pointing his cigar at Anchylus. Accepting an unuttered denial, he continued with the exposition. ". . . used to be a knocking parlor, an elegant one in spite of the impish advertisement painted on the staircase—did you see it?—by some wag or another. One night, so I am told, a contract worker stabbed a customer, whereupon the lady in charge sought pastures new. I moved in—and I'll keep publishing till Birnam Wood shall come to Dunsinane. How would you answer this?" he shouted with sudden venom, his teeth flashingly meanly in his handsome sallow-dark face. "Read it, read it," he said, pushing a letter into Anchylus' hands.

> To the Editor:
> Dear Sir:
> I take exception to the language of menace and aspersion you have cast at me. Nor will I permit you to hide behind a mimicry of morality or religious scruple in an effort not to face the music. I stand ready to engage you at short notice with whatever weapons you elect. If not, I will shoot you down like a dog.
> I beg to remain, sir, yr. obed. servant,
> Rev. Hamilton Dawes

Anchylus reflected.

"He's one of those nuts," he said. "I'd give him a biff on the jaw."

Rupke slapped his leg. He threw his head back zestfully and opened his mouth as though shaking with laughter.

"Capital! By George, you'll do. You'll *do!*"

He sat down. Putting up his right hand, he negligently took the sheet of copy paper from the gray-haired man. He read it, clenching his jaw muscles, his black eyes fixed and staring in a murderous concentration. Once he moaned sharply, stabbing the paper with a pencil so hard that he made a hole in it.

"Cistern is spelled with an *i*, not a *y*," he said.

Releasing his brain from the clamp in which he had held it to do his reading, he handed the paper back in the same abstracted way that he had taken it.

"Not bad," he said.

A look of slavish gratitude appeared in the gray-haired man's long, tired hound face.

"What will I slug it, Mr. Rupke?"

"Anything you like—anything. What does it matter?" Rupke said, waving him away. "Isn't it enough that I correct your slovenly grammar-school spelling," he shouted with sudden irritation as the gray-haired man started back to his desk; "do I also have to wetnurse you? 'What will I slug it'!"

Deaf to all this, the gray-haired man did not stop his walk toward the desk. The only change in him was that an old pain now replaced the gratitude that had poured from him a moment earlier. He sat down and began to write once more.

Rupke's jaw clenched again. He clashed his teeth together, then said softly, "Slug it—'Tumefaction in City Council!' "

"Tumefaction?" the gray-haired man repeated stupidly.

"Yes—tumefaction. Certainly! Meaning a pustular liquescent swelling, a degeneration of the tissues. Good word, eh?" Rupke cried, swinging around on Anchylus. "How about that?"

"You're right," Anchylus said. He looked at his new employer with genuine awe. He had never met a man with such a vocabulary, and at this point in his life he felt that the possession of a good vocabulary was the highest of human accomplishments. Also, in spite of Rupke's dandified clothes, bad temper and abrupt, unreasonable changes of mood, there was something exciting and wonderful about him. He was the sort of man Anchylus felt an editor should be—though none in his own experience had ever been this way.

"Fine!" Rupke said. "Now to business. This, dear fellow, is no sinecure. Far, far from it. We publish a daily on a battery of presses which includes three Ramages much like those used—as you'll recall— by Benjamin Franklin, possibly just as old. Ever see a Ramage? Ha! You've an experience coming—the frame, platen and so forth? Made of wood! Now the linotype," he added in a lower tone, as if issuing a memorandum to himself. "Very well. *Toujours de l'audace!* Have to go down to the Embarcadero now and have that linotype shipped up here. Finest in the world if I can get someone to—"

The editor got up. He picked up his gold-headed cane and took his hat from its anatomical hook on the statue.

"Mr. Rupke," Anchylus said, "what do you want me to do?"

"Do?" Rupke stared absently at the statue. "Yes, by George . . . All right! You go downstairs," he said, fixing Anchylus hard with one of his black, darting looks, "go down there and tell Damon you're hired. You see, I've decided to accept your story. Not that you're a writer or a salesman, mind—but let's put it that I sense some capability in you. Hell, what does it matter for twelve dollars a week?"

4 THE FOG had turned to rain. Anchylus walked through it whistling, his hands in his pants pockets. It was past one o'clock by the big timepiece in the Ferry Building, but he felt fresh and lighthearted. He walked fast, not with the wary intentness that had characterized him on the way to meet Rupke but simply in the way of a man who wanted to get somewhere in a hurry.

It had been a remarkable day—the most memorable and perhaps the most fruitful of his entire life to that date. After reporting to the press foreman, as directed by Rupke, he had spent three hours repairing one of the Ramage presses. Neither this press nor the rest of the equipment in the basement pressroom to which he had been sent was as bad as Rupke had indicated; it was the policy of his new boss, as he found later, to spread the view that the paper was tottering on the brink of a collapse into which it would surely sink, never to rise again, if all hands did not work harder without asking for raises. In this way, he kept expenses down, his chief preoccupation. According to the information Anchylus picked up from the other printers, *The Day* was an excellent money-maker and Rupke a rich man; if it had not been for his insistence on doing everything in the cheapest way possible, including necessary repairs and of making his employees double, wherever possible, in two or more jobs, *The Day* would have given stiff competition to its rivals in the morning field.

The pressroom was shorthanded: purchase of the new linotype would make it more so. Although a linotype operator had still to be hired, Anchylus guessed that he owed his job to the new equipment. His presence would release a skilled man from more routine tasks. Also, now that he understood more of the paper's organization, he saw that his own statement that he could both write and attend to business matters had made him appealing to Rupke. Versatility, at *The Day*, was a convincing recommendation.

When that night's runoff was completed, Rupke came down to the basement. Twirling his cane, with flashing eyes and smiles and mercurial speeches, alternately coaxing and commanding, he had made the printers unload the linotype when it arrived on its dray, pulled by six huge brown horses. He had danced around excitedly, getting in everybody's way.

"As the monks said, 'ora et . . .'; the hands and muscles, lads. That's it. All together now, heave on it."

Anchylus laughed. Striding along in the rain, he bunched his muscles. He stretched out his hands, palms upward, flexed like powerful hooks, wet with the streaming rainwater, and stared at them.

"Let him find out," he said aloud, "the crazy bastard!"

5   HE WALKED WEST awhile, then south through an area of flophouses, pawnshops, seedy hotels and tenements. He was wet through now. The water had soaked down his legs into the tops of his good shoes, the soles and sides of which resisted it; his steps made a squishing sound.

He raised his eyes. Straight ahead, near the end of the block, a wooden sign hung over the pavement. The sign was shaped like a fiddle. The weather had long since obliterated its lettering; a few musical instruments, covered with dust, could be seen in the window of the store to which it was attached.

To one side of the store an open doorway led to the floors above.

Here Anchylus stopped. He shook off his cap, then put it carefully back on his head. He went through the doorway and up three flights of wooden stairs. No light showed on the lower floors, but on the third—the top floor—yellow threaded a closed door and a rich, warm smell of women, cooking, and drying laundry leaked into the hall.

Anchylus looked at the light with satisfaction. He tried the knob of the door, turned it, and stepped quietly into the room beyond. Water in big drops splashed from the ceiling into a tin basin set in the middle of the floor, each drop whanging loudly. The room was warm and pleasant. A lamp, turned low, burned on the table, the glow of it amplified by the coals of a wood-burning stove which stood in the corner, its fire door hanging loose. More than a third of the room's living space was taken up by a large double bed; in this bed two women were asleep, one lying down and one sitting up.

The woman lying down could not be seen. She was rolled in a blanket from which nothing of her emerged except a tassel of dirty black-gray hair. She was a tiny person. Even with the roll of the blanket to bulk her up she hardly made a lump in the bed. She was an old Italian woman, Rosa Falconi, who made artificial flowers. She had no place of her own but sponged on other people for shelter; the thread, colored paper and shears used in her flower-making were scattered on the table near the stove.

Anchylus looked at her with distaste. He had been hoping she would not be here.

He turned his attention to the other woman. Evidently she had been waiting, trying not to doze off, and had fallen asleep while she sat, her head tilted back against the hard iron bars of the bed. She was a deep-bosomed woman with a tender, childish face. Her head was small. Enormous quantities of red hair covered it and sluiced down sideways over her long round neck. Her only garment was a yellowish, soiled Chinese kimono, and this had fallen open almost to the navel, showing large portions of her skin. Her skin was silky and milk-white except where, on her thighs and the upper part of her belly, it was covered with a fine soft mist of the red hair to which she owed her nickname, Red Margaret. Her body was beautifully shaped. Her long eyelashes made soft, reddish semicircles on her full, broad cheeks. Her mouth had fallen open. She was snoring loudly.

Anchylus stood beside the bed. He stared gloatingly down at the red-haired woman. There was something almost frightening about her beauty when she was asleep, stripped of the quick angers and overanxious tenderness that animated her when awake. He put out his mashed knuckles and stroked her gently on the shoulder, where the kimono had slipped off. She stopped snoring at once; when he touched her again, she opened her eyes. A look of joyous welcome filled her face, a look which she quickly repressed. She remembered that she had sat up for him till late and that he had not come. A pair of weary, spiteful little lines appeared around her mouth.

"Well," she said, "look what the cat brought in!"

Anchylus said nothing. He stood in front of her, staring down with the same gloating, secretive expression, turning his hat in his hands. He grinned. He tossed his hat onto the floor at the foot of the bed and cut out a wild dance step, his heavy boots clacking on the bare board floor. The red-haired woman watched him, puzzled. She had never seen him behave this way.

"Are you drunk, then?" she demanded, rising up on the bed. "Is that where you've been, out on a skite?"

Suddenly seeing something in his face she had not seen before, she jumped out of the bed. She stood up, fastening her arms around his neck.

"You've found work," she cried. "Why didn't you say so?"

With a yell Anchylus seized her. Picking her up as if she were a doll, he waltzed around the room.

"Tararaboomdeay, tararaboomdeay," he shouted. The woman kicked and struggled in his arms, trying to reach him with her hands, finally wrapping her legs around him.

The flower-maker in the bed woke up. She stuck her head out of the blanket, then ducked it under again in terror. "Madonna!" she whispered under the blanket.

"Not just work, Marge, not work," Anchylus said, putting the woman down at last, breathing hard from his wild antics and the feat of holding up her heavy weight. "More, much more. I found—a fortune. A bag of gold. A mountain of it. Well, believe it or not . . . and that's the truth . . . I'm hungry. . . ."

"Wet is what you are," the woman named Margaret said. "Sit down now and take off those filthy things. And tell me more."

He sat down on the bed, heedless of the tiny flower-maker, who had jammed herself against the wall as the bed tilted under him.

"Do you remember how I said this morning it would be a lucky day? What have you got to eat?"

He began to pull off his jacket, shirt and pants while Margaret, squatting in front of him, tried to unlace his shoes.

"A cutlet. Soup and potatoes too."

"Ha!"

He glared at her. He had not given her any money for weeks and was suspicious and jealous if there was food in the house. He knew she whored up the money to buy it. Usually she told him she had been paid for telling fortunes in tea leaves, but this tale was wearing thin even though many of her friends insisted she had the true gift of reading in the leaves; she had quite a reputation for it in the neighborhood.

"What are you going on about now, for God's sake? It was Father Felice himself give it to me. For when I cleaned up the parish house for him that time."

"Well, you can give it back. We're rich. Here's how it was. . . ."

Scratching himself as his skin began to itch in the warmth, he recited the events that had taken place since he had left her—how, coming late to Docker's, he had heard about the man with the gold-headed cane, how he had gone in search of him and found him, how he had felt in his bones that he would find him, and that something great would come of it. He walked around the room thawing out mentally and physically, scratching himself and talking.

Margaret took his wet clothes. She hung them in front of the stove to dry. Then she warmed the food and put it on the table. She prompted him with questions, waiting on him with a placid and contented air. She took pride in all she did for him, like some pioneer woman in a log hut whose man has just come back to her from a dangerous exploit.

"Twelve a week!" she said uncertainly. "Is that all he'd cough up?"

"Christ, but it's not that—drop in the bucket. There'll be a barrel more. I'll handle him. A millionaire! And when he hired me, he sat me by his desk for a half an hour telling me about the paper. Sizing me up! He knows all right. This is what I've been waiting for."

"But twelve a week."

"Who cares about it? There'll be a mountain, I'm telling you. He has no one in the shop with a brain in his head, tries to do it all himself. All right. I fixed his stinking press, not that a baby couldn't have done it. 'We'll see if you can write,' he says, 'but first downstairs.' So I went down. Don't think they haven't a pressroom, and a big one—fifteen thousand the first runoff."

"Ah, you're the one all right," Margaret said softly and mockingly. She watched in delight as he shoveled the food into his mouth.

61

To her, the tale of his success at the new job was natural. It was impossible to think of him as anything but successful and conquering. It was because of this quality, something irresistible, superior and exciting, that she had brought him home with her in the first place, after meeting him in the street.

Anchylus sat back, sopping up the gravy from the cutlet with a thick slice of bread.

"The foreman is a snotty runt," he said. "I'll have him out of there one of these days."

As he finished the meal, Margaret went over to the bed. She gently shook the flower-maker and said something to her. The old woman got up. She put on her shoes, stockings and hat, and gathered up her thread and other stuff from the table. Then she crossed herself, tied her dress together in front with a piece of string and went out of the room. For a short time her slow steps, in her loose, floppy shoes, could be heard descending the stairs. Then she was gone.

Red Margaret lay down on the bed. She took the kimono off completely and stretched out, wiggling her loins luxuriously against the mattress. When Anchylus, who had been sitting at the table in a sort of stupor, got up to approach her she moaned with anticipation. She fought against the tendency to cry out, closing her mouth and clenching her small, sharp teeth. Anchylus too stretched out. With his mashed hand he slowly caressed her smooth skin with its delicious veil of ruddy silky hairs. Suddenly he embraced her. Their bodies merged. The loose iron headboard of the bed banged loudly against the wall.

In half an hour they were both asleep. The wood in the stove stirred now and then as it fell into ashes, and the drops from the leak in the roof splashed loudly into the tin pan.

6 ANCHYLUS KEPT a list of the better words in Fabian Rupke's editorials. He looked up their meanings in Webster's Dictionary.

In one week the list included the following words: necrophilic, libidinous, pederastic, prurient and lubricious. Most of these terms had been applied in some manner to personalities prominent in the government of the city or state, as well as cavernicolous, dandyprat, lorette, demirep, drab and punk (a noun).

Anchylus tried to use such words himself in the stories he took off the police blotter and wrote up after he got the paper on the press. In the furnished room which he shared with Red Margaret, he read *Lives of Illustrious Americans, Great Speeches of the World, A Scene in Devil's Den, The Doctor Book, The Life of Horace Greeley* and *Cleopatra* by H. Rider Haggard.

All the books on great men of the past, with whom Anchylus privately aligned himself, mentioned the fine appearance of such men. Anchylus tried to improve his own appearance. Within a week after Rupke had hired him, he had got rid of the shabby clothing he had worn while looking for a job and bought himself a fine suit, new shoes and a derby hat on credit. These clothes made him the best-dressed man in the pressroom. He did not find it inconsistent that he was also the lowest paid. That condition, he felt, would soon change—as in fact it did.

Men who worked with him at this time recalled that as a press-man he dressed like a star reporter; when promoted to be a reporter, he dressed better than the managing editor. By the time Rupke let him fill in as assistant city editor, Anchylus sported a gold watchchain as big as a bank president's, worn across fancy waistcoats imported from England. Already he had established the sartorial style which he was to retain all his life.

Through subsequent months the circulation of the paper grew steadily, but Rupke was still not satisfied.

"We must stun them, boy—flabbergast them! That's the way!" he said, marching up and down in front of the alabaster statue. "But how? How?"

"Buy some brains," Anchylus said. "That's what the other papers do."

Fabian pointed his cane at Anchylus. He was wearing his meanest smile. "Your own brains, my dear boy, will have to be adequate until others are available."

Fabian's temper fits came and went, but Anchylus got his salary raised three times in eighteen months. He fired the gray-haired man, employed some better reporters, moved himself up from the press-room to the City Desk. When news was scarce, he invented his own ways of getting it in the paper. One day while Fabian was working on an editorial, three men in masks romped into the city room. They kicked a proofreader downstairs, broke the big mirror over Fabian's desk and put out the lights with shotgun fire.

Anchylus slugged the street edition THUGS ATTACK S.F. DAY. He

63

brought Fabian a petty-cash slip made out in the amount of fifty dollars and asked for immediate payment in cash.

"What do you mean 'recreational expense'?" Fabian said. "What in hell is this for?"

"For the fellows who shot out the lights."

"That wasn't recreation."

"It was for them."

"I won't pay to make news happen," Fabian said, glaring at the slip. "It costs too much."

"It costs a damn sight more when it don't," Anchylus said. "We boosted street sales nine hundred."

When not called on to lay out money, Fabian gave Anchylus a free hand editorially. He let him run a sports story on page one and plant a political cartoon five columns wide and eighteen inches deep right beside it. He approved when Anchylus headed some raffish testimony in a divorce case NAUGHTY NAUGHTY and another, OH YOU KID!

The Day went from eight pages to twelve. Thus more space for advertising was available, which Anchylus proceeded to fill; and when the advertising force had failed to get good enough results, he left his own assorted editorial jobs to make personal solicitations. He was quite ready to exert unusual forms of sales pressure and did so when the occasion seemed to require it. An incident attributed to this later period concerned a sales call on a retailer who had shown a marked preference for having his advertising appear in such stable media as *The Chronicle* and *The Examiner*. Anchylus stood looking out a window while the merchant enumerated reasons why he would not use *The Day*. Suddenly, he pointed downward.

"Say," he exclaimed, "isn't that where your pappy's saloon used to be, down there off Sansome? . . . Tremendous! There was a man I admire, from what I've heard about him. That hole in the floor, to drop the sailors through. That's what I mean by his *keenness.*"

"If you're implying that my father was a crimp, you're laying yourself open to—"

"Don't call him dirty names," Anchylus said genially; "that was just ordinary business in those days, same as you and I are doing now. Mean to say you don't remember what I'm talking about? I bet your sister would."

"My sister is a married woman," the retailer said shakily. "We will resist to the . . . full extent of the . . . foul attempt at extortion."

"My friend," Anchylus said sadly, "you don't appreciate my point of view. What's your sister's present address?"

"We'll sue. One word of this and—"

"History, sir, can't be the basis for suit. Now, scandal—that's different. I always heard your mammy went through those sailors' pockets, but that's *hearsay*. Don't you see the difference? We'd never print stuff like that. Just wouldn't do it," he finished with a quiet self-righteousness. "All I'm saying or have ever said is that the old days shouldn't be forgotten. Too much entertainment in them. Leave you to write up the contracts, any way that's easiest for you, just so *The Day* gets a parity with the other papers. We know our space *pulls*."

At the time of which we are writing such deals were still outside Anchylus' scope, as they were outside his function with *The Day*. His one connection with reality, and with the future, was Fabian Rupke's interest in him. This was the key which would open all doors and without which, for the time being anyway, he could get nowhere.

7 UNDER THE ABLE TUTELAGE of his employer, Anchylus' journalistic style developed as fast as his sales techniques. Two years after he had joined the paper as a press repairman he was made chief editorial writer. He celebrated his promotion by composing and printing a vivid analysis of the candidates nominated for city electoral offices in opposition to those supported by *The Day*.

For Mayor:
The King of the Dora Street Hoodlums.

For Sheriff:
A Fenian with a record of four jailbreaks.

For School Superintendent:
A dunce who failed to obtain a third-grade certificate.

For Assessor:
A political barnacle scraped off a garbage scow.

For Tax Collector:
A seller of Chinese lottery tickets.

For County Clerk:
An undergraduate of Berkeley college.

For Surveyor:
A thief who has run away with $1000 of his party's slush funds.

As a reward for such diatribes he was occasionally allowed to occupy the city editor's chair when the latter, a convivial spirit, had been taken drunk. Anchylus enjoyed this job most of all. He conducted himself in it with a zest which later prompted a competitor to say of him, "He runs his desk as if life were a cornhusking, San Francisco a barn, and himself the life of the party." Dressing in ragged clothes—possibly the same he'd worn while waiting for a job outside the warehouse—he went begging to six San Francisco churches, then wrote a story telling how he'd been turned away without alms; he sent a reporter to Mexico to find out how opium was being smuggled into Chinatown. *The Day* printed that story too, much to the annoyance of the police department, which had been making a good thing out of the opium pay-offs. It was during the opium investigations that he went to the police paymaster in Chinatown, Ling Tung Chow, a man to whom he was to turn twice, later, for much-needed help at moments when he felt his own career to be in danger.

The first of these occasions was a quiet Sunday afternoon. Anchylus, who had slept until the sun was low, woke to the sound of fire alarms. The blaze was on the waterfront. Anchylus hurried there. A grain ship and a lumber freighter which had berthed the night before were burning brightly; the flames had spread to a lumberyard and a produce warehouse across the Embarcadero; an all-city alarm had gone out and large crowds had gathered, interfering with the firemen, rushing in to help with pails, sand, fire extinguishers and hoses dragged from their offices and homes.

A big fire is scary news in any city, doubly so in San Francisco. People remember how the gas mains exploded after the earthquake of 1906 and flames ran wild. To be scooped on a fire story meant immense loss of prestige—yet although Anchylus saw the *Chronicle* and *Examiner* had staffers on the scene, no *Day* man was present. He took some rapid notes, then rushed back to his office. Here he found things as he had feared: the city editor was out on a spree. There was no one in the office but a cub reporter who sat in a corner tapping out a column on that morning's sermons.

Anchylus sent the cub to the Embarcadero to get the rest of the fire story. However, even if printable, it would be hours late. The emergency was an unusual one. It called for unusual procedure. Ling Tung Chow's office was only a few blocks away. Anchylus went there. He felt that the opium matter could be overlooked and Ling Tung's help secured if overtures were made in the right medium—cash. Fabian kept a supply of this in the office safe: Anchylus, who knew the combination, took some with him. This he laid on the desk. He made certain requests.

Ling Tung Chow, though not unsympathetic, shook his head. "I cannot get Chinese to do this for you, Mr. Saxe," he said.

Anchylus reached to take back the money.

"But I can get Irishmen," Ling Tung Chow said quickly. "Irishmen in San Francisco will do anything if they are paid. But it will cost you a little more."

Two hours later *The Day* was on the streets with a fourteen-page Fire Extra. No *Chronicle* or *Examiner* coverage appeared for some time. The reason was a mechanical failure. Circulation wagons at that time were still principally horse-drawn. As the rival papers' trucks lined up to be loaded, certain mysterious attackers armed with knives sprang at the horses and cut off their harnesses, causing a number of runaways and a suspension of newspaper distribution.

Police action followed this coup. Charges were filed against *The Day*, Anchylus, Fabian Rupke and various John Does. Nothing, however, was ever proved, and after a series of court delays, and the enrichment of several judges, the matter dropped out of sight.

This, as we have said, was the first time Anchylus turned for help to Ling Tung Chow. The second occasion, though no less pressing, took place a great many years later, and under very different circumstances.

8 "WHERE ARE THE CLIPPER SHIPS? What's happened to them!" Fabian demanded. He capered in front of Anchylus, glaring at him accusingly. As usual when in orating mood, he went on without waiting for an answer.

"Grand creatures, like birds, those ships. Hauled in the gold hunters. Hauled in the pianos, the whores, furniture and pickaxes, my boy, and the Chinamen; those ships changed this burg from a tenth-rate Spanish outpost to what you see today. The lovely ships! Where have they gone now? Can you tell me that?"

Rupke picked up the skull on Anchylus' desk—the sole memento of the discharged editorial writer whom, for the moment, Anchylus was replacing. As Fabian pranced up and down the room soliloquizing in his usual style, he kept tossing the skull up and catching it like a baseball.

Anchylus detested the skull. He had wanted to throw it away, but

Rupke had insisted on keeping it—to remind him, as he said, of man's mortality.

"Well, speak up," he demanded. "That's an important fact, the fate of ships like that. What about it? Eh?"

Straddling a chair, Anchylus thought it over. In his puzzlement the heavy, bony knobs of his large face made him look dull and clownish.

It was after three o'clock in the morning. The two men were alone in the newsroom. Such late sessions had become quite common with them, Anchylus having to stay late due to his double function as press hand and reporter, while Rupke, according to a well-established habit, was always the last man to leave the office.

Tonight they had been discussing the long-projected move of *The Day* into a new building. Architects' drawings for this project had been prepared years before; Rupke had taken them out to show them to Anchylus, then veered off to tell how his father, Jacob, a Philadelphia job printer, had come over the Sierras in the eighteen sixties "with a shirttail full of type" to start a printshop and, later, a small throwaway newspaper. Fabian had given an eloquent description of the Round-the-Horn and China clippers, as seen by him in boyhood ("Damned masts like a varnished forest . . .").

It was hard to tell when Fabian expected an answer and when he would resent one as an unwarranted interruption. In this case, some reply seemed indicated.

"I guess they've been replaced by steamers," he said tentatively.

Fabian snorted. "You guess! Facts, laddy—facts. When you guess you're farting up a breeze. Had another gazebo just like you here, begged me to let him write. All right, I said, go out and get a story on the buggering Salvation Army. He was gone a week. 'So you know all about the buggering Salvation Army, sir?' I said to him when he got back. 'Yes, sir, I do,' he says. 'All right, then, my boy, when they come in at night, where do they hand the bass drum?' He didn't know. I fired him on the spot. What about that?"

"You did right, by God," Anchylus said.

"Of course I did right, sir," Fabian Rupke said. "I happen to know my business. There's no more to be said."

He spun around like a dancer. Seizing his hat from the statue, he jammed it on his head. He pranced up and down the bare strip he had worn in the carpet.

"Those clipper ships are hauling fish today. Fish from Washington. Ice from Alaska. *Tempus fugit.* But don't you forget—I saw them as a boy. Hell, if you lived in Plymouth, Massachusetts, that would be the same as having seen the Mayflower. Understand that and you'll

68

start understanding something about San Francisco, farmer boy."

Now in full flight of rhetoric, Fabian fixed Anchylus with his mean, narrow stare.

"So what happens," he said balefully, "what happens when the lovely ships are hauling fish and the mine tailings are worked out and the railroads have been built and the madames have married the leading citizens? Do we persist in our frontier tradition? Do we perpetuate the indigenous costume—whiskers and leather breeches for the men, rice powder and Sweetheart perfume for the gals? Not at all. We seek, instead, styles copied from New York, London and Paris. Are we willing to share our last sourdough biscuit with the needy stranger? On the contrary, we'll steal his watch. We have stopped being the sort of people who hang Chinamen over precipices with a few well-sharpened chisels and instructions to start chipping out a locomotive tunnel."

"I see what you mean," Anchylus said.

"I doubt it," Fabian Rupke said. "There is a moral as well as a social lesson in all this, if I can get around to it. Let me give you an example. Just before the nineteen-o-six Fire and Earthquake we printed a story. Item: a lady in New York had been arrested when she was seen smoking in an open carriage. I tell you we received more mail about that item than about the Quake. People were horrified. Because the lady was arrested? By no means. They were horrified because she'd come in contact with a cigarette. It could never have happened in San Francisco. She wouldn't have dared to smoke!"

"I know some that like to smoke," Anchylus said. "They'll smoke anything."

"I'm referring to ladies. The mood of the city is what counts. We have a limited society here and they control it. The noose of the vigilante has been superseded by the dowager's lorgnette. Only in secret does respect for courage and liberality survive among the natives as the worship of the Minotaur persisted, out of sight, after the Greeks had set up city-states in Crete. To this vestigial loyalty *The Day* will always cater and to this we owe our success. You, too, dear boy, are a throwback—the recrudescence of an earlier type. You resemble the brutes from whom the present heirs have sprung. Never change. I have a feeling that you will go far."

One night when Fabian was holding forth in some such manner, the door of the newsroom was pushed open. A girl came in. She advanced a little way and stood still, listening. The light on Rupke's desk outlined her silhouette on the wall, a tall girl, fashionably dressed. She waited until Rupke had stopped to draw a breath or light a new cigar. Then she spoke in a soft, urgent voice, apologetically yet firmly.

"Father—"

Fabian spun around. "Oh, it's you, Jessie. What in the world—"

"I was worried, Father," the girl said. "Why did you stay so late?"

"But I always stay late," Fabian Rupke said with a pretense of irritation. Actually he seemed pleased by his daughter's unexpected visit. He went up to her with the old-fashioned, exaggerated gallantry which he sometimes affected and, offering her his arm, led her out of the shadows where she was standing.

"My dear," he said, "I should like to present my acting city editor, Anchylus Saxe—my daughter, Jessica."

9 Anchylus got up awkwardly. He bowed, acknowledging the introduction. The girl barely glanced at him. She was anxiously defending herself for coming, explaining to Fabian the reasons for her concern.

"—All those threatening letters. I was sitting home and all of a sudden I was terrified. Suppose something had happened? Then I couldn't start the electric car. So I came in a cab."

"The very fact that you were thinking of me, dearest, should have been protection enough," Fabian said. "No assailant, if there is a God in heaven, would prevail against a father beloved by so beautiful a girl."

"Oh, Daddy. What a pompous speech. And how impossible you are!" She turned to Anchylus. "What can one do about the chances he takes, staying here until all hours with no protection?"

"No protection, is it!" Rupke cried before Anchylus could say anything. "Why, we've a whole arsenal. Wait."

He began to pull open the drawers of his desk, tumbling out papers, cigars, dental powder for his false teeth, line cuts of political cartoons and other objects; finally he found what he wanted, buried under a mass of debris—a large, heavy, rusty pistol of outmoded design.

"Here," he said triumphantly. "Perfect, eh? This will do it, but don't touch—dangerous, you know—always keep it loaded."

"Father," the girl said soberly, "I can well believe it's dangerous. You have never shot a pistol in your life."

"Eh? Well, perhaps not—that is, I . . . But Anchylus here. A farmer boy, my dear! The stuff of heroes. He can deal with anything."

"Mr. Saxe," the girl said warmly, "looks wonderfully competent.

Even so, I wonder . . . have you ever handled such a weapon as this, Mr. Saxe?"

Standing stiffly, his large hands pressed to the sides of his breeches, Anchylus had never taken his eyes off her.

"I have handled weapons," he said. "Whether any of them were like this I couldn't say."

The girl laughed as if he had said something very witty. At the same time she turned slightly away from him, a movement which showed off her figure. Her features were aquiline, the nose high-bridged and small, the chin weak, the mouth curiously soft and girlish even for a person as young as she was—she could not, Anchylus estimated, have been more than seventeen or eighteen. All in all there was something independent and yet hopeless about her, as if she had not yet been completely formed or trained for whatever it was she had to do. The best thing about her appearance was her eyes, extraordinarily handsome eyes, dark, brilliant and bold, their force belying the tenderness and girlishness of the rest of her.

"Handle one and you've handled them all," Fabian said with energy. "Here now, you shall be the bodyguard." He stuck the pistol into Anchylus' hands, seized his coat and started them all toward the door. "If there's a reader of *The Day*—one of the homicidal ones, you know—standing across the street to wing me, shoot him down. All right? Come on then, off we go."

He switched off the light over his desk. Followed more slowly by Anchylus and his daughter, he ran down the steep flight of stairs that led to the street.

10 THE CAB had gone. Fabian decided to walk. Jessica took his arm and they went on ahead, laughing and talking with their heads close together. Anchylus was left to bring up the rear, the heavy pistol dragging his coat down on one side. He tried to hear what the girl was saying to her father. Not that he cared. The point was that he liked the sound of her voice.

How she walked! She took long steps—longer than Fabian's—her body raking almost sideways with the turn of her hips. Fabian was always talking about *ladies* as distinguished from *women*, and his daughter was a lady of the first order. No doubt of it at all. Beautiful as well. And intellectual! How could she be otherwise, having such a father?

Anchylus felt that he had behaved stupidly. He had hardly found a word to say to her. He could not have impressed her favorably yet somehow he would, given the chance. He would make her see what sort of man he was! At least, she had trusted him to act in the capacity of bodyguard—a relationship of a sort. It could be the beginning. The idea, of course, that anybody would attack Fabian was farfetched; still, it would be fine if some idiot were really lying in wait, making it necessary to discharge the pistol. What a sensation that would be and what a headline it would make!

He wondered whether, when they reached the Rupke house, Jessica would ask him in. He had heard that it was a grand house and would have loved to see the inside of it. However, when they reached it, Fabian and Jessica seemed to have forgotten all about him. Fabian said a casual good night, opening the big door with his key, while Jessica, turning on the doorstep, thanked him briefly for escorting them home.

Then she followed her father inside.

Anchylus felt baffled and angry. He had expected different treatment—he didn't know exactly what, but certainly not this. The publisher had always kept his private affairs separate from his activities at the paper. His life in the raffish old building where *The Day* was printed was walled off from the other he had here in this big, elegant house where, a widower, he lived alone with his fashionable, beautiful daughter. Sometimes, on the rare occasions when he was ill or for some other reason couldn't come to the office, copyboys had taken proofs up the hill to him, and reporters and editorial people had gone there for conferences. No one else had seen the inside of the mansion though rumors had circulated in the pressroom concerning its grandeur and the unique features to be found in its interior. An orchestrion, for instance, which was some kind of organ, playing rolls like a piano, with pipes stretching all over the house so it could be heard in every room. Also a conservatory where, in a man-made jungle of plants, located behind a big glass window, perched mechanical birds which would burst into song at the touch of a button.

Anchylus understood Fabian well. He liked and respected him and felt that he had formed the basis for a friendship with him, but he also knew how, granting the division between Fabian Rupke's work life and home life, he could expect now, and perhaps always, some measure of social rejection at his hands.

From Fabian. Not from the girl.

From Jessica, because of her attractiveness, her girlishness, and because he felt that in spite of her poise and worldliness, her low-pitched, confident voice and fine clothes, there was something soft, something

72

alluring and shy and yet accessible about her, a streak in her being which Fabian did not own or control, from this girl who had spoken to him in such a friendly, casual way in the office, as if he and she, the two of them, were somehow in cahoots against her father, from her any rejection, even for a moment, was not acceptable or understandable; it was infuriating, bewildering, not to be tolerated for a minute; and if it had been invoked against him, then this was a condition which must be changed, nullified forever, and as soon as possible.

Because of his defeat at the hands of the girl—for defeat he felt it to be, even if a temporary one—Anchylus did not leave at once. He didn't want to let the house out of his sight until he had devised some plan for returning. He had to challenge the authority of the walls behind which Jessica had retreated and which, for now at least, ruled him out.

He retreated across the street. Here, in the doorway of another mansion—all the houses in this part of town seemed to be large, imposing ones—he stood looking at the Rupkes' house for a long time, studying it with the intentness of a burglar.

The house was four stories high. It was so wide on the side facing the street that it looked like two houses put together. It was built of red sandstone cut in big blocks, heavy, like a fortress. On its upper stories, galaxies of bay windows prodded out sternly in the city night and at one end of it a curved piece of roof made entirely of glass glowed like a fruit. Its front door, a huge affair of glass and wrought iron, displayed the number in brass.

Anchylus watched as one light, then another, went out on the second floor; he wondered which bedroom was Fabian's, which Jessica's. The glass roof, which he concluded must belong to the conservatory, where the mechanical birds were, continued to glow, and he had a sense that other lights were still burning downstairs even though they could not be seen; the windows on the street floor were barred outside and covered on the inside with draperies so thick that a two-story fire in the rooms behind would have come through dimmer than candleshine. And if thick walls, snoutlike windows, heavy window coverings and the great, formidable door were not protection enough for those within against the forces without, there was in front of the door a yard or court, and around this a low, stout wall with a black iron fence on top of it.

Anchylus took a cigar out of his pocket. He clamped his teeth around it without lighting it. He had a bad feeling. As far as the people inside the house were concerned, he could stand out in the street forever looking at the walls that protected their elegant, effortless life. Why, he was as much an outsider as when he had stood outside Docker's warehouse waiting for a job.

A cold wind came up the street. It knifed through his thick clothes. Still he had little inclination to move. Looking at the house told him much about the Rupkes. Here was where the money went, the money that geysered out of the newspaper like an artesian well. Ink and melted lead and men's brains trapped this money. It was not grubbed out of a mine or collected by a conductor or racked up on a meter. It was a voluntary contribution made by readers who were thus enabled to participate in the rich, complicated life of the city and in great, far-flung events.

Fabian owned the paper, lock, stock and barrel. He wanted no partners. He wanted the money—to use in the great house, to pay for the grand entertainments, to buy the elegant clothes that the girl wore and the books they both read, the books from which came the knowledge that made them superior, conquering individuals. Nothing, nothing short of a bank or a public utility, made money like a newspaper, once it was well started, and *The Day* was already a magnificent producer of money.

Yes, indeed. Locked out. Be a bodyguard. Fix the machinery. Write the stories. Be Fabian's friend down at the office. Not here. Good night, Anchylus. Thank you so much.

Suddenly some gossip he had heard popped into his mind. Fabian's daughter was being courted by George Dudley, rich young attorney, fashionable buck around town.

Surely there should be a way to put an end to that!

Anchylus threw his cigar into the middle of California Street. Yes, the walls were thick, the door was strong—but there was a side entrance. The girl! Get her and you got it all. You stopped being an underdog forever. Then your abilities didn't have another man's name on them. They had your name on them. People paid attention to you, the money worked for you, not against you; no force in the world would ever be strong enough to push you down where you had been before, lined up with the fog-colored men who had no hope.

The girl was the answer. And what a girl! Not a homely girl but a beauty, in many ways the most alluring girl he had ever seen in his life: a girl who was herself a treasure.

The day that Fabian had hired him Anchylus had had the feeling that he'd found his fortune. He had said as much to Margaret. But even so he hadn't seen, then, how this feeling would be fulfilled.

He turned away from the house. Slowly he walked down the hills, his head full of dreams, into the web of the sleeping city.

11 THE SUN had tilted past the zenith. It made a dazzle of light over the harbor, the gardens and the clump of big stucco buildings, of a brindle shade, lying in a scoop of earth. Beyond were sand dunes and water and nearby, between the buildings, banks of flowers, crisscrossed with pink paths. Jessica, who had been to the Exposition before, said the buildings were "travertine"—though whether this term applied to their color or their architectural style Anchylus wasn't sure. He made a mental note to look up the word when he got home.

Meanwhile he had other things to think about. He stared into the air. Here, from an edifice called the Tower of Jewels, millions of brilliant specks reflected the sun, giving one a floaty feeling in the huge spin of the sky.

Jessica smiled at Anchylus' expression. He seemed so determined to enjoy everything to the full, even when it hurt.

"It's not good for the eyes, dear, to look too long," Jessica said. She put a light pressure on the hand which, so companionably, she had placed in the crook of his arm.

"Shall we go?" she asked.

"Certainly. But where to?"

"I don't know. Just let's ride a little back, toward the California Building. Then we can decide."

That word *dear*: she had never used that before either. Anchylus' throat felt tight. He stretched out his hand to help her into the electriquette, a small wicker-bodied cart that they had hired—the distances in the Exposition Grounds being too far to walk.

"Would you like to drive?"

"Oh, no. You do the driving," she said, with a pretty assumption of helplessness—a social grace only, for although Anchylus still did not know much about her, he knew definitely that she was not helpless. "If I were to try," she was saying, as if trying to give some foundation to her plea, "I know I'd have an accident. Why, I can't even drive a carriage team."

"A carriage team is harder," Anchylus said. "This runs by itself, almost." Still he took the lever and they started. Silently but with a finer feeling of ease than they had ever had together they rolled on, side by side.

The day's outing had been planned for a long time. Anchylus had thought of it in February when the Exposition had opened—but at that time he hadn't as yet taken her out. Their contacts had been limited to the times when Jessica called for her father at the office late at night, usually in the family electric. To make doubly sure of his safety on these occasions she had asked Anchylus to come along with the pistol, as he had the first time.

Since that first night Anchylus had acted as bodyguard, there had been a great increase in threatening letters. All the letters had been signed with different names but they were oddly alike in wording. Anchylus had written them himself. Sometimes, from ironic comments which his boss let fall, he thought that Fabian suspected this— but the strategy had certainly worked out where Jessica was concerned. As a result of the relationship set up during these journeys she had invited Anchylus to a Saturday-night supper. Then he had taken her to see Miss Elsie Ferguson in *The Outcast* and later to hear Ignace Jan Paderewski play a concert for the benefit of the Poles stricken by the dreadful Germans.

There were always concerts and benefits designed to help the poor people of this or that European country. Jessica had been quite strong in her sympathies, and there was no doubt of it, the Huns were pretty bad. Jessica had studied French and told him how to pronounce the names which *The Day* was always running and rerunning in black studhorse heads.

Mons, Aisne, Ypres, Verdun—Verdun, Ypres, Aisne, Mons.

Anchylus, personally, had not taken sides with regard to the war. Mr. Hearst, in *The Examiner*, was advising neutrality, and *The Day* followed Mr. Hearst's example. The war was on the whole remote from the interests of San Franciscans, occupied as they were with the Exposition.

He wondered now why she wanted to go back to the California Building. He had taken her there to lunch, wishing to avoid the cheaper and more popular attractions which he thought she wouldn't like—the pitchgames, the rides and the Clairvoyant Horse. The lunch had been delicious and she'd commented on the Hawaiian orchestra, but they hadn't danced; he'd wanted to ask her but had been wary of pushing his luck just when everything was going so well.

Was dancing what she wanted to do now? He hoped so.

He was about to suggest this when she touched his arm again. In her most charming manner, but with eyes averted, she said she would like to go to the Turkish Building.

Actually, he had mentally classified the Turkish Building as out of bounds, at least for today. One of its principal features was the performance of a bellydancer, much discussed throughout the city. There was also a lounge, said to be a perfect reproduction of the Sultan's Harem, where one could buy coffee so thick it had to be spooned. A rather rakish place—still, he would be safe from criticism of its faults, if going there had been her own idea.

Inside, they headed for the lounge at once. Jessica walked past the bellydancer with a quick, short, interested look which for a second gave Anchylus an entirely new picture of her mind. It was as if, just for that second, she was matching herself against the wriggling, dark-skinned woman, point for point, not as a person, but purely as a woman. She gave her this one look, then moved on with her beautiful raking walk, her profile averted, as if the momentary contest had been decided against the dancer.

"She's very pretty," she said decisively. "I hadn't realized that she would be so pretty. . . . I should like to have some coffee."

They had found a table in the corner. The bellydancer's music, now at some distance, floated toward them. Jessica ignored it. She removed her attention from Anchylus and fell into one of her silences.

Several times, when they had been together in the past, these queer moods had overtaken her. Once, after the Paderewski concert, she had refrained from speaking to him for a long time. They had gone to the Palace Court for a late supper, and here, breaking painfully through the shell of irritation or abstraction which had encased her, she had begun comparing Anchylus unfavorably with Fabian Rupke. "My father attacks people because, fundamentally, he has a respect for them. He can't bear it when they aren't what they ought to be. He is an idealist, so he is defenseless. You have no ideals and you expect nothing from anyone. That makes you formidable. No one is irreplaceable to you . . . and, besides, you don't care for music."

There had been no use assuring her that he had enjoyed the concert very much. She had formed a contrary opinion, triggering her attack on him with this view. They had parted with coldness.

Some such mood had evidently returned now. With downcast eyes and a withdrawn, cold expression, Jessica sat stirring the sirupy black liquid in her cup, hardly tasting it, while Anchylus made efforts at conversation. Perhaps, he thought, the Arabian Nights atmosphere of the coffee lounge had upset her. Or it might have been the dancer.

He had been a fool to bring her here, even though she'd been the one to suggest it.

"We can go if you like," he said.

"Why?" she demanded. "I haven't finished my coffee."

She spoke in a very different tone from the one she had used less than an hour before, when she had called him "dear."

"I don't know," he said. "I thought maybe this place disappointed you. You don't seem to be having a good time."

"It doesn't disappoint me," she said in a low voice, "and I'm having a fine time. I've enjoyed the day very much. Perhaps too much."

"Too much!" he said, puzzled. "How could that be?"

"It could be," she said broodingly, "for lots of reasons. I've been wondering all day if our being together has any point in it. Whether we should keep on, or—"

"There is a point to it if you're happy," Anchylus said, his heart sinking. "Have I done something wrong?"

"No. Of course not."

"Then why—"

"You must forgive me," she said. "I have a bad habit. When I'm happy I can't let myself alone, I start probing at my feelings. And I wonder sometimes if—" She broke off.

"You wonder about us?"

"Yes."

"In what way?"

"In all ways."

"You don't like to be with me?"

"I do. You know I do. But we're so far apart. Almost completely opposites, in our background and everything else. Happiness has to be related to something, and—"

"I have happiness," he said harshly; "I have happiness when I'm with you."

"That's not the point. Oh, it all sounds so serious, and I hadn't meant it to. It was so nice of you to bring me here today, and—perhaps we shouldn't talk about it—"

"I want to talk about it," Anchylus said. "You've got something on your mind and I—"

"All right, then. I have something on my mind. As you may have found out," she said, hurrying along so the words were hardly distinguishable, "I'm a moody person. I suppose you'd call it that. Aren't people apt to be that way when they have lost one or the other of their parents? My father has been everything, and then, I've read a lot. That is the way I am, that's all. I've thought about my life."

"As it relates to me?" Anchylus said. He put his hand over hers, looking into her eyes fiercely and fixedly. She let her hand stay as it was for a moment, then withdrew it, but slowly, as if to tell him he was not to regard this as a rebuff.

"In a way I've never been in love. If, or when, I ever fall in love it will mean—everything. My whole life!"

"Jessie—"

"Please don't misunderstand me. I'm speaking quite impersonally."

"Naturally."

"I know," she went on after a moment, "I know that I have a very intense nature. Idealistic. I make too much of—well, of my feelings. And I can be hurt too easily sometimes. I'm afraid of that."

"You're afraid of being hurt by me?"

"I don't know. By myself. Or just by life. I need someone so badly and I—well, I can't afford to make a mistake. I suppose that sounds frightfully selfish, but it's true. I keep a tight check on myself where actions are concerned but I've read and I've thought so much . . . about everything. I read and then I think and think. Do you believe that's wrong?"

"No, no of course not!"

"Oh, not in a certain sense, I suppose. But you know what I mean."

"It isn't wrong," Anchylus repeated. "I read too, and I think too. I think deeply. All the time."

She looked at him with a sudden smile—a smile that seemed to burst from her face.

"The words you use sometimes—"

"That I misuse, you mean?"

"Oh, no," she said emphatically, worried that she might have hurt him, "you don't misuse words. You use them correctly. I get furious when father calls you 'farmer boy.' He knows better."

"Well, that's what I am, I guess."

"You are *not*. You may have been once, but you've risen. You have such drive!"

"Jessie."

"Yes?"

"Jessie, I've never known a woman in the same class with you. Not one who could even compare with you."

He took both her hands now in his mashed one, and this time she made no effort to draw them away.

"You shouldn't say things like that."

79

"I've offended you?"

"Of course not. You can't offend a woman by paying her compliments, especially such handsome ones. Only what you say isn't true."

"It *is* true."

Her soft, girlish-looking mouth was partly open, tugged down at the corners as if by some sensuous, unusual feeling. He tightened his grip on her hands. Though the Harem Lounge was full of people he had an impulse to pull her to him and mash his own lips on hers.

"Have you ever read anything by Thomas Love Peacock?" she asked softly.

"I can't say that I have."

"He's one of my favorite authors."

"Then I'll have to read him. What books has he written?"

"Oh, nothing that you have to read but he says so much sometimes. So much that I feel myself."

"I'll certainly get some of his books."

Anchylus finished his coffee. He wondered how to get back to the frame of feeling which they had been experiencing before she got into this.

"You don't need to. I don't think most men would like him, though he writes so beautifully. *Nightmare Alley* is my favorite. One of his characters, a girl named Stella, expresses what I feel about love, how I look at it. I memorized one of her speeches. Would you like to hear it?"

"I would."

Jessica raised her head. She looked squarely at him, her black, blazing eyes flashing, and the mood which he had thought destroyed returned full force.

" 'If I ever love,' " she quoted, " 'I shall do so without limit or restriction. I shall hold all difficulties light, all sacrifices cheap, all obstacles gossamer.' Isn't that a beautiful sentiment?"

"Jessica—"

Under the table Anchylus jammed his legs against hers. He took hold of her arm in a fierce grip.

"Anchylus, I didn't mean by the words I quoted to make you feel that—"

"You didn't make me feel anything I hadn't felt for a long time. I love you and I—"

"Please stop."

"—I want," Anchylus said relentlessly, his head lowered like a bull, glaring at her under his heavy eyebrows, "I want—"

"People are looking. And you're—"

"—to marry you," he said heavily.

"You're hurting me. My God!"

With surprising strength she broke away from him. While he fumbled in his pockets for money to leave on the table, she walked out of the lounge; he could see her through the doorway, weaving her way through the crowd around the bellydancer.

He found her standing in front of the building. Tears were streaming down her cheeks. Wordlessly he handed her a handkerchief. She dabbed at her face. When she seemed to feel a little better they turned, by mutual agreement, toward the main gate.

His face was set. Though it was clear he'd made an ill-timed move, he didn't care. He had meant what he said. He would carry out his intention.

"I think . . . we'd better not see each other any more," she said at length.

"Is that so?"

"Yes."

She stopped and he stood facing her, heedless of the people strolling past.

"To be quite honest, I have decided *not* to see you any more."

"That remains to be seen," he said.

"No more," she said firmly. "You have apparently—you have acquired certain ideas about me. You have said certain things, and—well, I'm not ready to hear things like that from you or any man."

12

THE FARM in Michigan where Anchylus had grown up had been a small, infertile, rocky patch ringed with trees. Every day when time could be spared from other tasks, the men of the family attacked the trees in an effort to make the farm bigger. The axes made a song of courage in the lonely place whose life was geared to their wild rhythm; early in the morning the song would begin, his uncle's ax tuned to a note different from the slower, thuddier blows struck by his father.

Silence would fall when a tree was cut through. The monster, a conquered enemy, unaware of its own death, creaked weirdly, standing for a last moment with nothing holding it. Then male shouts of joy and warning filled the air. The creak that spoke of the tree's death turned into a splintering roar as the tall, feathery top tilted against the sky, then tipped grandly and helplessly—done for now—to go crashing down among the lesser trees.

The farm grew every year and living became easier. Then the growth stopped. Anchylus' father, then his uncle, enlisted in Teddy Roosevelt's Rough Riders. They were tired of the lonesome, pounding life on the farm. A spell of soldiering would be a vacation, and the grandparents, with the savings set aside, could look after the women and kids for a while.

Anchylus' father never came back. His uncle, a brown ghost so thin the family didn't at first recognize him, stepped out of the woods one day and sat on the porch for a year to continue dying. One of the grandmothers made Anchylus a suit by cutting down his uncle's uniform. When the soldier had wound up the process he had come home to attend to, Grandpa Saxe put Anchylus, in his new suit, in the buggy and drove down the road offering the boy as a labor hand to all the farmers in the neighborhood.

When spring came Anchylus ran away. A kindly, elderly man and his wife, operating a small printshop in a town across the state line, gave him his first job. When he found he was still working for almost nothing, though he now knew a trade, he began the wanderings which brought him finally in front of the warehouse where he first heard of Fabian Rupke.

Anchylus approved of his own beginnings. Reading the biographies of the great, he found that many successful men had started out in some such way. It was almost a formula, a folk story of America, its components varied so little: the farm, the poverty, the printshops, the road, the loneliness, the books, the better job and at last the success. Fabian was always telling him he was the last of a breed, a throwback. That fitted in too. Anchylus rather liked the idea. It went properly with the saga of himself which he had started in his travels and was still composing.

He was in love. He had not been lying when he said that to Jessica. Regardless of the motives that had first set him courting her—and even these motives had by no means been without a sense of her attractiveness—it was true now that he was in love with her. As for wanting to marry her, he had wanted that, of course, before love had come into his calculations.

So—that was his position. What was hers? An unknown quantity, a very ticklish and uncertain quantity until that day at the Exposition, that day when she had said so firmly that she wasn't ready to hear such words.

Not ready! Why, she was more impatient than he, or at least equally; she had gone further than he, in this direction, since she had already conceived of the words, the situation as a reality to which she was coming, or to which they were both coming, but for which certain preparations had to be made, preparations of an inward sort not yet completed, but the completion of which was anticipated by her—and not only anticipated but certain.

What else could she have meant by saying she wasn't "ready"? She had been readier than he, in spite of all her doubts and misgivings, for he himself had never thought about being ready or unready.

If I ever love, I shall do so without limit or restriction. . . .

She had been doing more, when she said that, than quoting from a book. She had been speaking of the two of them, using the words of a book for her own feelings. And what words they were! He remembered the sensual little droop of her mouth as she'd sat thinking about them, before she said them, looking at her cup of Turkish coffee. He'd never known a woman who could talk about love—bring it into her mind while still feeling it in her nerves—but the fact that she could find words for it, even words out of a book, didn't mean that she felt it less. Maybe the opposite. And, besides, there was an air of searching about her that made you know she had the feelings, that if she ever let herself go she would behave exactly as the words indicated.

I shall hold all difficulties light, all sacrifices cheap, all obstacles gossamer.

He couldn't see that there was much to worry about; as for her insistence that she'd never see him again, that was silly. He'd have to go slow for a while, that was all. Act as though he'd lost her, make her sorry for him. Write notes, send her flowers, until she relented and went out with him again, then slowly build back to the point at which she would be "ready."

No trouble there. The one trouble, the one danger—and that a real one, not to be held lightly—was Red Margaret.

He had been stupid about Margaret. He faced that fact realistically. He'd underrated, first of all, her feeling for him—a bad error, inexcusable considering that they'd been together now for going on two years. She wouldn't give up easily. Then his second big mistake had been in failing to consider her craftiness, the female practicality that had made her hide her suspicions that he was seeing someone else, then take out after him and tail him in a taxicab. She'd confessed all this, not in any way ashamed of it, but with infuriating righteousness, as if her actions had been absolutely proper, only his being wrong and faithless. She even admitted checking the number of the house on California Street against the city directory so as to find out who lived there. Jessica was now mentioned by name in their arguments—a fact which itself gave him the creeps, knowing how Margaret's tongue wagged and how gossip spread, no matter how far down the scale it started.

Jessica was so sensitive, so idealistic! And in spite of all her reading and dreaming and her instinctive response to life, she had been very sheltered. If she even got a hint of the truth of things—that he had been living with another woman while in the process of courting her—there would be no telling what she'd do.

That was where he blamed himself. He should have gotten rid of Margaret a long time ago. Then everything would have been simple.

Only . . . to hell with it. He hadn't wanted to get rid of her. She suited him. She was somebody to come home to, to brag to about the great things he had done. She suited him and he was used to her and in some ways she couldn't be improved on. Even now, she still had great appeal for him. If she hadn't carried on like a mad woman over his courtship of Jessica, he would have tried to keep up some sort of relationship with her. That skin of hers! The beautiful, soft, fiery down on her like a soft flame burning. And her shape! And she'd always been so easy to get along with, warm as the stove in that first room they'd shared—the one for which she'd paid the rent.

It was awful, horrible, that she couldn't look at things more reasonably, but she couldn't. No use hoping for the impossible. Anchylus wanted no recriminations after the separation had taken place. Margaret wouldn't go away without some recognition of his liking for her and and at least a reasonable guarantee of security for the future.

Anchylus drew out all the money he had in the bank. In spite of the better apartment, the clothes he'd bought for himself and Margaret and the occasional outings with Jessica, he'd lived frugally because he was used to it; out of the series of raises given him by Rupke over a two-year period he'd saved almost a thousand dollars. Red Margaret could have all of it—more later, if she wanted. All he'd ask would be to be left alone.

He brought the money home in an envelope and put it under a board in the kitchen. Then he nailed the board down again. He would wait for a critical moment, when she was upbraiding and accusing him, threatening to leave and so forth; he would get the money out and slap it in her hand. She would take it and go. That might seem brutal. In a way it would be taking advantage of her temper and passionate nature—the very traits which had helped to make her important to him. Still, it couldn't be helped. It was the only way out and must be taken even if his conscience plagued him for it later.

Trying for the present to behave placatingly—hoping thus to make the guilt for the final quarrel hers rather than his—he waited for the crisis that would put an end to his dilemma. It wasn't long in coming.

13 ANCHYLUS had known at once that something was up. In the week that had passed since their visit to the Exposition he had stayed away from Jessica. He had wanted to see if she would make the first move to mend their quarrel. Today she had telephoned the office to say she wanted to see him. Could he come by the house during his dinner hour?

Often, as she knew, he didn't take any dinner hour, eating some sandwiches at his desk; when he did have time to eat he usually chose 5:00 P.M., immediately after the home-delivered edition went to press. Naming this hour as the only one possible for him, he left the office as soon as the presses began to run. With a bad, foreboding feeling, he traveled up California Street in a cable car.

His sense that something unfortunate or at least out of the ordinary was about to take place seemed borne out by the fact that the servant who opened the door did not show him to the library, where he generally went to wait for Jessica, but escorted him upstairs to a sitting room on the second floor, a room in which he had never been before.

Jessica came in at once. She looked thin and very pale. She had on a dark tea gown of some clinging material which emphasized the erectness of her bearing and the smallness of her waist. Her eyes were red, as if she had been crying, but her manner was calm—icy, in fact. She walked past Anchylus without responding in any way to his greeting. Except for one scornful, flashing glance of her black eyes, she never looked in his direction.

"Mrs. O'Boylan called on me today," she said.

Anchylus was astounded, as much by her strange manner, after the increasing tenderness which she had shown of late, as by her words.

For a moment he couldn't think whom she meant by Mrs. O'Boylan. He knew Red Margaret as Margaret Tighe, the name she generally used. Then he remembered that she had once had some connection with a fellow named O'Boylan and had called herself this way at times, especially when she wished to strike an air.

"I see," he said.

"You see!" Jessica echoed. She still did not turn but stood with her hand on the marble mantelpiece, staring down at a small coal fire which was burning in the grate.

"Men!" she burst out. "I can't, never will, comprehend the perfidy

85

of men. This, well, this to me is . . . vile. Unspeakably vile and . . . awful. Lower than anything I had ever thought possible. Well?" she asked, turning around at last, "have you anything to say? No, of course you haven't. There is nothing anyone could say, if it's true, except admit it and then—"

"Jessica, I—"

"Just answer one question," she flared. "Do you admit it or not?"

"I admit it," Anchylus shouted.

He wasn't angry. He shouted because he felt he was cornered and that a show of anger was the only available defense. "I admit it," he added more guiltily, "but I ask you, for God's sake, to let me—"

"Please, Anchylus," Jessica said. She sat down in a gold chair. Though she was still breathing oddly, she seemed to have regained some of her control.

". . . let me explain," he finished. But she, twisted sideways away from him, shook her head, begging him not to go on. Silence fell. It lasted several seconds—perhaps longer. He could feel her trembling. At last she lifted her head.

"We had a rouser," she said with sudden, incredible placidity. "A real rouser. The classic scene, woman to woman. Oh, my God—" She buried her face in her hands, her thin, broad shoulders heaving. Anchylus couldn't tell whether she was laughing or crying but he suddenly had the feeling that all might not, after all, be completely lost.

"I respect your taste," she said through her fingers. "She's beautiful, in a coarse way. I'm weary of the whole sordid affair. Really!"

"What did she have to say?"

"She wanted me to give you up, of course. She indicated that she had a prior claim. I think she's right, don't you?" Jessica uttered these words in a cold, ironic way. Then, dropping her handkerchief, she slipped from the low gilt chair onto her knees. "Anchylus! Why? Why?"

"I don't know, dearest," he said. Hardly able to believe that events had taken this new turn, he caught her in his arms, holding her against him as he remained seated in the chair.

"I know, I know why," she said. "I don't have to ask. Asking was cowardly, but—never mind. You had her because of . . . needs. Your needs as a man that you would not have dared to ask me for and that I would have refused you if you had asked. Oh, I've faced that. I've had a session with myself. Would you like to know what I decided?"

He nodded. He did not trust himself to speak.

86

"I have decided that it was my fault," Jessica said. "Oh, I'm not absolving you, not entirely, but . . . it still was basically my fault. I decided that. I had not intended to tell you because I may never, and I'm quite sure I never shall, really forgive you even though it *was* my fault. I also decided that if I broke off with you, as I first intended to, you'd find another woman immediately since all women—everybody, in fact—is replaceable to you, as I've told you before. And do you want to know what else?" she demanded, taking his face between her hands, feasting on his face with looks of ravishing tenderness. "I decided that we should announce our engagement right away. Yes, and get married right away. Before anything else can happen, while we still love each other better than anything. That is, if you want me, now that you've seen my temper."

"Want you!" Anchylus broke in. "Jessie, I . . . but you must listen—"

"No, don't say anything. I may as well tell you this one last doubt I have because it's a doubt, just a suspicion from something she said. Well, just toward the end of our set-to she hinted that she had a winning card or something. I don't know what. Some reason why you would never really be free of her, no matter how angry you were about her coming here, or how much we loved each other. 'There's a reason,' she said. And she looked so—I don't know how to express it—triumphant or something. 'A reason.' That's what she said. Of course, I stood my ground; oh, I wouldn't stoop to ask her to explain, but I wondered what it could have been."

Anchylus felt his bowels crawl. A *reason!* He also in the last few weeks had had suspicions regarding Margaret—suspicions which he was not just about to bring up with Jessica.

"I'll be damned if I know," he said.

Some of the ecstatic, rapturous joy faded from Jessica's expression.

"Because," she said, "if it was a real *reason*, there is only one thing it could be. And if it were that, I don't know what we'd do. I just don't know."

14 THERE WASN'T a cable car in sight. Anchylus turned down the hill on foot. At the foot of California Street a wall of white fog marched in from the Golden Gate, heavy and thick as a glacier.

He was happier in a sense than he had ever been in his life before. He had won Jessica. It was no longer a case of her being "ready";

she loved him, she had said so. She was his completely, all his, barring the one final act of physical possession, and even this would soon come to pass, with marriage promised for the near future. Or perhaps—in her present outgoing, giving and rapturous state of mind —even before marriage, or so she had hinted.

God Almighty! Had he been lucky! He had certainly thought there for a while that he'd lost her, and then, the proof, in her living tenderness, the proof of her determination to hold "all obstacles gossamer." It was perfect, marvelous, and yet in all its wonder, tucked away there in a corner of his mind the hint of the damned *reason* thrown out by Margaret. What had she meant by it? And had this *reason*, whatever it might be, given her the notion of going to California Street—just as he'd somehow always feared she would— with her wild claims and demands?

Well, she had gone too far this time. She must know it, too. She must know this meant the end between them. So maybe it was all for the best. Here was the chance he had waited for, the release from the old bonds of affection and friendliness which he still felt, damn it all, in spite of his anger.

Goodbye to all that now. They were through and he'd tell her so. The scene ahead of him, he could tell, wouldn't be easy, because of both his own feelings and Margaret's resourcefulness. She would try all her wiles on him, tell lies, make excuses by the dozen, finally appeal to his pity, remind him of all he owed her, as he did, of course. Damn it. Let her, though. This time it wouldn't do her any good.

He hurried south on the familiar block, climbed the stairs to the apartment, then unlocked the door with his key. Usually, when he came home unexpectedly, it was his habit to yell out as if he had expected her to be standing there waiting for him—she, a piece of property wholly his even though, with eventual parting in view, she had been on kind of temporary lease from fate, a rental, about to be vacated.

Tonight he didn't shout. It was not a night to be likened by any habitual, unthinking act to any other night of their life together. He didn't feel like shouting anyway, and then, even before he had closed the door behind him, it struck him that Margaret was not there. There was no sense of a person in the place. There was an empty feel to it as there could never be to a place which Margaret charged with her spacious vitality, not to mention the trailing clouds of perfume and the rich smells of Irish cooking that she brought into being wherever she was. The parlor looked neat, a way it never looked if she was home, even if she had just cleaned it. A sterile neatness, too. Almost a desolation.

Hold on a minute. He'd been wrong. There was someone here after all, someone in the kitchen where he'd heard—he didn't know what. Also the lights had been turned on there.

Anchylus gave the kitchen door a shove. He stood looking down at Rosa Falconi where she sat on the kitchen stool, backed into a corner with a tray of knives and forks in her lap, which she'd been cleaning.

"So it's you," Anchylus said disgustedly.

Rosa Falconi looked at him calmly. She had always been mortally afraid of him. He knew that she tried to time her visits to Red Margaret at those periods when he was sure to be at work. Sometimes when he left in the morning, Margaret would say, "I guess I'll have Rosa over today," as if to prepare him, put him on notice not to glare at the flower-maker and terrify her the more if she was still around when he came home, licking up warmth and a crumb of friendship like a charity cat.

"Where's Marge?" he asked.

Rosa Falconi didn't look afraid now. She had a sharp and spiteful look.

"*Se n'é andata*," she said.

He nodded. He got the drift of this, even though Margaret was better than he at understanding the Italian, mixed with a little mispronounced English, which Rosa spouted.

"Where?"

Rosa shrugged. "*Non só*," she said. "*Non só dove. Ma ti ha lasciato una lettera*." Since it was clear from Anchylus' expression—one of bafflement combined with rising annoyance—that he did not understand, she added in English, "Come, I show."

The letter had been written on a sheet of drugstore paper evidently bought for this purpose (Anchylus later found a box of the same in the bedroom wastebasket). The letter had been placed in an envelope addressed with his name and fastened to a bed pillow with a pearl-headed hatpin which was one of the few, if not the only, personal possessions left behind by Margaret in her departure.

DEAR HEART:

I am sick all through me writing this now the last word of goodbye between the two of us not that you are worth the tears I shead. No man is and you least of all running out be-

89

hind my back my curse is on you. [This was scratched out.] No. I put no curse on you because I know the evil thot you had when it cum into you to be like the fellers in the books you told me that married the Boss his daughter. That was it. I was about to curse you but you know I have the Gift my curse would dam you forever Anchylus Saxe. I hold back my hand. Instid a curse I bless you for the love was once between us I kin feel no other way. I went to her and told her to her face that much she is sure to tell you but I never told the Reason. Maybe she thot I was lying let her think so God in his mercy put her eyes out and plug her Bung falsehearted thing she is to take what is not hers. I seen the new nail shining like a juel and took the mony onder the Bord it is mine be rights tho I would rather crwl on my Ass from here to chicago than tell her the falsehearted thing she is the Reason you will always be my own it was made known to me be a doctor I am carin your child in my Wom that is the God's own turth so help me God. Whin I follow my face out of your house I go to bare the child and raise it where yuel never find it. God be good to you my Pulse and now it is time to say Goodbye.

MARGARET TIGHE (O'BOYLAN)

III

The Party

"Mr. Roosevelt was essaying a vast experiment in conservatism designed to . . . restore life to institutions that were beginning to decay."
—San Francisco *Examiner*, November 1934

1   "Now, Matt," Angela Wilke said, "you have to get all this straight, because it's all very important, and if anything goes wrong and one of us has to be crucified it will be me, not you, and you wouldn't want that to happen, would you?"

"God forbid, honey child," Matt Brody said. He put his arm around Miss Wilke, dropping his right hand gently downward.

Miss Wilke terminated contact with the hand by a slight shrugging motion.

"And we'll have none of that either, you oaf," she said.

Matt Brody was the only member of the editorial staff who got fresh with her—possibly because he was the only staffer who came into the office much—and he only got fresh in a nice sort of way, as if conveying a feeling of esteem. At this time Matt was one of the youngest and brightest staffers on *The Day* and he was frequently called up from his regular duties to perform special chores for Mr. Saxe. Mr. Saxe liked him and said Matt would go far. He had made this remark several times in Miss Wilke's hearing, and it was no more than the truth. Matt would go far and he did, almost every day, traveling around the city and doing the kind of errands which couldn't conveniently be handled by one of the secretaries or by someone connected with the Saxe household.

Miss Wilke liked Matt Brody too. You couldn't help it. He was efficient and nice looking in spite of his sloppy clothes and his artificially tough ways.

Miss Wilke felt much older than Matt. She had already been one of the front-office secretaries for two years, and her sense of seniority was one of the factors which made her repel any pass directed at her by Matt. That she would have felt an equal obligation to repel a pass if he had dated her away from the office Miss Wilke did not know and didn't have the chance to find out since, so far, he hadn't tried to date her. He might, of course, sometime. That was a possibility, even though perhaps a remote one, and Miss Wilke didn't wish to lose sight of it entirely. She moistened her lips, looking up at Matt with her number one smile. She continued to stand beside him near her desk, which she had been about to leave when he entered, holding in her hand a sheet of paper headed: THINGS TO SEE RE SAXE DEBUT BALL—7 Oct. 1934.

"Did you get the quail for Griff Williams?" she asked.

Matt Brody groaned. "Those quails," he said, "cost this newspaper about ten bucks apiece. I promised two guys from circulation, guys that know how to shoot, two bucks. Then we had to buy their shells and licenses, hire a car for them, and put in for beer. Three cases."

"That's a lot of beer for two dozen quail," Miss Wilke said. A frown like a Chinese letter appeared between her eyes. Evidently the beer appeared to be the only budget item which, in her opinion, did not tally with the results.

"I'll say it is," Matt Brody said. "Guys have to roam the woods. Trained hunters, armed to the teeth, blasting birds out of the trees. They walk miles, fill the air with lead, sweat like hell, sop up beer, burn gasoline—all so a band leader, playing a paid engagement, gets quails as a tip. Why does Williams get quails? I don't see the point of it."

"Griff Williams likes quail," Miss Wilke said. "He's in big demand. It seems the Saxe girls want to make sure he'll be there. Did you contact the lady from—" Miss Wilke consulted the memorandum in her hand—"the California Society for the Preservation of Native Flora?"

"Yup," Matt Brody said.

"How much beer did *she* want," Miss Wilke said sardonically, "or

94

did you let her have some of what the quail shooters kicked back to you?"

"Suspicions will get you nowhere," Matt said comfortably. "If there had been a kickback it would have been whisky. I don't like beer. I doubt if this lady likes anything."

"What did she want?"

"Wanted to know, was it true Baldocchis were doing the boss's ballroom in Sierra stuff. Pulling up manzanitas by the roots and gobbing up the joint with sagebrush. She said the Society was putting through a law against cruelty to sagebrush and could she inspect to see if we'd amputated any pine boughs. I said no, all the stuff had been brought up from *southern* California. That seemed to satisfy her. Is it on the level? Are the mountains being stripped for this cotillion?"

"The décor," Miss Wilke said, quoting from her notes, "will be that of a secluded canyon. I don't suppose it will be too secluded, with six hundred people invited, but that's the décor. By the way, I finally arranged with the police department to rope off Taylor Street and make California Street one way there between nine and ten-thirty. You can tell Mr. Saxe in case he asks you."

"I doubt if I'll be seeing him," Matt Brody said.

"You certainly will be seeing him," Miss Wilke said; "that's the most important thing of all. He wants you to be there."

"What for?"

"In a tuxedo," Miss Wilke continued. "What size do you wear? I figured forty-two. I hope that's right. I called Selix's and they're holding a rent for you. It comes with shirt, tie, shoes, socks and garters. You don't own one, do you?"

"Hell, no," Matt Brody said; "but what's the pitch? What am I supposed to do there?"

"That's what I'm trying to tell you," Miss Wilke said, "and please pay attention, because this is the most important thing of all. Letty Meeker has an exclusive on this party. I repeat. An Exclusive. She asked for it, and Mr. Saxe told her she could have it. After all, it figures as a *Day* exclusive with two imperial daughters coming out the same night and the party right in their own house and all. *The Examiner* and *Chronicle* get handouts. Letty has them all written. You don't have to write them."

"If I had to write them you could get yourself another boy."

"You not only don't have to write them," Miss Wilke said, "you will under no circumstances be permitted to write them. This is a

95

society event, dear boy, not a police-court nasty. You, in your tuxedo, size forty-two, complete with shirt, tie, shoes, socks and garters, will be on hand to see that no one from the *Ex* or *Chron* sneaks in. Letty is nervous about it. She knows that Millie Robbins or Ethel Whitmire would never try to make it themselves but she's scared they might send over some staffer from Cityside. You know the staffers; you keep them out. What's the matter? You no like?"

"I like everything," Matt Brody said; "I love my work."

"That's what I thought," Miss Wilke said.

"I love," Matt Brody said, "every phase of it. Organizing quail safaris. Fighting off ladies who preserve sagebrush. Renting size forty-two suits when I wear thirty-eight short. All I want to know is the full extent of my duties. Besides keeping out the staffers, do I also have to mount guard on the family silver and debutantes' minks?"

"Burns detectives," Miss Wilke said, "will take care of that part. For your information there will be not one but two Burns detectives on the premises. So if the staffers you identify don't want to be thrown out, the muscle men will help you. Now you'd better get down to Selix's and pick up the thirty-eight short, or whatever, before they close. And don't—" she finished, deftly checking another attempt at physical exploration by Matt "—try to do that to the girls tonight. They might not be as sweet about it as I am. They're not as nice girls. Goodbye, now."

"Goodbye, Love Bucket," Matt said.

As he left, she was telephoning Mr. Kruger, head of the Palace Hotel's Catering Department, to inform him that if, as she'd been informed, he couldn't supply a hundred extra chocolate ices molded in the form of typewriters, the suggested substitutes—pineapple sherbets shaped like lyres—would be all right.

2 ANCHYLUS DRESSED with care, putting on a full-dress suit. A full-dress suit was indicated if you were giving a ball—Jessica had emphasized this—not to say a ball at which you were introducing to society not merely one daughter but two. He realized, struggling somewhat awkwardly with his white tie, that he, no less than the girls, would be on exhibition.

Tonight the people of the city would be coming to see what he had made of his house and his family. They would be coming with more than the common amount of curiosity.

He settled the white piqué vest on his shoulders, twisting an arm around behind him to adjust the strap. Almost twenty years had passed since he had first rigged himself up in a contraption like this (he had worn tails to his wedding, an evening affair held in this very house). Nineteen years, to be exact.

His mind took another jump into the past. Nineteen years, and almost exactly fifteen since the event which, more conspicuously than his excellent marriage or even more so, perhaps, than his rapid rise in the city's affairs, had focused attention on him. This event had taken place on an October night in 1920. A few months previously, Margaret Tighe, once again identifying herself as Margaret Tighe O'Boylan, had unexpectedly initiated and then haphazardly dropped a suit against him in the state of Washington charging him with paternity of her fatherless daughter. Then came the October date and the appearance of a youngish, red-haired woman with a little girl at her side at a charity home near Eugene, Oregon. The woman had left the child with the home, stating that she could no longer provide for her. She had added the information that the child's name was Pamela and that her father was Anchylus Saxe, editor and publisher of *The San Francisco Day*.

"Are you ready, dear?" Jessica spoke around the partially opened door connecting his dressing room with their shared bedroom. She was ready ahead of him, as she always was, and as if to prove this, if it needed proving, she pulled the door wide enough for him to get a glimpse of her in her satin dress made by Nelly Gaffney for tonight's occasion. The dress was rather daringly cut in front, according to the new style, and its creamy color set off the rich olive tints of her skin and the blackness of her hair. On her head, a veritable crown, perched the tiara Anchylus had bought her for their fifteenth wedding anniversary. She had not been sure, at first, that she should wear it. Wouldn't a tiara, at a ball in one's own house, seem ostentatious? Not until he'd mentioned—rather subtly, he felt now—how becoming the tiara was to her, even though purchased primarily for the opera, had he won the argument.

In any costume at all, or without any, Jessica was a damned good-looking woman, and at this moment she looked positively dazzling.

Anchylus turned and smiled at her. "Pretty near," he said. "What do you think about having a little nip up here before we go down?"

"Oh, I don't think so, dear," Jessica said. "It's almost nine. I really think I should go down, just in case someone comes in a minute or two early. I think Pamela's gone down already."

"All right," he said, "you go ahead. I'm going to tie this stinking tie once more; then I'll be right with you."

"You look very nice," Jessica said, "I wish I could send Temple up to help you, but he's really terribly busy."

"Oh, I know that," Anchylus said. He jerked at the ends of the tie to even them up.

"The Palace men don't know where anything is. He's had to show them. And dear—" Jessica paused until Anchylus rolled an eye, indicating that he was paying attention to her "—if you do have a nip by yourself, don't take more than one. There is nothing worse than a man standing in his own receiving line breathing the fumes of alcohol on his guests. I've had the experience and I know."

"Don't worry about it," Anchylus said.

"I won't," Jessica said. "I've made up my mind not to worry about anything. I just know that everything is going to be perfect."

"Why not?" Anchylus said. "Of course it is."

Jessica now opened the door fully. She took a step into the dressing room. "It's really a milestone in our lives together. You feel that way about it too?"

"I do, honey," Anchylus said.

"I'm glad," Jessica said, "and I want to thank you for everything you've done to make all this possible. I'll always be grateful to you and I know the girls will too. Now I'm going downstairs. Please don't be long."

"I won't," Anchylus said.

He took the tailcoat off its hanger and wriggled into it, working the starched cuffs through the tight sleeves. There was Jessica for you—thanking him for something that was much her own doing. It was she who had brought the girls up so well, given them the know-how they needed, the poise of true ladies (which they were, of course; let nobody dare to contradict that, ever), thus making them eligible for honor and conspicuity, for the triumph of being ushered into adulthood, as it were, in such a splendid, almost brazen way as this—by a ball in their own house! And the house itself had been, to start with, Jessica's—the great house her grandfather had built and which had come down to her in the estate of Fabian, who, as spirited and articulate as ever, spouting quotations and irritated directions to those around him, had gone to his death in the early twenties, prodded over the brink not by an assassin's bullet, as his daughter had always feared, but by a gangrenous appendix.

Anchylus pressed his wide feet into patent-leather pumps. Jessica had picked them out for him: pumps with large black bows on them, the height of fashion. They'd been expensive, like everything else that had to do with tonight's festivities. (Anchylus, whose great problem in his wandering days had been to keep himself well shod, reckoned the cost of shoes carefully, though he paid little attention to other budget items.) He grimaced, feeling his toes bunch in their pointed scabbards. What was a cramped toe or two, if your daughters were coming out? What was money? He was spending more of it tonight than anyone had spent for a private party in San Francisco in a long time. In the Depression, people had lost their nerve about parties; it was time someone showed them the way to get it back. He'd stood firm on that, and Jessica had been delighted from the first with his notion of bringing out both the older girls at the same time. So had Alexandra, who loved show for its own sake. They'd turned a little, had been dubious as his plans grew, but he'd laughed off their objections.

"If we're going to give a ball," he said, "let's give a whing-ding."

"What do you think, Mother?" Alexandra asked.

It was Alexandra who always put everything up to her mother, as a court of last resort, while Sharon put things up to Alexandra, and Pamela, the quiet one, put them up to herself.

"I think," Jessica said, "that we'll wind up giving the kind of party your father wants."

"Not that I don't adore your ideas, Father," Alexandra said, "only, I must say, the way you're talking about it, it sounds more like a New York party than a San Francisco party."

"Fine," Anchylus said; "then let people imagine they're in New York."

He'd been glad to spend the money. What else did you have it for? In any business operation you set aside money for institutional advertising, for prestige, and this ball, in his eyes, was that kind of spending. Looked at another way, it was the kind of spending you put out to hire a good lawyer if you were in a jam—an expenditure for honor, for justification.

Let the people come and look. They would see how things had worked out—the people who were friends, and those who weren't, and those who were neither friends nor enemies but would come now because they had sons or daughters, or both, who were "on the list," but above all because they were curious. He knew very well the way they'd all talked, friends and enemies alike, and what some of them had said at the time Jessica and he had brought Pamela into the house.

The comment of Helen Wilkins—Mrs. T. W. Wilkins, herself a

99

friend and married to a friend—was typical, if repeated accurately, and he thought it had been. "The Saxes are turning a scandal into a glory. That's making the family a law unto itself."

If that was the kind of remark you got from your friends, you didn't need enemies. Not that it made much difference to him. He was running a newspaper, so to hell with it. Sooner or later, if you were running a newspaper, you got in the last word.

Jessica was the one he'd been thinking about. She'd known what to expect; she'd grown up with these people. Take Helen Wilkins: Jessica had gone to school with her, made her own debut the same year. Yes, indeed, she'd certainly known what to expect, but to Jessica's everlasting credit she hadn't hesitated a second. When the call came through from the people in Eugene she'd gone up there and got the little girl and brought her home.

It would have been an easy thing to dodge. Almost too easy. The red-haired woman hadn't left a name and the kid hadn't even had a birth certificate, not one that anybody could locate. Legally, apparently, she hadn't been born—but there she was, a living, breathing kid, confused, lonesome and bitched up so bad that for a while she wouldn't even talk to anyone. A kid not listed in the books, but the right age to have the dates check out. Red Margaret's kid. That much her physical resemblance established beyond a doubt.

That had been enough for Jessica. She'd packed her up and taken the next train. Neither he nor she had ever later wanted to mess around with the blood tests to determine paternity or any of that rigmarole. The child could have been his, and so for Jessica she was.

"If you'd had a child by a Hottentot or an Indian, I would have felt it was ours," she'd said to him once; "any child of yours, anywhere in the world, is ours, not any other woman's. Mine. Because you're mine."

He'd almost laughed at the romanticism of that. But, again, that was Jessica for you. He'd asked her seriously, and he thought sensibly, if she hadn't wanted to have the Bureau of Missing Persons check for Margaret. Jessica said she didn't. He'd had a hunch that Jessica felt the woman was dead, that leaving Pamela in the home had been her way of checking out. And there had been no doubt of the fact that she was very ill.

One thing was for sure—he'd had no regrets. Or perhaps only one— that if it had been in the cards to work out this way it couldn't have happened a little sooner. That way there would have been less division among the girls themselves, growing up; as it was, Alexandra, then four, and Sharon, almost three, had been a unit, knit together with kid-stubbornness and kid-snobbery to resist the new-little-sister and dear-little-girl-for-you-to-play-with build-up that he and Jessica had given Pamela.

Kids were that way. There wasn't anything you could do about it except wait for the hoard of humanness and slowly experimenting friendliness that kids put into all their activities to take effect and, little by little, overcome the resistance and strangeness—a resistance and strangeness exaggerated somewhat, perhaps, by Pamela's being the way she'd been then: a silent and suspicious little thing.

Nobody could say it hadn't come to be all right. It had, and if, as young adulthood set in, the girls had tended to go their separate ways again, that, too, was to be expected. There was no harm in it. They were vital girls, all of them—each a force in her own way and each interesting.

Let the people come and look. They'd see. They might even find out a few things they didn't know; and if they still felt Jessica was a traitor to her class and he some kind of illuminated upstart or, as Fabian Rupke had once called him, "a throwback," that was all right too; they would be dancing to the traitor's music tonight, they would be drinking the upstart's wine.

Anchylus Saxe drew a slow breath, testing the integrity of the piqué vest. It held. Pleased with this, he dabbed with gold-backed brushes at his iron mop of hair. In front of him, in a small vase, tilted a white carnation, put there by Jessica with instructions as to what was to be done with it. Anchylus, as directed, stuck it into his buttonhole. He went down the great stair of his house to the place where, midway between the foot of it and the open door of the ballroom, the receiving line was to be and where his wife and his adopted daughter Pamela stood in position as in a military review while Temple, the butler, hovered at the front door, ready to open it at the ring of the first guest.

"Where's Sharon and Alexandra?" he demanded.

"I'm afraid they may be dawdling, dear," Jessica said. "Perhaps I ought to go up and call them."

Anchylus pulled out his watch and looked at it. He still had it on the gold chain he'd bought while he worked in Fabian Rupke's press-room.

"No," he said. "It's nine o'clock, straight up. Pamela and I don't want to be left here all alone. You'd better tell Temple to do it."

"All right," Jessica said. "Will you please, Temple?"

And Temple, with a ducking, assenting movement of his pale, blue-veined butler face, toddled off toward the house telephone in his pantry.

3 BOTH Anchylus and Jessica knew that the girls had been moving apart as they grew up. They had sensed this fact without seeing the extent of it or knowing how it had been prodded along by neighbor talk and school talk and backstairs servant talk.

Children got to find things out. After they did, they took action. Several incidents had shown which way the wind was blowing, one in particular—although knowledge of this had leaked through to the older people only in snatches, its real scope and significance not being revealed until much later on.

This certain Saturday Gertrude Donovan, a girl in Alexandra's class at Miss Burke's, had invited Alexandra and Sharon to have lunch at the Fairmont and go to a matinee of Katherine Hepburn in *Little Women*. Then at the last minute Gertrude had come down with a cold. Mrs. Donovan telephoned Jessica to suggest that her husband, Oakleigh, could still meet the girls and give them lunch. He would enjoy it, and it would be far better than calling off the date. Jessica agreed with this; but it appeared there was one hitch. Oakleigh Donovan could not stay for the picture. Did Jessica mind, Mrs. Donovan inquired, if he just took the girls to the theater and bought their tickets? They could see the movie, which was said to be quite wonderful. Then Jessica could pick them up or they could come home in a taxi.

Jessica said she didn't mind. It would have been better if the car could have picked them up after the theater. She would have felt a little easier about it, that way. Still, Anchylus was using the Pierce Arrow and she herself had an Altar Guild meeting at the Cathedral. So under the circumstances a taxi would be quite all right, provided Alexandra and Sharon came straight home.

The lunch turned out to be pleasant. Alexandra had lobster cocktail and lamb chops and Sharon had fruit cocktail and roast beef and they both had baked Alaska for dessert. Mr. Donovan had a hard roll and five martinis. He made jokes all through lunch. After signing the check and having one martini for the road he took them to the theater and bought the tickets, leading them right to the ticket-taker before he left them. When he took off his hat to say goodbye he shook hands with Sharon, then put his arm around Alexandra and kissed her. Sharon felt that without the martinis he would not have done this. She had noticed in the last year or so even old family friends who had been in the habit of kissing them both now seemed to concentrate on her older sister, especially the men. Alexandra's dimensions were very good, and you missed none of them in the dress she was wearing. She was the only girl in Miss Burke's who could look beautiful in a plain wool dress with a white Buster Brown collar, and it was her dimensions, Sharon felt, that did it.

"I hope you both enjoy the show," Mr. Donovan said.

"We will, Mr. Donovan," Alexandra said. "Thank you so much for the tickets. And for the lunch."

"Thank you so much, Mr. Donovan," Sharon echoed dutifully.

But Mr. Donovan had already put his hat back on and turned away.

Alexandra made Sharon go in ahead of her. As they walked out onto the thick carpet of the lobby, the head usher flipped his hand up. He produced one finger from a bunch of fingers with a snappy motion, like a person opening a spring knife, and intoned, "First aisle to your left. . . ."

Alexandra didn't move. She was looking back toward the curb, where Mr. Donovan's taxi could be seen driving off.

The main feature had just gone on. People were still pouring from the lobby into the darkened area in front of the screen. The head usher asked Alexandra if he could see her stubs but Alexandra said, "There'll be no need of that," and dropped the stubs on the carpet. To the usher's amazement she took Sharon and dragged her out of the theater.

They went along Market Street toward Montgomery.

"What is it, Zan?" Sharon asked, hanging back and almost weeping in her disappointment and annoyance. "Why can't we see the show?"

"We're going somewhere else," Alexandra said, "so shut up. And when we get there, let me do the talking."

They went to the offices of Galt, Winterhalter & Dudley. Alexandra asked the girl at the reception desk if she could speak to Mr. Dudley. Both girls knew Mr. Dudley because he frequently dined at the California Street house, and it was a relief to Sharon to realize that in this strange place they were about to see someone they knew. She had not yet recovered from her disappointment about missing

Little Women. She felt miserable and fidgeted on the slippery seat of the big leather chair in the waiting room. Alexandra sat quietly, holding her gloves and looking at the wall.

They had not been waiting long when an inner door opened and Mr. Dudley came out.

"Well, for heaven's sake," he said. "Alexandra! How are you? And Sharon! Well, well! Is anyone with you, or did you drop in all by yourselves?"

"We dropped in by ourselves, Mr. Dudley," Alexandra said.

"Well, I'm delighted to see you," Mr. Dudley said.

"Could we go into your office, Mr. Dudley?" Alexandra asked.

"Why, of course," Mr. Dudley said in a more professional way, grateful for being prompted. "Won't you come in?"

Mr. Dudley was a cheerful, squarish man with a pink, fleshy face and thick, black eyebrows. He had very shrewd yet kindly blue eyes, and the hair on the top of his head was starting to get thin. Sharon rather liked him. In the office where he now took them she wiggled in another slippery-bottomed chair and studied the gleam of skin that could be seen through Mr. Dudley's hair on top.

"I thought at first the girl might have sent in the wrong name—that she meant *Mrs.* Saxe instead of the *Misses* Saxe. What in the world are you two doing way downtown?"

"We came down to see a movie," Alexandra said, "but we left."

"I see," Mr. Dudley said.

Sharon opened her mouth to say she had not wanted to leave, but Alexandra shut her up with a look.

"My sister and I," Alexandra said, "would both appreciate it if you didn't mention to our parents that we came to see you. It is rather confidential. We happen to need some advice on a legal point of law."

"Well, that's what we're here for," Mr. Dudley said good-naturedly, "lots of people come in all the time with just the same idea."

He spoke lightly, but some of the glow had faded from his manner. Until Alexandra mentioned law he had perhaps suspected that the girls lacked cab fare home or would request financing for a couple of chocolate malts.

"You see, Mr. Dudley," Alexandra went on, "there is an adoption matter in our family. It happened some years ago. You know all about that, I'm sure. That is what my sister and I have come to ask you about."

Mr. Dudley had become quiet. From being rosy and spread-out, his face looked narrower. He pulled up his gold watch chain and carefully rubbed the Phi Beta Kappa key which hung from it, as less well-established men might rub a rabbit's foot.

"Well, well!" he said.

"There are one or two things we'd like to know," Alexandra said.

Mr. Dudley poured some water in a glass from a carafe on his desk and slowly sipped it.

"I'm flattered, my dear, that you come to me," he said, "but don't you think that any questions on this subject could be answered more fittingly by someone in your own family? Your dear mother, for instance."

"Mother won't tell us anything," Alexandra said, "at least, she never has. Of course, we know more than she thinks. We know Pamela is a bastard. Illegitimate, that is."

At the words *bastard* and *illegitimate* Mr. Dudley's body jerked as if he had been stuck with a pin. Sharon also, though she did not jerk, was shocked. Never had she heard Alexandra use these particular words. She hadn't even used them in their talks alone at night when Alexandra used quite a number of odd words, and to hear her use them now, in these strange surroundings and to a grown person, gave her a choked-up feeling. Language of this sort could be terrifying to someone who only the week before at Miss Burke's had been sent to detention for saying *ain't*.

Mr. Dudley sat back in his chair jiggling his watch chain and studying Alexandra with the same narrow look.

"We know that for sure, Mr. Dudley," Alexandra said.

"Not many of us, in the law business, know anything for sure," Mr. Dudley said. "However, without inquiring how you came by this piece of information, my dear, may I ask what else you want to know?"

"We want to know what relation she is to us."

"I don't think I quite see what you mean."

"I mean," Alexandra said, "is she our sister or isn't she? Because being a bastard and living with us wouldn't necessarily make her our sister, would it? Or wouldn't it? That could make a big difference and we'd like somebody to tell us."

Mr. Dudley looked at her again, but differently this time. "Well, well," he said. He turned sideways in his chair then and looked out the window. "Yes," he said, "well, yes. I suppose it would."

"That's what we want to know," Alexandra said. "You can speak freely. I know that sex comes into it, but we know about sex. At least I know about it and I've explained quite a bit of it to Sharon. She'll understand whatever you have to say. We both will."

Mr. Dudley was quiet for a moment or two. Then he said, "Alexandra, was coming here to see me your own idea, or did some other person suggest it to you?"

"It was my—our—own idea," Alexandra said.

"I see," Mr. Dudley said. "How old are you, Alexandra?"

"I'll be seventeen in two and a half months," Alexandra said. "I'm making my debut in October. Mother said I didn't have to wait until I was eighteen. She thinks I will be mature enough when I am seventeen and three months."

"She might have something there," Mr. Dudley said. "How old are you, Sharon?"

"Fifteen," Sharon said. "Almost fifteen and a half."

Mr. Dudley reflected. He got out of his chair and walked up and down the room. "I'll be damned," he said; "excuse me, girls." He sat down again and looked straight at them, first at Alexandra and then at Sharon, who was now sitting up better and trying to look older, since age seemed to have become such a big issue in this talk.

"Well, girls," Mr. Dudley said, "I've been in law practice eighteen years, and this is the first time I—but never mind. . . . You've asked me a grownup question and I'm going to give you a grownup answer. You may as well get the facts straight. I think you're entitled to that."

"Yes, Mr. Dudley," Alexandra said.

"All right," Mr. Dudley said; "now about Pamela. She came into the world as the result of a love affair, as you seem to have heard. I should certainly suggest that you do not try to judge the rights and wrongs of this until you are much older or perhaps never. Such matters are often—and in fact generally—puzzling even to much older persons. Whatever happened, you must realize that in all likelihood it was less your father's fault than that of the . . . er . . . other person involved. She was most unhappy and misguided, as such persons always are. It was a most unfortunate situation. Actually it concerned nobody but your father and mother, and your mother and father reached a complete understanding about it. Your mother behaved with great courage and . . . er . . . nobility, and you should never have the slightest feeling for either her or your father that is not one of admiration for the way in which they faced this difficult situation."

Mr. Dudley stopped and took another sip of water. He rubbed his Phi Beta Kappa key again. Alexandra and Sharon sat perfectly quiet and waited for him to go on.

"There was," he said, "the problem of the little girl and her terrible position, and in this emergency your dear mother did a most courageous thing. She went and fetched the girl, Pamela, and took her to your home. She gave the whole world to understand that she and your poor father did not cast off this child but acknowledged her and that she was to be brought up as one of you, as she has been. Those are the facts. They reflect nothing but credit on anyone concerned."

Alexandra by-passed the last remark as being editorial in content. She drove at the gist of what had been communicated. "You mean, she was adopted?"

Mr. Dudley nodded. "Yes," he said, "she was adopted. Not in a formal way, but she was adopted."

"And her name is Saxe?"

"Yes."

"I don't see how that can be," Alexandra said.

"I shall explain it to you," Mr. Dudley said. "Damn it all anyway. I don't know how I ever got into all this."

"Please, Mr. Dudley," Alexandra said.

"Well, now," Mr. Dudley said, "there is a specific law that covers what you've asked me. I think—yes, by George, I'm going to let you read it for yourselves. Also—but one more thing! I'll keep my bargain with you not to tell your parents that you've been to see me but I won't bind you to the same deal. If at any time, remember —at any time—you want to say where you obtained your information you can say you got it from me. Is that clear? You can say I thought it best to answer you explicitly."

Mr. Dudley flipped a switch connected with a box on his desk. He spoke into the box. "Cal Civil two thirty, Wickett," he said.

Having given this order, Mr. Dudley sat back, watching the door. Alexandra and Sharon watched it also. Time, which had flown so fast till now, dragged painfully, though it could only have been a minute or two before the door opened and a sharp-faced, sandy-haired man in a black coat came in carrying a thick book which he handed to Mr. Dudley.

"Thank you, Wickett," Mr. Dudley said.

The sharp-faced man lowered his sharp nose a little, then raised it again. He turned and left the room.

"That was our librarian, Mr. Wickett," Mr. Dudley said.

He picked up the book, which had a slip of paper in it to mark a place, but Mr. Dudley did not seem to need the place marker; his pale, well-kept hands flicked through the pages like the hands of a pianist running over a keyboard. His fingers seemed to find the place without direction from his brain.

"This is Section Two Hundred and Thirty of the Civil Code of California," he said. "I believe it will remove the doubts that seem to have been bothering you. Alexandra, you may sit here in my chair and read the paragraph which I am marking. Sharon, you may stand beside her. If, when you have read it, you have any further questions, I shall be glad to answer them."

Mr. Dudley pressed back the covers of the book so that it would lie flat. He laid a paperknife along the inner margin of the right-hand page, marking a passage with his pencil. Alexandra crossed round to him and he made her sit down in his chair, showing Sharon where she was to stand beside her. All his movements now were executed with a precision of manner which, later in life, Sharon was to observe in lawyers when they handled books in courtrooms. Or perhaps it would be truer to say that, though she had never been in a courtroom, Mr. Dudley's manner gave her her first impression of one.

The paragraph was marked with a light bracket. Alexandra read it through slowly and in silence; Sharon, looking over her shoulder, did the same. Memorizing things in school was never easy for her, but she memorized this paragraph when she had read it twice and for a long time afterward was able to bring it before her mind with little effort.

> The father of an illegitimate child, by publicly acknowledging it as his own, receiving it as such, with the consent of his wife, if he is married, into his family and otherwise treating it as if it were a legitimate child, thereby adopts it as such; and such child is thereupon deemed for all purposes legitimate from its birth.

4 AFTER HIS CALLERS had left, George Dudley sat at his desk for some time. He didn't feel quite easy in his mind about the interview which had just taken place, and after giving it some thought he decided that it might be well, in order partially at least to forestall repercussions, to inform the firm's senior partner, Hiram Galt, of what had happened.

Hiram Galt had been disturbed.

"All right, Hiram," George Dudley had said, a little defensively, "what would you have done if you'd been in my shoes? They come in here with their little bare faces hanging out and ask about their bastard sister. What would you have told them?"

"They called her a bastard?"

"They most certainly did. Or at least the older one did, Alexandra. She was the one who carried on the interrogation."

"It sounds to me as if she'd pinned you to the mat."

"Maybe she did. I'm ready to admit she took me by surprise. But she had that much information. Of that I am positive."

"Perhaps she was only fishing for it."

"No. It didn't come out like that. She also told me, by way of introduction, that I could speak freely since they both knew all about sex."

"Good God."

"I can't help it if you approve or not, Hiram," George Dudley said; "I think I did the only thing possible. If I had refused to tell them they would have found out eventually from someone else, maybe gotten a completely mixed-up version. This way they know where they stand."

"I wish I knew where we stand," Hiram Galt said glumly. "Just let their parents get wind of this and some other firm will be handling the Saxe Trust Estate. Not to mention the San Francisco Day Publishing Company."

"I am more worried about the old man, to tell the truth."

"I can't tell about him. He might go along with your thinking. It's still even money that we lose both accounts."

"I suppose we could, but I doubt we will."

"Just let those kids start quoting Cal Civil two thirty around the house and we will. Honestly, George, there are times when I wonder about you."

"Let's wait and see. I just don't know what else I could have done."

"You could have kept your mouth shut, my good friend."

"Is that what you would have done?"

"I believe so. Yes! I think I can honestly say it is."

"Saying so is easy, Hiram," George Dudley said, "but just keep in mind you were never in the spot I was in. Damn these things anyway. They're tough on kids. I wanted to help them."

"George," Hiram Galt said, "you're a great man. A gentle, kindly man. But next time you want to help some kids by expounding the law of bastardy, pick kids where we don't handle their family's legal business."

"All right, Hiram," George Dudley said.

"Be a Girl Scout master or something," Hiram Galt said, "tell them about the birds and the bees."

"Take it easy, Hiram," George Dudley said.

5 ALEXANDRA SAT in front of the mirror in the Lilac Room, the quarters which she shared with Sharon on the second floor of the California Street house. She was busy making up her face. Jessica had told her quite definitely that she could use lipstick, since the other girls were using lipstick, but no make-up. Alexandra had chosen to ignore the order. She was the only person in the family whose will was strong enough to oppose her mother's but even she, pitting herself against Jessica, relied on guile more than on strength; a head-on collision would result in her undoing. She had planned therefore to dress first, just in case her mother came in while she was dressing, and put on the make-up last—a judicious amount of base and rouge, of mascara deftly applied, and above all not too much, to both upper and lower lashes, and of eye shadow just enough to bless her with the haunted, dissipated look she felt she must have for her debut in society: the look that was all the rage. It wouldn't do to be ready on time; she must be late, or late enough, even though this was her debut, so that there would be no time for Jessica to object to her appearance or to order her to change it. She was studying the effect in the glass when the telephone rang; she spoke into it briefly, then dropped the small white receiver carelessly back on its cradle.

"It was Temple," she said; "they're down there waiting for us."

Sharon shivered. This was the moment—the hour when something started, she wasn't sure just what but more than a ball, however grand that might be. A moment of decision.

"Gosh, Zan. We'd better hurry."

"Hurrying is gauche," Alexandra said.

She took a long, slow look at herself in the mirror, then turned her head above her tapering, creamy shoulder and smiled at her sister.

"How do I look, Chicken?"

"You look . . . divine."

"Divine is a gauche word; you ought to stop using it. But thanks anyway," Alexandra said.

She stood up. She twisted her body in front of the mirror so as to study the smallness of her waist as compared to the fullness of her breasts and the outthrust curves of her thighs in the soft dress. She stood so for almost a minute.

"You look nice too," she said without turning.

"Thanks, Zan," Sharon said.

Alexandra didn't seem to hear. "I think," she said softly, speaking to her glittering image in the glass, "yes, I do believe that tonight I'm going to like me. And, I'm going to find out . . . something. But I'm not going to tell you. Anyway, not yet."

"What, Zan?" Sharon demanded breathlessly.

"You'll find out."

"Will you tell me?"

Alexandra considered. "I believe . . . yes. I'll tell you. Only you. But not until I'm sure. All right?"

"Oh, yes, Zan. Of course."

"Then it's agreed, Chicken," Alexandra said.

She looked at her sister in a wild, conspiratorial way. Then, suddenly, she laughed. When she laughed, perhaps because of the smallness, sharpness and evenness of her teeth and the full, sumptuous way her lips curved, showing her sharp little tongue, she looked reckless—vicious almost, Sharon thought. She loved Alexandra with a consuming, awesome love, and all her life, despite the fact that she herself got better marks in school, she had been led by Alexandra as by a person immeasurably older and wiser.

"Is it . . . about a man?" Sharon ventured timidly.

Alexandra's face changed. Her cheeks sucked in warningly. "You mustn't ask me, or—nothing. Wait. That's all I can say."

"All right, Zan," Sharon said.

She didn't understand Zan. That was the most exciting thing about her—that you never understood. It was baffling. Even about the party Alexandra had been baffling. Sharon had never thought that, after the visit to Galt, Winterhalter & Dudley, Alexandra would stand for making a joint debut with Pamela, yet she had not resisted the idea, had actually seemed to like it. This was all the stranger since at first, when she and Sharon had discussed what Mr. Dudley had told them, she had seemed to dislike Pamela intensely.

"I don't want to share my parents with anyone," she'd said darkly.

"Well, I know," Sharon said, "but in a way it isn't her fault, is it?"

"Who cares whose fault it is?" Alexandra said. "I won't have her putting on airs, that's all."

"You mean you mind her being here?" Sharon asked, puzzled.

Of the two of them, Alexandra had on the whole been nicer to Pamela than she had, right from the start—now so long ago.

"I never minded her being here," Alexandra said.

"Then what?"

"I just don't care too much about her having *rights*," Alexandra said. "That's where she gets the airs that she puts on."

"Gosh, Zan, I hadn't noticed," Sharon said, "you mean she's been putting them on lately?"

"She's always been putting them on," Alexandra said, "only I never noticed either. I just *wondered*. Now I know. Well, they'll find out."

"Who, Zan?"

"Everybody."

"You mean you're going to *do* something?"

"You're darn right I'm going to do something. She's a big phony, and she's made everything else phony. That's what it is."

"Maybe she can't help it," Sharon said weakly. She felt it was up to her to defend Pamela somehow, even at the risk of losing her closeness to Alexandra, yet she didn't know what arguments to use in her defense.

"It's the *situation*, not her," Alexandra said. "The situation just goes with the airs she puts on. Don't you see?"

"You'd better tell me, Zan."

"Well, it's very simple. We were supposed to be so proud of everything. *Our* house, *our* school, *our* manners. Blah, blah, blah. We had to give bigger parties and have better manners and get better marks than anybody to make up for *her*. That's why it's all so phony. And I'll tell you something else: everybody probably knows about her. They know everything about you in this town. It makes me sick."

"Probably," Sharon said desperately, "probably a few people know, but not everybody. We didn't even know until—"

"If a few people know," Alexandra said, "then everybody knows. Well, I'm not going to stick around here long. That's one thing they can count on."

"But where will you go, Zan?"

"Don't worry about that," Alexandra said.

From her face, Sharon knew that she was thinking about men, a subject they had covered in many previous discussions but still somehow never quite summed up to their mutual satisfaction.

"After a person has her debut," Alexandra said, "she can do what she wants. Or else what's the point of having one? She can

112

go where she wants, too. There's no reason," she said with intense, surprising bitterness, "why I have to hang around this pile of timbers. I've had about all of it I can stand."

The telephone rang again. Sharon stared at it blankly. She looked at Alexandra for directions and, since none was forthcoming, moved her hand as if to pick up the receiver. Alexandra caught her arm.

"Let it ring," she said; "we know what it's for, don't we?"

Scooping up a small bouquet ordered so she could hold it in the receiving line, she led the way out of the room.

6 OUTSIDE the Lilac Room a mild circle of light splashed downward. It came from a gas jet which was always kept burning there. At the time it was built in the late nineties the Saxe Mansion, as it was then called, had been equipped with both gas and electricity, the architects not having any secure faith that Mr. Edison's tricks with illumination would be of any permanent, practical worth. The gas had burned there when Jessica had been a girl growing up in this house and it burned there now, a mild votive offering to the past, kept as it was. Jessica liked things to stay the same, and then, too, gas was cheap.

Just past the circle of light, in a sudden plunge of darkness, the staircase dropped in a steep, powerful coil to the festive hall below. Around it the other rooms rose in layers, like rows of ascending balconies, four stories of bedrooms, sitting rooms and rooms for reading, games and entertainment, the grand tiers starting on the ground floor and ending in the section of artificial sky, made of imported glass, designed as a roof for the stairwell and equipped with miraculous, slowly turning galaxies of simulated stars.

The staircase itself was a splendid thing. The stairs were broad, ever widening, twisting down tremendously. Upon their solid surfaces was a rich and still handsome old carpet, dating from Fabian Rupke's time, woven in a design of gray and rose diamonds. On the inside of the stairwell, put there for ornament as well as protection, was a tulipwood banister, the top rail as thick as a railroad tie, smoothly polished, spiraling in a way that would have been perfect for sliding and had constituted a perpetual temptation to the girls when smaller, since banister-sliding had been sternly forbidden. The very soul of the house seemed to live in the stairwell, bottled up there in the central and yet empty place, a soul locatable and traceable by the huge and mysterious collection of smells which the stairwell held in its vast wooden clasp, where the air had not changed since the house was built and would not be changed until it was pulled down. True, the staircase did not go all the way down to the basement (this, and the cooking quarters, being reached by two smaller, fumed-oak staircases, put in principally for the use of the servants), but the basement smells found their way in too. Once your nose became skilled in the language of the smells, you could identify the furnace smell pushing up from where, with its battery of copper boilers, flanked by bins of coal, the furnace snaked up its arms through the floor like a surrendering octopus, its fire door sparking redly—the octopus' eye—tended day and night by a half-witted but sweet Polish furnaceman, Gogi, who lived, ate and slept down there in the coaly warmth. Upward also, wonderfully rich and penetrative (though nobody, Jessica was in the habit of saying, could actually smell *cooking*), came the kitchens smells by which you knew, happily and surely, that people ate in this house, and ate well, just as you knew with a relaxing sense of comfort that the house was sure to be heated or cooled, winter or summer, at just the right temperature.

In the staircase the air currents from the house mingled: from the water closets, the linen closets, pungent of cedar, from the dryness and mousy dustiness of studdings and boards in the attic, with its stores of trunks, valises, carryalls, and hampers, many of them stamped with labels reading Grand Hotel, Shepheards Hotel, Claridge Hotel, Adlon Hotel. There were the separate, individual climates of the eighteen bedrooms, each with its characteristic atmosphere—the guest bedrooms scented by the shaving water and perfume and body odor of the last guests to occupy them, bland and neutral or exotic and stimulating but always acceptable as being first-class and *comme il faut*, as Mademoiselle, the French governess, would have said; when doors were opened and closed there spiraled up the valiant smells of whisky and cigars and wood fires and upholstery and the chalk and leather pungence of the billiard room, and in the mornings the smell of coffee and brass polish and the soap and water and fresh, beachy smell of wet brick when the forecourt was hosed off. The air of the staircase retained all of these wonders, smoothed them out and stripped them of identification, filing them away forever in its large, impartial, dateless tube of reference.

Under the gaslight the two girls in their ball dresses crossed to the head of the stairs and stood looking down at a future they couldn't discern while around them, unheard, gabbled the childish

114

voices of their past, to be dismissed tonight—at least where Alexandra was involved—forever. One such, coming that moment into both their minds, was Pamela's voice as she did French lessons with Mademoiselle—a sound Alexandra and Sharon had listened to every night as they started down to supper. Sometimes Alexandra, annoyed by the cultural efforts upstairs, mocked them with wild cries, imitating the syllables Pamela was pronouncing. Now, as if able to hear again Mademoiselle's stern command to "*répétez après moi*," she said under her breath, with a derisive air, "*Pou tou mou lou . . . moi loi roi choi poi . . .*"

Sharon laughed. As always, she was there, faithful and impressed, ready to be an audience for her sister's every whim.

Alexandra got another idea.

"Here," she said, shoving the bouquet into Sharon's arms, "hold these."

With a movement of ferocious, balletlike speed and grace she jumped onto the banister rail. Folding her arms, leaning sideways to balance herself, giving warning of her descent with one loud yell, she slid down like lightning, ending with a bound that shot her ten feet past the stair end. She landed on her feet, almost in front of her angered and dumfounded parents, her adopted sister and the assembled servants.

Jessica's serene party face betrayed no trace of surprise. She chose, in this extraordinary moment, to correct her daughter's effrontery by ignoring its effect.

"Straighten your dress, dear," she said. "You've crumpled it behind."

Alexandra gave a pull to her skirt. She started to say something to her mother, but at that moment the doorbell rang and Temple, showing a composure equal to his mistress', stepped forward to open the door. Sharon ran down the last part of the staircase. She handed Alexandra her bouquet, and the two girls took their place in the line as the first guests, having yielded up their outer clothing to the housemaid, stepped forward to be received. The guests were Mr. and Mrs. T. W. Wilkins, Sr., he looking every inch a proper bank president, she trying to compensate for social lacks by anxious bunched diamonds and a toothy smile.

The night was dark, windy and damp. Little puffs of fog came in each time the front door was opened. In the middle of California Street, east of the house, a policeman diverted traffic so that the line of limousines and taxis inching along the right-hand side of the street could have a clear passage into the courtyard. Soon the downstairs hall became crowded with formally dressed people, young and old, fathers and mothers, and in some cases grandparents of debutantes having been invited, along with younger brothers and sisters, waiting their turn to pass down the receiving line. Temple called out the names of arrivals in a voice like that of an auctioneer.

The party had begun.

7 It was just like Alexandra, Pamela thought, to steal the show, sliding down the banister. Even if the show was designed for her, she still had to pull off some trick like that. Also she had on make-up. Pamela had known she would have. No matter how beautiful you were, you weren't beautiful enough if you were Alexandra; you had to be crazy too; no matter how much money your parents were spending, you had to try harder to please, with smiles, with pressures of the hand, blown kisses, loving publicly even people you didn't like, and of course men, all men; you had to try, and try harder, than girls whose parents never spent a cent and who, themselves, didn't have a chance.

It was stupid. What made it all the stupider was that it was so dated. Alexandra insisted on being dated, old hat, to use one of her own expressions. She wanted to model herself on the girls they'd read about in books when they were younger: Iris March in *The Green Hat* and Lady Brett in *The Sun Also Rises*. They had been forbidden to read the books just as they were forbidden now to put on make-up and to drink liquor, although Alexandra drank, too. That was another thing Pamela knew, although she'd never tell anybody. Alexandra kept bourbon on her dressing table in a big bottle that had once held Nuit de Noël. She also drank with men who brought flasks, in the dated way Alexandra thought was so smart, for girls who were too young to drink at the bar. Poor Alexandra, wonderful, breath-taking Alexandra, whose one passion was to be ahead of everyone, to be the mode, the rage, mascaraed and all, page-boy bob and all, she who as a little girl had twisted her long blond hair up in curls and ringlets and spitty little ear-puff dabs in imitation of Vilma Banky and Greta Garbo and Olga Baclanova. All so gauche, that was the tragedy of it, at least a tragedy for Alexandra, whose favorite word was gauche, as meaning something you must never be.

Standing next to Alexandra in the receiving line, Pamela couldn't help stealing little looks at her half-sister instead of keeping her eyes straight ahead as Jessica had told her to do when they rehearsed all this. They had stood here, lined up the day before, all three of them, while Jessica, acting the part of different guests, young and old, men and women, passed down the line schooling them in the right how-do-you-dos—the right smiles, the pressures of the hand, the way of accepting compliments, if they were offered, the warm look of the eyes and the so-glad-you-could-come turn of the softly parted lips. No handshakes, girls; handshakes are gauche. Just allow your fingers to rest in the man's. (Pamela, of course, never could help giving a handshake if someone shook hands with her, but that she was powerless to fix.)

The trouble was that she was scared. Not so much now as she had been, but still a little scared by force of habit. When Jessica had first brought her to the house, she'd been scared, and it had lasted from then on. Jessica had noticed it. She noticed everything. She kept trying to reassure Pamela that everything was going to be all right. Pamela could live here always. No one could take her away. She could share and share alike. Absolutely equal—her own room, her own dresses, her own governess, her own napkin ring. You must realize, dear child, that the sad experiences you have known in the past are all over and will never come back. We won't ever talk about them and we will try to stop thinking about them, won't we? This is our home now. All the kindness and the big rooms, the little bunch of violets in the vase in the Pierce Arrow limousine in which Alfred drove them all to Miss Burke's, his red ears sticking out like handles on each side of his chauffeur's cap. All for her and she mustn't be scared—although what scared her and froze her down to the middle of her bones was that they'd find out that she didn't like it. Then they would hate her for sure; she would be disgraced. They must never find out. Day and night she had to live with the fear that they would find out and at the same time the longing to tell them, to yell it at them.

All the awfulness is gone now, dear, and it will never, never come back. Why would it never come back? Was the world so horrible you couldn't even have a hope that the awfulness, as they called it, would come back, since it had been so wonderful? You weren't supposed to talk about your mother or think about her, but the truth was Pamela had loved her vague, sweet, boozy mother and there hadn't been a minute of it that had been awful except the worm that had crawled out of the piece of penny candy that had been her birthday present when she was three and they had lived with the colored family in Oakland, and Livey, the colored man, had taken her fishing in the bay and called her missy. Where was Livey now, if she could see him, hear his easy, sliding voice just for one minute, see the pale quiet insides of his hands as he baited up the hook with a piece of shrimp so she could catch a bullhead? None of it anything but wonderful or anything but what she wanted and had to get back somehow and find her mother again. What had happened, what had gone wrong? None of it awful, even the two sailors fighting in the bar that time and her mother crying and then talking so sweetly to the cop about her baby that he'd let her go and had only pinched the sailors, and the time her mother couldn't wait and had to go on the floor of the taxicab. That was bad because you were supposed to find the popo no matter how badly you wanted to go, and her mother teaching her five foot two eyes of blue and Charleston the way to dance it so the fellows in the bars would throw nickels quarters and even fourbit pieces at her because there had to be some way to eat and a threeyearold kid with such talent was wonderful, had a fine future before her.

The cough. It had all gone wrong because of the cough and finally the spattering bright plume of blood across the pillow, the mattress and onto the floor and the taxicab always taxicabs and her mother talking to the driver the way she knew so they wouldn't have to pay and the drive through the rainy Oregon night to the place where they'd made her so comfortable and she'd shivered all night with the first absolute desperate hopelessness of her life knowing her mother wouldn't be there in the morning and, sure enough, she hadn't been. Instead, a few days later, Jessica had come.

Lying in bed in the California Street house with the door open in a crack into Mademoiselle's room and a little light showing because now she was afraid in the dark, Pamela reasoned it out, her face with the soft dust of freckles over it and the turned-up nose aimed at the ceiling. People got over coughs eventually, no matter how bad; there had been a misunderstanding somewhere along the line and she had to do something about it.

One day she did. She'd saved up her allowance, fifty cents a week, the amount set at this figure because Alexandra, who was six months younger, also got this amount. It was even Stephen and share alike, just as Jessica had said. She saved up and when she had twelve dollars she packed. The only thing she wanted to take was Dixie, the parakeet they'd given her. She hated dolls; always had. She got one of Mademoiselle's shoeboxes and cut a hole in it because a bird had to breathe and tied a string around it and bought a bus ticket to Eugene, Oregon. She was seven years old and it had been three years since she had been there, but the lady in the home remembered her perfectly. The lady was so sorry, they had never heard from her mother, they didn't have the least idea where she had gone.

Pamela still had two dollars left. She planned to go on looking in the morning but she was pretty tired. She had the same bed again, and she put the box with the bird in it on a small shelf right beside her. This time Anchylus was the one who came to get her. She had never liked him. She knew he was her father. She had heard her mother say so, both to her and to the lady in the place. It made very little difference that he was her father; she hadn't liked him even as much as she liked Jessica. Now he was nicer. He drove all over town with her, looking for a place to buy seed for Dixie; then he took her home on the train. He was large, pale, tired and discouraged; she hadn't ever thought anything could get him down; his voice was just as raspy, but she knew with a child's sure knowledge that he was hurt because she'd run away and she felt sorry for him. She knew that in his eyes she had done a bad thing and she wanted to make up to him for this. She had kept this in mind ever since, reminding herself to feel sorry for him, and they had got along all right.

"Congratulations, Pamela dear. You look truly lovely."

"Thank you, Miss Meeker. I'm so glad you could come."

Letty Meeker twinkled at her and passed on into the ballroom with a whiff of lavenderish five-and-dime-store perfume and a glint of nameless, worthless little jewels. Pamela turned to greet Mr. and Mrs. Oakleigh Donovan, who were followed by their daughter, Gertrude, and Gertrude's escort, Timmy Wilkins, Jr.; Timmy was especially smiling and beguiling because he was moping for Alexandra, whom he had taken to all the parties that summer in Atherton, where the Saxes had their summer place, but who had recently dropped him, along with all her other beaux, in favor of some unknown fellow nobody knew anything about.

"Save me a gavotte, Pam," Timmy said.

"You bet," Pamela said.

She knew he would never dance with her. That kind of fellow never did. She didn't care. There were always fellows that would. It was share and share alike; and if she suffered by comparison, it was only by comparison to Alexandra, by comparison with whom anybody suffered. Certainly she was at least as attractive as Sharon, with her straight black hair, suspicious glare and body like an ironing board. All debutantes at their own debuts were beautiful, just as all brides were beautiful. "The three beautiful Saxe sisters," Letty Meeker would say in her report the next day, "received with their parents at a ball given in their own house, wearing identical dresses of . . ." and so on. Letty in the course of years had put out enough reporting on herself and Alexandra and Sharon to make a series like the Five Little Peppers: *The Saxe Sisters at The Horse Show, The Saxe Sisters at the Opera, The Saxe Sisters in a Submarine, The Saxe Sisters on a Cloud.* And talk about being scared, Jessica and the girls seemed to be scared of Letty because she would take digs at anybody, and Anchylus let her say anything she wanted to.

"Hello, Pamela dear."

"How do you do, Mrs. Tewcomby, Mr. Tewcomby."

"You look most charming, dear."

"Thank you so much, Mrs. Tewcomby, Mr. Tewcomby."

Arrivals were thinning out. Alexandra had already asked her mother for permission to dance—trying to steal the show again. Pamela determined to stick it out. She was not competing with anyone, but if they wanted her to have a debut she would have one, she would do her best. The debut was part of the deal but afterward she'd have to see. Maybe now she was caught up for letting go of the dearly recalled awfulness of her life with her mother.

Maybe now they'd let her have a room somewhere and look for a job. Quite a few girls had done it, girls known to the Saxes; some even had to do it, due to the Depression. Maybe she could still find a little Depression around somewhere to give her an excuse.

". . . and my sister Pamela, Prince Shimenko . . ."

"How do you do, Prince Shimenko," Pamela said.

Prince Shimenko kissed her hand.

God knew where Alexandra had picked this one up, a thin little man with a long nose and black eyebrows, wearing a black-tie suit that didn't fit. Alexandra was mad about men with titles, another proof of the Old Hat way she looked at things. The receiving line had finally disintegrated and Pamela found herself dancing with Prince Shimenko, listening to the spiel he was giving her about the estates his family had owned in Russia. As he talked she got the impression, she didn't know why, that he was scared to death, as she had once been, and accordingly the feeling-sorry-for-somebody business began aggravating her.

"Do you know what I think, Prince Shimenko?" she said when he ran out of material.

"What, my dear gorl?" the Prince said, pulling back and gaping at her with the monocle that was always falling out of his eye. "I think you're very nice, but I think you're a hell of a liar." The Prince beamed. His slimness, she saw, was only in part due to sickliness. He was really quite young, for an older man. "My dear gorl, I am nod. But what difference does it make?" Seizing her happily in his arms, he whirled her away at a fast, awkward clip, kicking up his heels on the turns.

8 The dancing was at its height. Vibrations of music and the rhythmed pressure of dancing feet ran through the whole house and were felt even in the cellar, where Gogi, who had refused out of shyness to come up and see the sights, sat on his stool with the fire door open in front of him, glaring into his furnace and puffing on his pipe. It was a great occasion, and Griff Williams and the boys were rising to it with sweet Guy Lombardo harmonies and crashing social Leo Reisman piano effects. Griff and the boys were out for blood, playing their first big house date after a long dry stretch. The beat, beat, beat of the tomtom and the sweet tenor sax blowing and drumming away the Depression mists, wiping away lonesome boarding-house nights, wino breath of little bars where the boys had passed the time when there were not only no house dates for society parties but no dates at all, everyone split up, playing in little combos around the city in order to eat. You're the top, they played, you're the Colt repeater, be still my heart. The object of my affection can change my complexion from white to stuff and stuff. You ought to be in pictures, you're the top, you've had a busy day. Bright and breezy on the bandstand in the Nob Hill home, they blew a moan for John Dillinger, stooled by a dame in a red dress, dead in the alley back of a Chicago theater, for Kurt von Schleicher, shot in the back, for Primo Carnera, kayoed by Max Schmeling. A hurray for Dizzy and Daffy, for the upswing, for the long gray Roosevelt freight ride out of trouble. I know that if I even took one whiff it would bore me terrif-icly too but I get a kick out of you, blew Griff Williams. Love thy neighbor, Ginger Rogers, Papa Dionne, Albert Einstein, Carole Lombard, Bruno Richard Hauptmann, Al Capone. You're the top. You're the Eiffel Tower. Stay as sweet as you are. It's love in bloom.

Each time Alexandra turned to a new partner, she put her soft, accessible body completely against him, giving up to him, adapting herself effortlessly to his style of dancing, sometimes only for a step or two, since there was always someone else waiting to cut in.

"Bye," she said with a ravishing look that was both a passionate farewell and a command to dance with her again as soon as possible; then she moved away, holding her arms up to settle them around a new dancer.

> *Can it be the breeze*
> *That fills the trees*
> *With rare and magic perfume?*

Anchylus, standing with Jessica, his craggy face beaming with pleasure, watched the success of his three girls, all so good looking, the blonde, the brunette, and the red-haired one, the girls in their bright dresses moving with so many others in a haze of tulle and silk and warm, perfumed young flesh around the island of black cloth in the center of the room that was the stag line.

> *Oh, no, it isn't the breeze*

When Alexandra and Pamela were on the floor, the debut had become official. Yet people hardly noticed whether Pamela was there or not. Alexandra's presence was the only one that meant anything; in it generated a force that changed the mood and even the architecture of the party. The stag line was pulled lopsided by the fellows bunching up around her—one dancing with her, one just cut in on, one cutting in, others waiting to cut in.

You could never tell about a girl, no matter how beautiful she was, until she had made her debut. Now Alexandra was proved up.

"She's a real belle, my dear," the older people said to Jessica and Anchylus.

At approximately thirty minutes before one, the hour at which supper was to be served, Alexandra walked out of the room alone. She walked through the press of maids and catering butlers in the pantry. Holding her dress away from her legs, she ran up the small stairway connecting the pantry with the servants' rooms and certain small, rarely used guestrooms. A few minutes later Schuyler Cutting, a young dancing man, reputed to have money, also left the ballroom. He stopped under the constellations in the hall long enough to light a cigarette and get his bearings. Here he chatted with an elderly dowager who insisted on detaining him to make comments on the party and congratulate him on his apparent success with Alexandra. (He had been her partner oftener than anyone else, and when he was dancing with her she sometimes refused to let others cut in.)

"Everyone is talking about it, *mon cher*," the dowager said, tapping him on the chest with her fan, "everyone. What a belle!"

"Thank you, Madame," Schuyler Cutting said.

"But where is your dear mother? I haven't seen her all evening."

"Ah, you know Mother," the young man said. "She's probably playing cards. . . . Please excuse me."

He went on up the stairs. On the third floor he stood still once more, counting the doors stretching away on the right side of the stairhead; picking out one which had been described to him, he went toward it lightly and quickly, his rather dull, white, heavy face, young and vain, quiet as a hunter's. He tried the knob, the door opened, he was inside the room, where it was dark and where, with no delay, a girl's body, soft, perfumed and expectant, light as air and also mysteriously heavy, settled against him, drawing on his with a rhythm that seemed born in it, while an eager, exploring mouth made his brains spin around.

"You took your dress off," he said rather stupidly.

The private little noise that she was making in her throat broke off, and from this throat now came a voice not at all like the voice used in flirtation, harsh in the small, darkened room.

"Don't talk," she said, "we haven't got much time."

9 IT HAD BEEN understood that Sharon was not to stay up for the whole party. There would be time enough for that when she made her own debut. For the present she was younger and would have to go to bed a little early, even if the party was still going on. Griff Williams had been hired to play until four o'clock, and it was possible that he might go on a little longer if there was a demand for encores, as there was sure to be. At a private ball an orchestra couldn't pour the spit out of the horns and pack up the drums and vamoose at the stroke of an hour, like a union band playing a lodge picnic. Also, even when Griff and the boys had gone, there were always a few guests who could play piano—Devereux Sansome, for one. So with one thing and another, plus scrambled eggs and bacon for those who wanted them, it might be six or seven in the morning before everything was over. Long before that time younger brothers and sisters and the old people and fathers and mothers would be in bed.

The hours between the end of supper and the onset of daylight belonged to the debutantes and their partners. Other people belonged in two categories—those who'd had their chance at this sort of thing and those who would have it in due course.

Sharon had said all right, if Jessica insisted, she would go up, she would take her clothes off and lie down but she wouldn't sleep. She didn't know anyone who could, with a party going on in her own home.

To her own surprise she went to sleep right away. She woke up an hour later because Alexandra was sitting on the bed and had turned on the bed light.

Instead of her ball dress Alexandra had on a woolen suit with a fur coat over it. There was a valise on the floor beside her. She had two letters in her hand.

"Chicken," she said, "I'm sorry about waking you up, but you have to do something for me."

Sharon sat up with a jerk. "What, Zan?" she said. "What's going on?"

"Nothing," Alexandra said, "except that I'm eloping with Schuyler Cutting. We're flying up to Reno. Schuy has a friend who owns a plane. So wish me good luck."

"I want to go too," Sharon said.

"I'm sorry," Alexandra said, "but it's absolutely impossible. We're not taking anyone or telling anyone. You're the only living human being that knows. So I've kept my word about telling you but you can't come with us. That's out."

Sharon began to cry.

"Please, Chicken," Alexandra said. "Don't start that."

"I'm going to miss you something awful, Zan," Sharon said.

"I'll miss you too," Alexandra said, "but I'm not going away forever, you know. I'll be back and we'll be together as much as ever. I promise."

"No, we won't," Sharon said. She dabbed at her eyes, shaking with large, dry sobs. "You can't fool me. You *are* going away forever. I hate Schuyler Cutting."

A flood of tears now poured down her face. She wiped them away with the sheet. "This is the end of everything," she said.

She spoke with great conviction—a conviction that welled up from the sleeping depths in which she had just been plunged and which took possession of her whole mind and body. Nor was she ever quite convinced later that she had not been right, at least in part. Alexandra's elopement might not have been the end of everything but it was certainly the beginning of a lot of things nobody had anticipated.

"Shar, I want you to stop that nonsense and pay attention to me," Alexandra said in a voice a good deal like Jessica's. "There's something you have to do. I want you to take charge of these letters and see each one gets to the person it's addressed to."

Sharon looked miserably at the letters. On the envelope of each a name had been written in the square, ornamental handwriting that all girls learned to write at Miss Burke's, with little circles used instead of periods and dots over the *i*'s. The names were

Mr. T. W. Wilkins, Jr.
Mr. Bradley Iverson

"But, Zan," Sharon said, "I can't go out now and trail all over town looking for two men. Mother would give me hell."

"You don't have to go out," Alexandra said; "that's the point of it. They're both downstairs dancing."

"They are?" Sharon said with amazement. "I thought the party was all over."

"Well, it's not," Alexandra said; "it's not even four o'clock yet. As a matter of fact. I don't want you to go down this minute. Wait a half an hour so that Schuy and I can get going. We don't want anybody chasing us. . . . Well, will you do it for me?"

"All right, Zan," Sharon said.

She had stopped crying. Suddenly she wrapped her skinny arms around her sister, clasping her in a hug of murderous power. "Zan, please . . . Zan . . . don't do it."

Now it was Alexandra who began to cry. "Angel! Chicken! I'm doing it because . . . But it doesn't matter. It's all settled, don't you see? Now look what you've done. You've made my mascara run. . . . Goodbye. Kiss me."

"Zan! I wish—"

"I do too, but it can't be helped. And I love you too. All right, once more . . . and wish me luck. . . ."

"I do, Zan," Sharon said meekly.

"Tell Mother I'll telephone her sometime tomorrow—today, I mean. But don't tell anybody where we're going. You're the only one that knows. Goodbye."

"Goodbye, Zan. Oh . . ."

"Goodbye. I'll talk to you too, when I talk to Mother. And don't forget the letters."

Alexandra took a tissue and a lipstick from her purse. Having carefully removed all traces of her tears, she replenished her mouth

125

and removed the smudges around her eyes. She smiled brilliantly at Sharon, picked up her valise and left the room.

10 For some minutes Sharon sat huddled on the bed. She felt wide-awake and yet exhausted. She had a temptation to close her eyes for a few seconds, except that doing so might make her break her promise to Alexandra. She felt that a whole world, everything she'd lived by till that moment, had come crashing around her, and there was no chance, no chance at all, for happiness any more—and all of this was terrible beyond words, yet exciting, and some good might come out of it. It was really time to get up and dress, if she was to go down with the letters, but she had no strength to do it yet, and while she waited for strength to come back she examined the letters themselves. Suddenly she was overcome with curiosity. She would have given anything for a look inside one of them; if Alexandra minded, that was just too bad; Alexandra would never know, and besides, if she herself was going to deliver letters, she had some right to know what was in them. She turned them over, studying the flaps. The letter to Tim Wilkins was very tightly sealed, but the one to Bradley Iverson was loose at one end, and by working her finger in the gap Sharon got it open without much damage. The letter said:

Dear Brad:
You were an angel to ask me to marry you, but after giving this most careful thought, dear Brad, I have decided against it. I am leaving tonight to marry Schuyler Cutting, with whom I am very much in love. I hope you can understand and forgive this decision to which I have given most careful thought, and that we can still continue to be friends. I am having this letter delivered to you personally, dear Brad, because I want you to be the first one to know. So, wish me luck, dear, if you can, and thanks for everything. In haste,
Affectionately,
Alexandra Saxe

Sharon closed the flap and stuck it down with spit. She held the other letter up to the light. She couldn't make out more than a word here and there but even so she was convinced its phrasing was identical with the first. Alexandra was not a person for finesse in minor matters, particularly when she was in a hurry. After all, would two gentlemen, even if they shared a mutual reverse of fortune, compare notes? At least she, Sharon, had found out one interesting fact—that Brad had asked Alexandra to marry him. Probably Tim had too. Else why would Alexandra be writing to him? And having the letter delivered at the very moment of elopement?

Alexandra had always been secretive about some matters. She had talked freely about men in general and matters pertaining to men in general rather than about her relationship to any particular men, even though such relationships were in some mysterious way the essence of her life. Outwardly she had preserved the proper decorum of a girl not yet "introduced" to such things—the introduction, supposedly, not having taken place until tonight. She had worn the middy blouses, the black ties, white collars and the black shoes, she had patted a ball around the tennis court and ridden, in the summers, on group rides on the trails around Atherton, but all the time she had presided like the legitimate pretender to a disputed throne, in exile but planning a coronation. Sharon had no idea how she had managed it, though possibly it hadn't taken too much management; men had swarmed about Alexandra since she had turned twelve, and not always the sort of men she was supposed to play with. Once, for instance, she had confessed to Sharon quite lightheartedly that on several occasions, left alone with Albert, the chauffeur, she had necked with him in the front seat. Sharon found it impossible to visualize this. All she could bring before her mind was Albert's handle-shaped ears sticking out on each side of his cap as he drove the three of them to school.

Oh, yes, men were Alexandra's specialty—a realm apart from the private, little-girl world she'd shared with Sharon, that cozy upstairs alliance of the two of them against all others—Jessica, Anchylus, the governesses, and of course Pamela. Their own world—only a fraction of Alexandra's, but Sharon's all. Now, all in a second, with a wave of goodbye and a smile, as it were, that world was gone. There was nothing in its place.

But was there really nothing? Sharon kept looking at the letters. Out of all the men who'd wanted her, Alexandra had chosen one. She'd gone away with him. She'd left all the rest. She'd turned them loose. Now it was no longer hopeless to wish to be beautiful, hopeless because Alexandra was so much more beautiful than she, Sharon, could ever be. Now she had a chance. Even these men to whom the letters were addressed, these might like her since they had liked Alexandra and she had the quality of being Alexandra's sister.

"One of them," Sharon said to herself, entranced and almost consoled by the thought, "why not one of them for me?"

Which? It didn't really matter, just so long as there was someone to fill the void left by Alexandra's going.

As she dressed, Sharon evaluated the persons designated by the names on the letters: the friendly, athletic, rather dull but so good-looking Tim Wilkins, "their sort" of person and of course possibly and in fact likely to succeed his father in Pacific Midland; and Brad Iverson, a little older, but also probably smarter since he was a writer and a good one, people said—he had once even worked for *The Day*. Thinking about them as she brushed her hair and got her feet, which seemed to have become enlarged while she slept, back into her dancing slippers, Sharon decided they were both fascinating. She didn't see how Alexandra could leave either of them or how she could have turned them down if it was true, as she surmised, that they had both proposed.

Either of them, she thought, would do in a pinch.

Either of them—and the one who got to know her would find out it was worth while. She wouldn't treat them the way Alexandra had. To her, a man wasn't something to be picked up or laid down the way Alexandra picked people up and laid them down. Only a person as wonderful as Alexandra and as glamorous and all could get away with that. She herself would never want to.

Alexandra could have told the fellows her sister would be with them. If she'd wanted to put something helpful in the letters she could have said it quite simply.

> DEAR TIM OR BRAD [as the case might be]:
> I am sending you this goodbye letter by my sister, Sharon, who is also my best friend. I suggest that you look her over carefully since there is more to her than meets the eye. She has an affectionate nature, can keep secrets and will laugh at your jokes. Now that I am going away she needs someone to love and I'm sure you'll find that she'll do very well. Obviously she isn't as good looking as I am, but remember, she is a year younger and there is a good chance she may improve. Hoping you will give this matter most careful thought, I am, etc., etc.
>
> ALEXANDRA SAXE

128

Sharon wondered whether there was any way, as she handed the two men the letters, she could plant such thoughts in their minds. Probably not, but at least the mail delivery would be an opening of a sort. Possibly one of the recipients, if not too stricken by the news in the envelope, might ask her to dance. Tonight neither of the two concerned had asked her, at least not yet.

Once more repeating the route she had taken earlier, in such a different frame of mind, she started down the stairs. In the hall she could feel the music, and as soon as she reached the stair landing she could hear it plainly as well as the party's great mingled gabble of voices.

> *You make time and you make love dandy*
> *You make swell molasses candy*
> *But honey are you making any money*
> *That's all I want to know*

There was quite a press of people in the hall, a good many of them leaving. Sharon wondered whether Alexandra's absence had been noted and whether she herself, by mooning upstairs, had let more time pass than she should have. It would be terrible if the men who were to get the news of Zan's elopement should have gone. With an anxious, disturbed look on her face she hurried toward the crowd below, carrying the letters pressed against her chest.

11 Tim Wilkins was a good sport. He read the letter, put it in his pocket, drank another glass of champagne, and went home. He had an air of feeling that the announced elopement might have been all for the best. Brad Iverson seemed far more upset. He stayed long after all the other guests had left. At half past seven he refused a second helping of scrambled eggs. At eight he started making calls to various hotels in Reno and the Lake Tahoe area to find out whether a Mr. and Mrs. Schuyler Cutting were registered.

"Be the first to congratulate them," he said. "Horrible thing to do, isn't it? Classic behavior of the jilted suitor. Be the very first and make 'em hate you forever after."

"You really should try to relax, Brad," Jessica said. "You ought to go and get some rest."

Brad finally accepted this advice. He was putting on his overcoat and silk top hat in the hall when there occurred a tremendous ringing of the front door bell followed by indications that someone was pounding on the door with his fists and kicking it with his feet. The servants had all gone up and the caterer's men had left with their van of equipment, so Jessica, who never went to bed as long as there were still guests in her house, opened the door herself and Letty Meeker walked in.

Letty had changed her clothes, but it was obvious that she hadn't been sleeping. Her face was a greenish color and she was very angry. She had with her an AP flimsy which she thrust toward Jessica.

"You knew about this. You knew, didn't you?"

"I can't read it, Letty, if you keep waving it around."

"Alexandra—she was married at six A.M. this morning by a Justice of the Peace in Reno. It's all right here!"

Jessica had taken the report. She was starting to read it when Letty snatched it out of her hand. She crumpled it and threw it on the floor.

"You knew she was eloping and you never told me. Why?"

"Letty," Jessica said, "if you wish to remain in my house you will refrain from addressing me in that belligerent tone."

"I want to know why I wasn't told."

"You weren't told because nobody knew. This came as a surprise to all of us."

"The Associated Press knew. They put the story out, and now everybody's got it."

"I imagine it went through the regular channels, don't you? A marriage is a matter of public record."

"Everyone has it now," Letty said unreasonably, still furious, "and it should have been *my* exclusive. If I ever had a right to an exclusive it's for stories emanating from this house. I don't believe Mr. Saxe was told of this. I don't think for a minute he would condone putting every other paper in town ahead of me with my own exclusive."

"You can ask Mr. Saxe about that yourself, Letty," Jessica said. "He will be at his office sometime today. And now, since you refuse to conform to a tone of courtesy or even ordinary civility—"

"You'll be sorry for this, Jessica," Letty said. "Alexandra will be sorry for it too."

". . . I must ask you to leave my house."

"Just tell her when she calls up to say how happy she is," Letty said, "tell her, 'Letty Meeker says you will be sorry for this.' "

She picked up the crumpled flimsy from the hall carpet and trotted out the front door, her small, underslung butt wagging viciously.

"Well," Brad said, "what got into *her?*"

These were the first human-sounding, un-sorry-for-himself words he had spoken for nearly six hours.

Jessica looked very tired.

"Letty is a coarse, ill-tempered woman," she said; "I've known it for some time. She writes well, but she tries to arrogate an importance which her position on *The Day* by no means warrants. I believe Mr. Saxe might do well to ask for her resignation. Now, we'd all better go to bed. No doubt we'll be hearing from Alexandra and Schuyler a little later."

Sharon followed Brad outside into the court. The sun was high now and the bricks in front of the house glowed with subdued red and brown colors; from their drying surfaces, wet with the mists of the vanished night, came a fresh, soapy smell. Traffic was stirring on California Street and the harbor at the bottom of the hill was wrapped in a gold-shot, glinting haze.

Standing on the front doorstep, Sharon noticed that her head was on a level with Brad Iverson's. She reached out her round, thin, girlish arms and settled them around his neck.

"I think Zan was an idiot to marry Schuy," she said.

So saying, she kissed Brad Iverson on the mouth.

IV

The Success

"The people quoted Edna St. Vincent Millay but they believed Henry J. Kaiser."

—Mort Sahl

1 ANCHYLUS had never been able to figure it out. He had tried to do so repeatedly and he tried once more, alone in his office the day Jessica died, looking back over their life together. Alexandra might have been a little too good-looking for her own good, perhaps also a little wild, but she had always seemed so basically sensible. Then, just to pack up and run off with a fellow she hardly knew and who had none too sweet a reputation, never saying a word to anybody. It was hard to get the hang of it.

Jessica might have come near the truth when she said, "I'm afraid we may as well face it. She didn't love this Schuyler Cutting. He was merely a means to an end. She wanted to leave."

Anchylus had opposed this idea. To believe it was to accept the very implication which hurt most about Alexandra's elopement—that he and Jessica, in spite of all they had done, had failed to seal up the crack in the family structure.

Once he had tried to verify Jessica's theory by checking it with Sharon. "Do you think Zan had any other reason for going, other than a yen to marry this guy?"

"I don't know, Anchy," Sharon said.

Anchylus looked at her sternly. Even the fact that she had called him "Anchy" instead of "Dad" seemed a little irritating at this juncture; yet, oddly enough, neither Sharon nor Alexandra, the daughters of legal wedlock, had ever used the familiar parental diminutives which proper children were supposed to use. Pamela was the only one who called him Dad. She had begun it when they were alone together up in Oregon, that time when she'd run away and he'd gone up there to bring her home.

"I just thought you might have some idea," he had said to Sharon; "you and she were pretty close. Didn't she ever talk to you about what she was going to do?"

"Not really," Sharon said, "but I don't think she was too insane about him, if that's what you mean."

"Your mother doesn't think so, either."

Sharon reached for a phrase. "Zan wanted to be on her own," she said.

On her own! It was the very phrase which Pamela, in quite a different sort of conversation, had used not long afterward when she'd said that she was going to take a job.

"Maybe so," he'd said to Sharon, "but she didn't have to go about it just that way. She could have asked to have a wedding."

"If she had," Sharon said, "would you and Mother have given her one?"

"Of course," Anchylus said, "of course we'd have given her one. We'd have loved it."

He'd spoken with complete conviction. Yet hardly two years later when Sharon, trusting him, had asked for a wedding on her own account, he'd tried to dissuade her from marrying at all! When had that been? Anchylus, who had the habit of identifying dates by headlines, let one zoom in at him:

HAVENNER WINS!

He chuckled. That was one he'd written himself, deliberately leaving to the lower deck all mention of a gentleman who had just been re-elected President of the United States by the greatest majority in history, carrying forty-six out of forty-eight states. Anchylus was rather proud of the headline and had justified himself, when kidded about it, by pointing out that Roosevelt was an eastern snob whereas Frank Havenner, a longtime supervisor, meant something to San Franciscans, who would like hearing that he'd been elected to

Congress. Secretly, he'd been rather pleased when *Time* pointed out that, as an example of home-angled news, his slug on the election bore comparison with *The Boston Transcript's* famous reportage on the sinking of the S. S. *Titanic* a generation earlier, with the loss of 1,513 passengers and crewmen. *The Transcript*, so legend had it, slugged its account of the disaster:

BOSTON WOMAN LOST AT SEA

Alone with his ghosts, he tried to remember how Letty Meeker had headed her story on Sharon's wedding.

NOTABLE NAMES UNITED . . .

Letty could be pretty dull, especially when she was trying to be respectful. Letty was never reluctant about taking potshots at Alexandra—she'd never forgiven her for ruining, by eloping, *The Day's* exclusive on the debut. However, as if to make up for her ill treatment of one sister by her devotion to another, she treated Sharon's doings with a seriousness that approached the ridiculous.

. . . IN SOLEMN CATHEDRAL RITES

Bradley Whyte Iverson was not, by any standard known to anybody, a notable name. He was a professor's son whose mother had some money and whose younger sister had come out the same year as Pam and Alexandra. A rather homely younger sister, as Anchylus remembered her—her homeliness, naturally regrettable, being doubly unfortunate in this case since if she'd been more of a belle her older brother might not have been sent along to see she wasn't stuck for a partner at the parties she went to. If that sister, damn it all, had just been a little lovelier, Brad Iverson might never have met either Sharon or, before her, Alexandra. Still, even with a homely sister to look after, a man thirty years old had no business at debutante balls, and one who was thirty-two had even less marrying a girl of eighteen. That was how Anchylus felt and that was what he had said, he recalled, in his set-to with Sharon. He didn't think his real objection had been that Brad, like himself, was a newspaperman; Sharon insisted that it had been, but Sharon had been wrong. He, Anchylus, knew something about newspapermen and even more about Brad Iverson, since he'd employed him for three years—started him off, as a matter of fact, a green kid with a brand-new diploma from the University of California.

Oh, Brad was bright. You couldn't gainsay that. He could also write, and had proved it to an uncomfortably large audience, but Anchylus still hadn't changed his opinion that Brad was the sort of newspaperman who was always brighter personally than the copy he wrote and always more political personally than the paper's politics and always bigger in his own estimation than any newspaper or chain of newspapers, no matter how important, that he happened to be working for.

Well, so much for the notable names. As for the "solemn rites," Anchylus supposed they'd been solemn if by that you meant a crew of ushers who had tippled slightly more than was good for them and a set of bridesmaids who looked ravishing in their white silk dresses and big June hats and a number of formally attired people who stood up with a tidal rustle as the slim, dark bride came down the center aisle of Grace Cathedral on her father's arm. Afterward he and Jessica had put on a bang-up reception at the California Street house, just as he'd told Sharon they would have done for Alexandra. At going-away time the forecourt had been full of howling guests assembled there to pelt the happy couple with rice. Sharon, very handsome in her blue wool traveling suit—she certainly had filled out a lot, just as her mother had said she would—stood on the running board of the Chrysler coupé Anchylus had given her for a wedding present and tossed her bouquet back toward the steps.

It had landed squarely in the arms of Pamela.

2 SHARON HAD been very glad to have the wedding, especially since it had seemed so likely for a while that she wouldn't. Anchylus' objections had taken her by surprise. She could have pretty well conceived, if he was going to object, that he'd use the argument about Brad's age, silly as this was, but she'd never imagined he'd come up with anything as corny as suggesting that she take a trip to Europe.

"I don't want to go to Europe," she said; "I want to stay in San Francisco, or right near it, and I want to marry Brad."

"If you like San Francisco so much," Anchylus said rather truculently, "why don't you marry a man who *writes* in San Francisco? I hear Brad's going to work in Los Angeles."

He couldn't have put more venom into the words.

"It's a promotion for him, Father," Sharon said. "He'll be bureau head there. Los Angeles is one of Hurd-Hudner's most important bureaus."

"Hurd-Hudner!" Anchylus said.

"Yes, Anchy," Sharon said firmly, "Hurd-Hudner, as you know very well . . . and what's wrong with that?"

"Well, Daughter," Anchylus said, "Hurd-Hudner is . . . well, it's a *chain*. There's a place for chains all right, as Mr. Hearst went out and showed us, but I'll be damned if I think . . ." He fell silent, chewing on the stem of his pipe.

"Yes, Father?" Sharon said.

"I don't think you can compare *that* sort of circulation with the sort of circulation we've built up for *The Day!*"

"Ha!" Sharon said. "Now it comes out!" Her eyes flashed. She had never spoken to Anchylus in just this way before. "I understand!" she said.

"You understand what?"

"Why you've got it in for Brad. You just can't stand remembering Brad left *The Day* to work for somebody else."

She could tell that this shot had struck home. Like the ganglords of the twenties, Anchylus never forgave a henchman who had changed sides. It also occurred to her that, combined with his dislike of all chain-operated newspapers, he particularly disliked Hurd-Hudner because in the depth of the Depression there had been some talk that Hurd-Hudner wanted to buy *The Day*, thus adding a San Francisco outlet to their sprawling newspaper empire.

"If he can better himself," he said, "I'm the last man to hold him back."

"Well, he *has* bettered himself," Sharon said. "They're talking about giving him a column. If they do, he'll be more than just someone who has bettered himself. He'll be *nationally known*."

Anchylus shook out his pipe. "Will that make him a better newspaperman?" he asked.

Sharon took a long breath. The time had come to be a little tactful. "He's getting better all the time," she said. "After all, look where he got his start."

She went on with an air of supreme confidence. "You mustn't think that just because he works for Hurd-Hudner he doesn't know how much he owes *you*, Anchy. Deep in his heart I think he's sorry he ever left *The Day*."

This last statement had been pure fabrication but good strategy—Sharon always looked back on it with pride. She knew it had gotten her the wedding.

3 HER EXILE in Los Angeles hadn't lasted long—less than two
   years. During this period, Brad's rise had been more than satisfactory; it had been sensational. With all modesty, Sharon knew
she had been a help. It was important for Brad to live nicely and do
some entertaining and as yet his salary by itself wasn't enough to
permit all this on the scale he wanted—and that he felt was suitable.
She'd worked hard on the entertaining and—why deny it?—the
money she'd been able to contribute to the household budget had
made life agreeable as Brad advanced toward his goals. Jessica Saxe
had fallen into the habit of giving all her daughters presents from
time to time in the form of common stock in *The Day*—a gift of
which the value had steadily increased. Now the dividends constituted a nice addition to the Iverson family picture, a fact as pleas-
ing to Sharon as it was useful to Brad. Yes, she had been proud of
her ability to help, proud of her ambitions for him—a man so much
older and so brilliant that most girls her age might have thought him
entirely out of reach. He was by far the more attractive of the men
to whom she had carried Alexandra's goodbye letters on the night
of the debut. This decision—that he was so much, much more attractive than Tim Wilkins—she had made that very night and she
had acted on it. It had been a long campaign, but in the end she had
attracted him and, what was important, had landed him.

Pride and ambition! These were expediters of success which any
loyal wife offered as a matter of course. If sometimes she bored
Brad with her questions about situations in the syndicate, there was,
still, no doubt that the information she thus obtained sharpened her
judgment, fitting her to give advice and stimulation when he
needed them. And what man didn't need them! Sharon never felt
more of a woman, more of a real person, than when Brad built a
couple of highballs and said in his offhand way, "Kiddo, sit down a
minute. There's something I'd like to kick around with you. . . ."

Entertaining was one of the principal directions in which she
could help—the sort of entertaining that was geared to a business
situation. Brad, to give him credit, fully recognized her talents in
this field. He often said that she had charmed Harold Hudner, really
hypnotized him, that first time Harold had come to their apartment
in Beverly Hills. It had been a simple party, just a buffet on the terrace for about five couples, with a young actress (Sharon had met
her at a beach party) invited to be Harold's date.

Very simple but really a fun evening. Sharon had bought a charcoal brazier so that Brad could barbecue the steaks himself, and after supper and a reasonable settling-down period with some old Courvoisier, they had gone on to the Trocadero to hear Duke Ellington. The actress had flirted most effectively with Harold Hudner. Her career hadn't been going well and it seemed possible that she felt that contact with a newspaper tycoon, and especially a young one, might turn out to be of some advantage. Harold Hudner had responded with enthusiasm. Usually a rather timid, although not an unattractive fellow, he had recently undergone psychoanalysis, which was just coming into vogue. Anyway, when on the dance floor with the girl in his arms he hadn't been retarded by inhibitions.

"Do you think I ought to say something to her?" Sharon asked a little anxiously.

"Are you kidding?" Brad said. "Hell, no."

"I just mentioned it, dear, because I thought she might be overplaying her hand," Sharon said.

"What she's overplaying," Brad said, "isn't her hand, but don't worry about it. That's the advantage of a joint with a five-dollar cover. Nobody gets thrown out."

"I'm awfully glad, dear," Sharon said; "I thought I might have made a mistake about her. She seemed so dewy and all, there on the beach the day we met."

"Leave her alone," Brad said. "She's doing fine."

"That night," Brad sometimes reminisced, "was what clinched the column. That was what did it."

"What clinched the column," Sharon always answered, "was you, Brad, and your ability. Just that and nothing else."

However, she was pleased. And certainly the party hadn't hurt anything. It hadn't done a bit of harm.

With an outfit as big as Hurd-Hudner you didn't land a column overnight. Brad had begun by guesting, with half a dozen other writers, for a regular Hurd-Hudner columnist on vacation; the following year he'd been the sole substitute when the columnist's annual holiday rolled around once more. This had been a mistake—one of the few Brad had made. The columnist's influence had still been strong enough to make his protest stick. Brad, however, started contributing special articles to the Hurd-Hudner feature page. He had been way out ahead as the columnist's eventual replacement when the latter's time off began coming at more frequent intervals and it turned out, to no one's surprise, that he was fatally ill. Brad immediately stepped into the job, while his predecessor, in accordance with H-H's generous policy toward aged or ailing employees, was pensioned off in Florida to die in peace.

Brad's column was to have a West Coast angle—a logical step. Most of Hurd-Hudner's circulation lay in the Rocky Mountain and Pacific Coast states. Harold Hudner held that columns angled around Eastern activities and personalities could be pretty tiresome. Take Walter Lippmann. Lots of papers bought him and some people liked him; but if you hadn't gone to Harvard the way he had, you didn't know, half the time, what in hell he was trying to say.

Brad's column was to be less commentary than an evaluation of American life. Some of the titles considered were "Nuggets and Tailings" (rejected on the ground that it sounded too much like a frontier throwback, with the added possibility that readers might not understand the word *tailings*), "The Lariat" (rejected as too cowboyish) and "Sombrero in the Ring" with a picture of Brad wearing a ten-gallon hat—a form of headgear he had never previously worn and in which he looked absolutely frightful.

The title finally chosen was "Pacific Periscope." Some Hurd-Hudner executives thought the word *Pacific* localized the point of reference, but Harold Hudner, when the discussion grew warm, held that localization might be an advantage.

Hurd-Hudner did not care whether Brad's copy moved on the wire out of Los Angeles or San Francisco; in fact, of the two cities, they rather preferred San Francisco as being more central.

Sharon was delighted. Now she and Brad could go home! They spent a number of evenings discussing the move and decided to rent in Burlingame, a place where both had friends and which was near enough to the city so Brad could commute. They soon found an almost ideal house—well within their budget and quite modern yet without the least suggestion of being pretentious. (If you had money in Burlingame it was always a good idea not to show it, since so many people were sure to have more.) Also, by fortunate coincidence, Hal Shirer, one of Brad's best friends when they had been in Cal together, sat on the membership committee of the Indian Pipe Country Club, and before the summer had run its course the Iversons received a flattering letter from Indian Pipe advising them that their application for membership had been accepted. Thus they entered a new and happy phase of their life together, a most agreeable life at that time for both of them, the only cloud on its pleasant surface being the incidents which, much to Sharon's regret, brought about a serious break in her relations with Anchylus.

4 LOOKING BACK on that summer, Sharon felt it had been one of
the best. The Depression had been over, barring a slight cy-
clical setback, and the saber-rattling in Europe could be
disregarded because Hitler himself said that he would never go to
war and President Roosevelt had come out flatly and said he hated
war. Sharon took Brad to the eight-sixteen in the morning and
picked him up on the five-thirty-two so they had a good deal of time
together, and this time was generally well occupied: there were club
dances every Saturday night preceded by dinner parties, and during
the week there were always smaller parties which ended earlier because the men had to take the train in the morning. The small
parties were almost more fun because then you could be with the
people you especially liked. Sharon liked almost everyone; she was
so glad to be in Burlingame rather than Atherton, where the Saxe
family had spent so many summers. She had inherited Atherton
but she and Brad had conquered Burlingame together. The friends
they had made there and the agreeable, busy life they led were another testimonial to the advancement of her favorite project—Brad's
success.

It was a different story when Anchylus started making a fool of
himself.

Brad should never have taken Anchylus to the club. That was the
start of it. They had met on the train one Friday afternoon and
Brad had suggested that they both get off at Burlingame and go to
Indian Pipe for a drink. It had been a friendly invitation on Brad's
part, quite a generous one, in fact, since he knew all about Anchylus' initial resistance to accepting him as a son-in-law. Whatever
reservations the two had been entertaining with regard to each other
were wiped out that afternoon—wiped out to such good effect that
a similar get-together took place a week or so later. Before long
Anchylus had started dropping into the club without the formality
of an invitation; once or twice he even brought with him guests of
his own—and of a type which occasioned comment among the
members.

Brad didn't immediately find out what was going on. By the time
he did, Anchylus' tippling sessions with the characters he brought
along to divert him had assumed the proportions of a scandal.

The first intimation, for the Iversons, of what was going on took
place on a warm day in July. Brad had been playing golf. He was

taking a shower when one of the stewards came into the locker room and told him that his "guests" were waiting; when Brad asked what guests, the steward said, "Mr. Anchylus Saxe and a friend."

Brad put on his clothes as fast as he could. He went straight to the bar. Here he found Anchylus seated with a man he didn't know but who was introduced to him as "Mr. Rudolph Ruggioni." Brad recognized the name. He had even written a column about his father-in-law's friend. Ruggioni was an ex-member of a murder syndicate; his testimony had turned state's evidence at the trial of one of his former associates. Recently *The Day* had been running his reminiscences as a feature of its Sunday Supplement.

"I'm happy to meet you, sir," Brad said rather formally. He shook hands heartily with Ruggioni. He then took a seat beside him at the table as if in very truth both Ruggioni and Anchylus were present by his own wish.

A quick glance around the bar had shown him the source of the steward's message—a group of older members seated at a near-by table with their gray or white or bone-colored heads close together. This group—known as the Cardiac Legislature—were all senior members of the club and also gentlemen of prominence in city affairs. Brad guessed that they had recognized Ruggioni and had chosen to ascertain, by sending the steward to check with him, whether or not they could ask to have him thrown out. Since his own presence made ejection impossible, the incident had passed off without public embarrassment.

Brad had been amused by the whole thing. Sharon, however, was furious when she heard about it.

"How could Anchy dare?"

"I don't suppose he thought about it, one way or the other."

"Of course he did. He just thought he was putting one over."

"I doubt it. It might even have been partly my fault. The first time I took him there I told him to drop in again any time."

"Oh, my God," Sharon said, "don't you know you can't say that kind of thing to Anchy? He's absolutely literal! If you said 'any time' he thinks you mean—"

"—any time," Brad supplied as emotion seemed to choke his wife,

"Exactly," Sharon said. There was a pause. "You'll have to tell him," she said, "that he can't go there any more."

"He can, though, if we invite him."

"We're not going to invite him."

"It might have been just a passing whim," Brad suggested, "or he might even have done it to impress this Ruggioni character."

"Ruggioni wouldn't know the club from a North Beach spaghetti house. It's not that, but there could be a reason—a real one. And the more I think about it, I think I know what it was. He went there as a deliberate sneer. He was laughing at us for taking pride in the club."

"Oh, come on, Shar," Brad said, surprised at her vehemence, "that's pretty farfetched, don't you think?"

"No, I don't. Please remember I know him a lot better than you do. He'd be proud to be in Indian Pipe if it was *his* club. But it's *ours*, so it's funny to him. He doesn't want any of us to have anything unless it comes from *him*."

"Well," Brad said, "he'll probably never do it again."

"I think he will. Or something just as bad. I think *you'd* better tell him to stay out of there."

"Good God, Shar! I couldn't do that."

"You couldn't? Well, I could," Sharon said. She turned her martini glass thoughtfully on its small paper coaster. "I love this place and I love the club," she said. "We've gotten them for ourselves and I'm not going to let him spoil them for us."

5 CAREFUL INQUIRIES among her friends reassured Sharon somewhat: none of them seemed to know that her father had even been at Indian Pipe the previous week, let alone that he had taken a gangster there. When another week passed with no reappearance of Anchylus on the club premises, she began to wonder if Brad had been right: Anchy might not go there any more.

The hope soon proved to be vain. Sharon had been playing bridge and was giving a lift home to Cordelia Feltrap and Cordelia's mother, Mrs. Bartley Stigmire, when Mrs. Stigmire asked with an arch glance at Cordelia how Sharon's dear father was these days.

"I'd never met him," the lady went on before Sharon could answer, "until we ran into him leaving the club the other evening. Such an interesting person!"

"When was this?" Sharon asked.

"Let me see . . ." Mrs. Stigmire said. "One night last week. He had a wee imp of a man with him; I believe he had something to do with horses."

"His name was Dowdy, Mother," Cordelia said. "Johnny Dowdy. He's a jockey."

"Yes, I've heard of him," Sharon said.

The Day had been giving considerable space to Dowdy, a rider who had brought in a record number of winners on California tracks that year.

"Mr. Stigmire and I were with Admiral and Mrs. Chumm," Mrs. Stigmire went on. "The Admiral went over at once to help Mr. Saxe."

"To help—"

"With the little horse person. I'm afraid he had been drinking; he couldn't walk very well at all. Your father made a most delightful remark about that. What was it he said, Cordelia?"

"I don't remember, Mother," Cordelia said shortly. She evidently felt her mother was laying it on.

"Oh, I know what it was," Mrs. Stigmire said. "He said this Johnny Whatshisname had 'stirrup legs.' Don't you love it? He said his legs were no good at all unless he had a saddle to separate them."

"I really don't think Sharon is interested, Mother," Cordelia Feltrap said.

"Why, of course she is, dear," Mrs. Stigmire said. She turned to Sharon. "You must have a most delightful time with your father and the individuals with whom he comes in contact. Such bonhomie! He and the Admiral folded the little imp, my dear; they bent him over like an envelope—an envelope, perhaps with too much inside it." Mrs. Stigmire giggled at her own joke. "Then your father's chauffeur turned up and they all drove off together. It was most refreshing."

Sharon gunned her motor. She was impatient to get her passengers out of the station wagon.

"How that old harpy loved giving me the needle!" she said later to Brad.

"To hell with her," Brad said.

"That's all very well, to say to hell with her," Sharon said, "you didn't have to listen to it. You weren't there."

"Well, no, I wasn't, kiddo," Brad said in a mollifying way, "I wasn't, but why worry about that kind of chatter?"

"If it was something that affected you, at Hurd-Hudner, for example, you'd worry about it."

"Well, maybe so," Brad said. "I'll try to find out what really happened. I hadn't heard a thing about it."

Sharon said, "For my part, I've heard all I want to. He's got to stay out of the club."

"Well," Brad said, "maybe we'll think of a way to put it to him."

"I've thought of a way," Sharon said. "I asked you once to do something about it and you didn't. Now I'm going to do something about it myself."

She could tell Brad didn't take her seriously, but she didn't care. She knew what she would do. She would protect the life she'd made. Anchylus couldn't have it. Not that he wanted it. To him the rules of a small community or even of a city were ridiculous. He was above rules. They were for other people. He could do as he liked. He made up his own rules.

Always as a child she had believed his rules. Then she'd found out they didn't apply. His idea that he could bring a bastard daughter home and raise her with his other children hadn't applied. It was legal all right. She herself and Alexandra had covered that point. It was legal but there was a class of rules beyond legality. By these rules and in the eyes of people who adhered to them he stood condemned. He'd done something that wasn't done. Breaking a rule like that meant that you were set apart. The walls of your house became transparent. The walls might be made of stone six feet thick, but the eyes of the people outside could see through them. You went on thinking that you in your grand house were lucky and privileged whereas actually you were far less fortunate than the outsiders in their lesser houses. You had to be more beautiful than they, as Alexandra had said once; you had to be smarter and more daring and give better parties because no rules protected you any more and stones could come whistling at any time with sharp, splintering crashes through the glass wall of the house and knock you down and turn you black and blue. You had made up your own rules and they didn't hold, no matter how secure and legal and worthwhile they seemed. You had to try harder than anyone else to live and breathe and be a person because you were living a lie!

That was where she and Alexandra had split off. They had stopped believing Anchylus' rules or even their mother's. Alexandra had split off first. She had gone so far she couldn't ever get all the way back, and because of her special talents and looks, that didn't matter so much to Alexandra, Sharon thought; but she herself had done differently. She had wanted to get back inside. She had wanted to live in a house with four solid walls, but here was Anchylus barging in again, big and laughing, strong and disdainful, ready to break out one side of her house and put the glass back in.

To hell with him. She was all through with him. She'd got this for herself and she was going to keep it. Indian Pipe might not be much. She had no illusions about that. When you came down to it, she didn't care about country clubs any more than Anchylus did. That wasn't the point. She had this club and the good opinion of the people of it. If he could spoil that he could spoil anything else she had or might ever get. She meant to stop him. She meant to make him stay out of her life from now on and the Indian Pipe issue was a good place to take her stand.

6
As soon as the eight-sixteen had pulled out the next morning Sharon went home and changed her clothes. Then she drove up to the city. Normally she would have gone up on the train with Brad, but though she knew she was deceiving him in this small way, and felt rather bad about it, the little deception appeared infinitely preferable to getting involved in an argument. Without bothering to telephone for an appointment, she went to her father's office and sent in her name.

There were the usual two secretaries in the outer office, the pleasant gray-haired Miss Wilke and a younger one. They looked at her curiously as she stood by the desk of the former, taking off her gloves, poised and suntanned, trim in her stylish cotton suit with the cultured pearls Brad had given her around her throat and the real diamond and sapphire bracelet Jessica had given her around her wrist—the boss's daughter, young and expensive and inimical. She could see her own image in a wall mirror and she was satisfied with it, although under her well-arranged exterior she felt an emotion resembling panic. Except for the time she had argued with Anchylus about marrying Brad, she had never matched wills with him on any issue—much less such a formidable one as this. There was a moment while Miss Wilke was speaking on the intercom when she didn't think she had the nerve for it. Then the door of the inner office opened and Anchylus himself came out with both hands outstretched.

"Well, Daughter! By God, this is a pleasure. Come in, come in and make yourself at home."

He drew her toward him, seemingly with the intention of kissing her—a contact which she avoided by turning her head sharply sideways. She tried to take the curse off this action, for the benefit of the staring secretaries, by a bright, false smile. A thickset man with a red face, not wearing any tie, was sitting by Anchylus' desk. He rose as they entered.

"Dan, you remember my daughter, Sharon? Guess you haven't

seen her in some time, though—Mrs. Brad Iverson now. Our secretary-treasurer, Mr. Daniel Winkler."

"How do you do, Mr. Winkler," Sharon said.

The red-faced man put his thick, round head on one side.

"A pleasure, Mrs. Iverson. I'd like to make a small bet you wouldn't remember when we met before. You were so high." Mr. Winkler indicated the height with his hand. "You and your sister came in here one day dressed up in your pretty white dresses and I took you through the plant. Circulation manager I was in those days. A long time ago."

"Of course," Sharon said, "I remember now."

She wondered, not that she cared, whether Mr. Winkler could tell from her face that she did not remember at all. She and Zan, it was true, had visited the Day Building on several occasions—birthdays and so forth. They had later eventually become rather bored with such "tours."

"Well, Anchylus," Mr. Winkler said, "I guess it's time I was moving. I know how it is when a daughter walks in on you. No more work that day—that's what mine always has in mind. So what can you do? We go out shopping. . . ."

He shook hands with Sharon again before leaving the office.

"Dan is getting to be pretty old now," Anchylus said, "like everything else around here. Still, we couldn't get out the paper without him."

He set out a chair for Sharon, moving around the desk to his own side and picking up a pipe as he sat down. The pipe was still going. Sharon remembered from her girlhood that her father's pipes, even when he laid them down on a table, never seemed to go out. She liked them much better, smelly as they were, than his cigars.

"Tell you what," he said, puffing, as she looked at him with a strained face, feeling for a sentence that would open her attack. "Dan said he knocks off work when his daughter comes pestering around. Well, if he can do it, so can I. I've got just two, three calls to make. Then what do you say we go somewhere and have lunch? Anywhere you like—that is," he added, sensing from her tenseness and strained expression that her call on him was not as casual as he had first supposed, "that is, unless you have something else in mind."

"Well, I have—I mean, I'm afraid I can't lunch with you, Father," Sharon said. "If you want to make your calls, I'll be glad to wait outside," she went on as Anchylus waved deprecatingly, dismissing this. "What I—the reason I stopped in to see you won't

149

take up much of your time. It's . . . something I have to ask you and it's rather private."

Anchylus peered at her under his heavy eyebrows through a cloud of smoke. He leaned forward and snapped the switch of the intercom. "No calls till I tell you," he said.

He sat back, his thumbs in his vest loops, waiting. "Go ahead," he said.

"I have to ask you," Sharon said in a thin, raw voice, "not to go to Indian Pipe any more."

She had taken the plunge. If it was not the tactful opening she had been groping for, at least it said what she wanted. The tightness in her throat relaxed and she felt in her handbag for a cigarette, her eyes fixed on her father. Because her own statement had required such an effort she had somehow expected an immediate, perhaps violent reaction on his part; she was a little surprised when none resulted. Anchylus' behavior was so mild, even stupefied, that she was not sure at first he'd understood what she said. He sat quietly smoking, rubbing his cheekbone with his mashed right hand.

"No?" he said. "Not— What's wrong?"

"It's just that, well, just that you can't, that's all," Sharon said, her voice a little steadier now. "A club has to have rules, you know, Father, sometimes very strict ones. While it's true that Brad and I belong and that I know he's glad to take you there from time to time, it's no good, just no good at all, to have you going there alone. Or taking your own guests."

Anchylus looked at her fixedly and quietly. It was now quite clear that he understood.

"Well, I'll be god-damned," he said.

"There's no use cursing about it, Father," Sharon said. She made the word *cursing* very reproachful, as if he'd used a four-letter word. She wanted desperately to find something about him that she could fasten on as a reason for the anger mounting inside her, the shapeless and almost objectless rage that she had brought in with her and that had been piling up perhaps ever since she had been a child.

"I said, I'll be god-damned."

"All right, Father," Sharon said. "I'd hoped you'd understand. It hasn't been easy to come here and say what I've had to say, but I felt it was absolutely necessary. Otherwise I wouldn't have come. We live in Burlingame, Brad and I, and we haven't lived there very long. I've felt we were both of us lucky to meet so many people and have them like us and to be asked to join the club. That has been very important to both of us, and it's absolutely impossible for you or anyone to treat this club, in Burlingame, as if it were a saloon where you can take all sorts of peculiar not to say objectionable and impossible people and fill them up with whisky till they're falling down drunk. A friend saw you leaving with that jockey, Johnny Doody or whatever his name is, and I know just what happened. I heard all about it and I can't tell you how I feel about it. It was, well, honestly and truthfully, revolting."

Anchylus sat square as a graven image in his heavy clothes, with his unreasonably pale and mottled face, digesting her words.

"Johnny Dowdy," he said. "Yes, that's right. The boy doesn't drink, not as a rule. Can't hold it. He was feeling no pain, no pain at all."

He grinned slightly at the memory and flipped with his hands on the desk. The flipping was an action Sharon had never seen him perform before. Although his hands were formidable, they seemed helpless as they did it, like fish jerked out of a pond and flopping on the bank.

"No pain," he said.

Sharon's carefully lipsticked mouth drew slightly open, showing her small teeth in a grimace which was not, however, humorous.

"It wasn't funny at all, Father. That sort of thing honestly isn't funny to me or to anyone else, and I want you to know that nothing like it can ever happen again. It's just too embarrassing to us and too . . . too frightful. So please promise you'll stay away from Indian Pipe from now on unless we take you there."

While she spoke she was watching his hands—quiet for a moment and then flipping again, the mashed right hand a little less conspicuously than the left. She would have liked to make him stop this flipping at all costs, the peculiar little action which told her that she had hurt him by what she said, that she'd driven the barbs of her words deep into some unprotected part of him. At the same time she wanted to drive on, to hurt him more and more.

"Naturally," she finished, "if Brad should meet you somewhere and invite you—if he should, I mean, take you there personally, that would be different, and in that case, of course, you would be free to go in like any other guest. I am not referring to anything like that when I ask you to stay away—only to these expeditions you've been making by yourself with drunken jockeys and Sicilian murderers and so on."

Anchylus now noticed the flipping of his hands. He brought it to an end by putting one hand over the other and holding them both against the desk. He nodded several times.

"All right, all right, Shar. Have it your own way. Slobs—most of them in that club. I know them, but I made— That's all, I guess; just as you say."

He glared at her, puckering up his mouth as old men do and munching his lips dryly.

"Sorry you can't have lunch. . . . Tell Mr. Winkler I'm free now, if he'd care to come back," he said into the intercom.

7 JESSICA was very angry when she heard about this conversation. She took Sharon heavily to task for it.

"You know your father doesn't understand about clubs," she said. "He keeps his own doors open. He doesn't see why people should band into groups to keep theirs closed."

"He understands better now, Mother," Sharon said.

"It's unfortunate he learned to do so from his own daughter. He may have been wrong in going to the club, but in speaking to him as you did you seem to have forgotten that children should respect their parents."

"Look, Mother," Sharon said, "I'm grown up now and I have my own life to live. I want to live without interference from him. That's something that perhaps even *you* don't understand."

At least her visit to Anchylus had accomplished its main purpose. During the rest of that summer and all the summers of the years following, Anchylus did not visit the Iversons even when his wife did, nor did he go to the club. When he and Brad met on the train they chatted as before but Brad got off at Burlingame and Anchylus rode on to his own station.

Severance from her father, though a relief in a sense, had one unforeseen result. It left Sharon alone to deal with her creation—the success of Bradley Iverson.

Success could be, but was not necessarily, a monster. Nor was she a female Frankenstein. If her time and thoughts and energy for a considerable span of years had gone into the project of making Brad's dreams come true, was that so strange? He was her husband: not to have helped him would have made her feel useless indeed. What was peculiar was that as time passed she took less and less satisfaction in the outcome of her efforts; in fact, she sometimes felt rather terrified of them. Sometimes it seemed to her as if the structure of her life resembled an illustration for *Gulliver's Travels*, one of the books Jessica had read to her, Alexandra and Pamela when

152

they were children. The figure in the foreground was a big type-writer to which numerous thumb-sized people were attached by threads, forced to depress the keys by jumping on them and to drag the heavy carriage back and forth. One of these people, in her fancy, was herself. The image was ridiculous, she was quite aware of that. However, there could be no doubt that her importance in Brad's life had lessened as the objectives he wanted were attained.

There was no use getting upset. Having persuaded him to accept his glory as his own creation, she couldn't very well take credit for bringing it about. She could only hope that when the dizziness engendered by his rapid rise had worn off somewhat, he might settle down and be his own sweet self again.

Never great, the chances of this solution's coming to pass were destroyed, together with a variety of other things, when the Japs attacked Pearl Harbor. Brad held an ROTC commission as a second lieutenant. When the nation flew to arms, he was sure he would be called up.

"Once soldiering gets into your system," he explained to Sharon, "you don't forget it. In the old days at Cal I could take apart the breechblock of a seventy-five and put it together again, blindfolded. And I mean blindfolded."

For once—possibly because her concept of Brad in uniform, with or without a blindfold, was so new to her—Sharon allowed herself a negative position.

"That's wonderful, dear," she said; "only, are you sure they still use them?"

"Use what? Soldiers?" Brad said with irritation.

"I only meant . . . that kind of gun," Sharon said quickly, pulling back to a prepared position.

"Weapons may change," Brad said; "it's men who are standard equipment."

He smiled at her, his equilibrium restored. He was making a mental note to use his comment about weapons in a future column. Sharon recognized this, but leaned across the small, candlelit table to squeeze his hand.

"Oh, Brad," she said sincerely, "if you have to go, I don't know what I'll do."

They were dining tête-à-tête in a restaurant—a sort of send-off dinner, with champagne and pheasant-under-glass. Brad had set the next day as the time when he would offer his services to the Army Recruiting Office in San Mateo. Sharon was very gay throughout the meal, and during the drive home she snuggled up against him. Their mood of closeness, culminating in the love-making which came later, successfully bridged not only the strain put upon him by the task of volunteering but the ensuing despondency when he was turned down. Actually, he was called back twice for medical examination. The whole trouble had been the knee cartilage he had torn while playing a sand shot from a trap on the second hole at Indian Pipe, an injury which had given him a lot of trouble.

Everything was soon different in Burlingame. Meat, gas and even whisky were hard to get in any quantity, and on the golf course now you ran into groups of servicemen in skivey shorts and government-issue shirts and government-issue pants playing free of charge—a courtesy extended to them by the Greens Committee. Sharon had taken up golf herself in preference to bridge. She couldn't stand sitting on her duff for four or five hours with the women who were perpetually yammering about their husbands in the service and their kids in school. She was lonely. If Brad had been somewhat career-minded before, he was twice as busy now that he had a war to comment on. He spent as much time in Washington as he did on the Coast. Sometimes she went with him on his transcontinental commutation trips, but this wasn't easy to arrange—Brad's priority for travel didn't include a wife.

Sharon thought of the period between 1941 and 1944 as a sort of limbo. The United States was putting forth the greatest effort in its history but for her this was stagnation time. Her one consolation was the fact that Alexandra, as beautiful and gay as ever, had come back to San Francisco. Alexandra had acquired a European way of looking at life and even a faint European accent which, though it was no doubt a little affected, seemed to go with her personality. She was wonderfully resilient. It was remarkable how little she'd been thrown off stride by her divorce from Schuyler Cutting. That marriage had never had a chance; while Alexandra had been awfully fond of Schuy, it was a little too much when he borrowed money on her diamond earrings and then lost it in one evening's activities at Monte Carlo. Finally, just before the war, and just when Alexandra had met a few people on the Riviera who were halfway nice, including Casi Dandopolis, a Greek who had invited them to go to Brazil on his yacht, Schuy had insisted on rushing to Paris, his mother having shown up there.

That had been the last straw. If people in San Francisco thought Mrs. William Bayard Cutting was a terror they should have seen her at the George Cinq with that dyed streak in her hair and her crazy twin chows on a gold-mesh leash. Her one saving grace was that she'd been decent about the property settlement—forking up out of her own pocket, since Schuy didn't have a cent in his own name. She'd paid some of his debts and carted him off somewhere while Alexandra came home by herself, bringing the Bentley she'd bought when she and Schuy had been in England. She'd left some of her clothes because she expected to go right back.

"I suppose," she'd said, "some Nazi general's mistress is having a ball in my Patou originals, probably still owed for by Schuy."

"Oh, Zan," Sharon said, "how horrible!"

It was pleasant to be Alexandra's confidante once more, almost like the old days at California Street come back again. In the loneliness of the life she was currently leading the meetings with Zan were a link with a carefree world from which, without realizing how it had happened, she had cut herself off. Alexandra for her part enjoyed gossiping about her new beau, a Hungarian nobleman who had recently left his own country, taking refuge in San Francisco, where he had friends. Though not wealthy, he cared nothing for money, only for fun. He was quite a noted horseman and had represented his country in the Olympic Games in Berlin before the war.

"You're sure it's not just the title that attracts you?" Sharon asked. She wished she sounded less like Jessica when she made this kind of remark. Alexandra, even before her debut, had shown a partiality for titles.

Alexandra smiled. "Just wait till you meet him," she said enigmatically, "just you wait!"

Nick Drobny turned out to be a tall, dark man, put together with a great length of heavy bone and a dissatisfied, impatient face. It was a little hard to believe that he had been, as Alexandra hinted, a notable hero in the Hungarian Resistance during the German Occupation; he was so agreeable in manner. Positively frivolous. He kissed Sharon's hand in a manner which made her reluctant to wash it for two days afterward. He also had a trick with a martini glass: after drinking its contents he would put the glass itself into his mouth and solemnly chew it up, pretending to swallow the pieces. Sharon thought he was one of the handsomest and most amusing fellows she had ever met, but neither then nor on the other occasions when they were together could she think of anything to say to him, and she wondered what subjects Alexandra turned to when she wasn't making love. She found to her surprise, however, that she was slightly jealous of her sister's good fortune, starting on a brand-new venture with such an attractive fellow while she herself was stranded, as it were, on a shoal.

One day she appeared at the weekly luncheon listless and fatigued.

"What's wrong, Chicken?" Alexandra demanded.

"I want a baby," Sharon said.

"Why, how wonderful," Alexandra said.

"Why do you say it's wonderful? I'm not going to *have* one. I just want one."

"That's what I mean. It's so marvelously normal and all that," Alexandra said.

"I can't help it, that's the way I feel."

"I wish I did," Alexandra said. "What makes you?"

"What makes me what?"

"Feel as if you wanted to . . . fecundate? If that's the word. Where does it affect you?"

"Good God, Zan, it doesn't affect me anywhere—physically. It's not like that. It's a state of mind."

"That's what's so amazing," Alexandra said. "I've always wondered about that."

"Haven't you ever *felt* it?"

"Not even remotely."

"I think that's rather odd, if you don't mind my saying so."

"There's nothing odd about it. I—"

"But most women do want children, Zan. Sometime or other. You have the equipment to reproduce. I suppose nature makes you want to use it."

"You only have half the equipment, dear," Alexandra said. "Men have the other half. Your half makes it easy to swell up and lose your figure and then get a lot of horrible pains. I never saw the point of it. If it's a state of mind, I must have had a mental hysterectomy. Doesn't Brad want a baby?"

"I don't think so."

"Did he ever say so?"

"No."

"Then he might be delighted."

"Well, I don't think so."

"Why?"

"If you mention babies and your husband knows you're for them, and he doesn't mention babies, you can figure he's against them. Anyhow, that's how I look at it. Wouldn't you? But I suppose,"

Sharon added, taking thought, "I suppose if *you* wanted babies nothing would ever stop you. Nothing ever does stop you."

She relapsed into silence, smoking moodily and playing with the silverware.

"Shar," Alexandra said with a gleam of suspicion, "do you swear you're not pregnant?"

"Of course."

"But if you want a baby so much—"

Sharon lifted her head. "*That* would never work with Brad. No gay little surprises. Anything you do with Brad has got to be a mutual undertaking. Carefully planned, with him in charge."

"Then put him in charge," Alexandra suggested. "Point out the joys and benefits of fatherhood."

"You don't understand, Zan," Sharon said. "It's different with Brad and me. I guess I can't explain it."

"How do you mean, different?"

"I suppose," Sharon said, "we started with a different conception of marriage. Brad was older. And so much more clever and all that. I made him feel that nobody would be able to love him the way I would—and did. He was supposed to be everything I'd ever need. So if I need a baby, that's a split. A new conception. Do you see what I mean? It's as if I were saying, Brad, you're not enough. I have to have some new person, even if I have to manufacture one. Far from being complimentary, it would be a lowering. And you must never lower Brad. That's rule number one. All this must seem horribly complicated."

"Not at all," Alexandra said. "It's very simple."

"I wish there were a simple answer to it," Sharon said.

"There is," Alexandra said. "Divorce him and marry a man that wants babies."

"I'd be miserable without Brad."

"Aren't you also slightly miserable with him?"

"Not nearly as miserable as I'd be without him. I'm not changeable, the way you are. My feelings are dismally permanent. I don't just want anybody's baby. I want Brad's baby."

"Then that's the answer, Chicken," Alexandra said triumphantly. "There's *no* split. Don't you see? No lowering at all. You want not less Brad but *more* Brad—another little piece of him. You're not changing the conception; you're making it bigger."

"Well, it's a thought," Sharon said dubiously. She blew out smoke.

"Yes," she said after an interval. "If I knew how to present that properly it might work. It just might."

"Of course it would," Alexandra said encouragingly. "Try it and see. I know everything will be all right. Where is Brad now?"

"In Washington," Sharon said.

"If I were you, dear," Alexandra said, "I'd go to Washington. I'm sure somebody can get you on a plane. I'd go there and tie on a whing-ding and then tell him. Tact is always better when there is a little sex in it, I don't care who the man is. And as I say, I know a little bit about—"

"You do, Zan, you certainly do," Sharon said. "And you've been a dear to give me so much good advice. I'll think it over, I really will."

"Whether you go or not," Alexandra said, "be sure and tell me how you make out."

8 SHARON DECIDED not to go to Washington. Brad's aversion to surprises made the trip seem ill-advised; also, he gave her a job to do. He telephoned one evening and told her to look for a house—he made it clear he meant a house that they could buy. When she reminded him that the lease at Bridge Road ran until the following June he said never mind the lease, they could always sublet. He'd decided it was time they bought a house in Burlingame.

"I've been thinking," he said. "It's time we stopped living like gypsies."

Sharon wondered if, through some telepathic influence, his thoughts had been moving in the same channel as hers. However, she successfully produced a light tone. "Not many gypsies live with two in help and a teletype in the den."

"You know what I mean, kiddo," Brad said with a touch of irritation. "We ought to have a house to *keep*. Don't you like the idea?"

"I love it," Sharon said quickly. "I'll start looking right away. Does this mean that we can spend more time in Burlingame? Because I'd love that too; you know I would."

"Maybe," Brad said laconically. "Hard to say for sure. I'll know more when I see you."

"It sounds as if something were cooking," Sharon said.

"Something is," Brad said, "something big. I can't talk now, though, and I've got a million calls to make. So don't ask questions. Just find us a house. I'll see you next week."

The business of driving around with agents to look at properties was stimulating. Sharon found herself living a fantasy life in each house she entered, clothing unknown pleasures in the mood of echoing halls and unexplored rooms. She could see winter fires blazing in the clean, blackened hearths the past owners had left behind; she could hear the babble of dinner parties in the stripped salons and the clink of cocktail ice on the empty terraces. And always there was a room—not always the grandest or sunniest, but always suitable—a room for the child or children which were part of all her imaginings these days.

She worked hard. By the time Brad returned she'd found a place on Floribunda Avenue she was sure he'd like. The price was high, but the war had put all prices up, since nobody could build, and this house served to combine solidity and charm in a way that was most unusual. There were four bedrooms, two with balconies, and a fine, rich lawn shaded with sycamores and Chinese elms. The dining room was small, but large dining rooms were starting to go out of style so this didn't matter too much, and the living room was huge, with dark oak paneling like the California Street library and a handsome fieldstone fireplace to give it a country air. The grounds were spacious. She was so sure of Brad's reaction that she made an appointment with the agent to show the house on the day of his arrival.

Brad walked nervously through all the rooms. He tried the closet doors and the watertaps and he rapped on the paneling with his knuckles to see if there were termites.

"Not bad," he conceded. "Not perfect, but not bad at all."

"It *is* awfully expensive," Sharon said. She felt the price would be the chief objection. If it were to be overcome, it must be faced at once.

"Well, yes and no," Brad said. "That doesn't bother me. We're in for inflation now and all prices are too high, but they'll go higher."

He sat down in an iron chair beside the empty swimming pool. Sharon walked back to get rid of the agent. Brad must not be rushed. It would be a good idea if he were left alone to think it over.

When he strolled into the house half an hour later, still abstracted but apparently satisfied, she felt that the deal was as good as made.

"You promised to tell me what was cooking at H-H," she said gently as they drove back to the small and now, as it seemed, pitifully inadequate house on Bridge Road. "Do you want to talk about it now?"

Brad chuckled. "The picture's been changing, Shar," he said; "it's been changing so fast it's hard to keep up with it."

When he said "picture" she knew she was expected to supply an automatic modifier—*the Hurd-Hudner* picture.

"In what way?" she asked.

Brad held up a finger. "Number one," he said, "the national angle. I'm not saying 'Periscope' has done it all—there are several factors to be taken into account—but we've been building circulation faster than a cat can spit. Then again—" he held up another finger— "the business angle. Have you noticed how I've been soft-pedaling it in 'Periscope' lately? Too much other writing is focused on business. *The Wall Street Journal* has piled up a lot of readership for the West Coast edition, which means we should maybe ease up on that angle. So, the gist of it is I'm to have complete autonomy. I can live where I want, write what I want. Harold is even talking about a new name for the column."

"A new name! Why, it took weeks to get 'Pacific Periscope,' and you've always been so pleased with it," Sharon said.

"I have," Brad said, "but as I say—well, Harold seems to feel that authorship, not locality, should be the key. You know the new name that's practically decided on? I'll give you three guesses—only when I tell you, keep it under your hat."

" 'Periscope'—without 'Pacific'?" she suggested hopefully.

"Nope. That was mentioned, but opinion was against it. Might sound too much like a naval affairs column or something. The new name will be . . . 'Iverson.' "

"Iverson or Iverson's?" she asked, not quite sure if she had heard him properly.

"Good God, Sharon," he said irritably. " 'Iverson's' sounds like 'Lloyd's' or 'Cook's.' This isn't an insurance company or a travel bureau. It's a syndicated column reaching better than three million readers. Just 'Iverson.' My name, or possibly 'Brad Iverson.' The brass is still kicking that around, which one to use."

"That's very flattering," Sharon said.

"You don't like it?"

"Of course I like it, Brad," she said. "I just want to ask you one question. If they're dropping the word Pacific, are they dropping the Pacific angle? Because if they are, I don't see why we're buying a house in Burlingame."

"They're not dropping it, kiddo. Far from it," Brad said. "You don't get my point."

"I'm sorry, Brad," Sharon said with quick contrition. She waited for him to go on.

"I've got to have a base," Brad said. "A home place, you might say. How much of the Pacific angle goes into 'Iverson' is up to me, and I intend to put a lot of it in. That's what autonomy can mean, in career terms. We've been yelling bad rice long enough."

"Bad rice?"

"That's what Chinese farmers are supposed to say when they have a good crop. To fool the gods. We've got it made now, kiddo, and our way of living should reflect it. Hence the house. Later, if need be, we can have a duplicate setup in Bethesda or Washington—sort of divide our time between there and the Coast. Too early to tell about that yet. But meanwhile, at least we'll be located. Do you know what I was looking at while I sat out there by the pool?"

"The trees?"

"Nope. They're all right. Good, solid trees, but you can take trees like that for granted when you have a solid house. I was looking at the old tennis court. What a place to put a suite! You know what I mean? A bungalow office suite like in a motion-picture studio. Did you ever look at that tennis court?"

"I did, Brad," Sharon said slowly. "I had an idea about it too."

"Honey!" Brad said, pleased. He put his arm around her.

"Don't give me credit where I don't deserve it, dear," Sharon said. "I didn't think of the executive suite. Perhaps I'd better not tell you my idea."

"Go ahead, Shar. If you want the tennis court we'll put the bungalow some other place. What was *your* notion?"

"I was thinking it would make a nice play yard, if we ever had children."

"Good God!" Brad said.

She waited for some clarification of his exclamation.

"You're not pregnant by any chance, are you?" he asked.

He didn't say it pleasantly. The die had been cast, and she'd lost.

"That's what Alexandra asked me," she said.

"You talked to her about the play yard?"

"No," Sharon said. "I just told her I wanted children. I said I wanted them and you didn't. That was when she asked me if I were pregnant. Well, don't worry, I'm not."

Brad drove for a few moments without saying anything. His profile looked handsome, rejective and annoyed.

"It's not a case of worrying, Shar," he said at length. "I wasn't *worried*. I trust your good sense."

"My good sense not to want a family?" The words burst from Sharon. She clasped her hands, twisting her fingers against her rings in an effort to regain her composure.

161

"Not at all," Brad said calmly. "I don't know where you got the idea that I don't want children. It's a matter of timing. If I had children I'd want to—well, take them on walks, read to them, and all that. Or just lie, maybe in a meadow, and look at a cloud. Do you know what I mean?"

Sharon said nothing. After waiting for a reasonable time for her reply, Brad put out his hand and laid it on her forearm. Sharon pulled quickly out of reach.

"Now, Shar," he said.

"Now, what?" she said.

"We don't have to brew up a storm about this, do we?"

"No," she said, "we don't. So suppose we drop it. All right?"

"Sure," Brad said. "Let's drop it. Only, I'd like you to understand my attitude. Frankly, I don't think you do."

"I understand it, Brad," she said.

"Children are a possible for us," Brad said; "they're *not* ruled out."

"I know, Brad," she said, "but can't we drop it, please? Pretty please?"

"They can always," Brad said firmly, "be placed on the agenda, for future discussion. I couldn't do the things I'd want to do with children, or a child, as busy as I am now. It's all a question of timing."

"Maybe the perfect timing would be never," Sharon said as if to herself.

"Now you're being unfair," Brad said sternly. "I'm afraid I can't discuss this any further."

"That's what I suggested," Sharon said.

Neither spoke again until they were at home on Bridge Road and the car was parked in the garage and Brad's suitcase carried up to the bedroom.

"You know, kiddo," he said in a friendly tone, "I'm sorry we had that argument about the tennis court. Because I like the house. I'm going to make an offer on it."

"The tennis court!" Sharon said.

"Of course," Brad said.

"Is that what we were arguing about?" she said.

Brad gave his attention to putting his suit on a hanger. "I'm sorry," he repeated, "because I bought you a little present. Jaeckel's is mailing it out. Now I'm sorry that I didn't bring it with me. It might put you in a better frame of mind."

"Jaeckel's?" Sharon said.

"That fur store in New York," Brad said. "Now I suppose you've

162

guessed what it is. So I might as well tell you. I can't afford it—neither of us can—but, well, I bought it for you anyway. Sort of felt like celebrating. It's a natural dark mink coat, like Alexandra's."

"Thank you," Sharon said. "That was awfully sweet of you, Brad."

"All right," Brad said, "go on being difficult. I think you'll feel different when you see it. I think you'll feel a little bit ashamed of yourself."

"I'm sure I will," she said.

"All right, all right," he said.

"A dark natural mink coat is something that I've always wanted," she said. "I can have an awful lot of fun with a mink coat."

She smiled so brightly that Brad, seeing her reflection in his bedroom mirror, looked at her sharply to see if she was coming around.

"Why not?" he said.

"Oh, but I will," she said. "I'm going to get a little book with a pink cover. I'll write down the mink's weight and the date when he says his first words and when he starts to walk."

"Very funny," Brad said.

"With snapshots, of course," she said, "and school reports."

"Oh, knock it off, Sharon," Brad said.

"Don't you think we ought to save the mink's first pair of shoes? We could cast them in bronze to use as paperweights," Sharon said.

"If you don't want it," Brad said, "you don't have to take it. But there's no sense ridiculing it. A coat like that costs a lot of money. We can always send it back."

"A dark, natural mink, dear?" Sharon said. "Oh, heavens, no. I'd never do that. But if it got to be a nuisance, of course, we could always put it up for adoption."

Brad gave her a furious look and walked out of the room.

Dinner was a strained affair—not at all a proper homecoming. Brad and Sharon spoke to each other only when Alfonse, the male member of their Belgian couple, was in the room serving. Later, one of Brad's secretaries came for dictation.

Sharon took her coffee out onto the patio. She sat there alone. She felt tired and mixed up. Why had she insisted on the quarrel? She'd known in advance—and put herself on record as knowing—Brad's views on the subject under discussion. She'd behaved stupidly, not like herself at all, for although perhaps not clever in many ways, or at least not thinking of herself as clever, she'd always, she thought, been clever in her handling of Brad. It had all been so unnecessary! He'd been thinking of her while he was back East. He'd even bought her a generous present. You couldn't hit him over the head for that, just as you couldn't point a pistol at him and demand he give you children.

And why the pitch on children all of a sudden? Was it really such a strong drive from within herself? She wasn't sure of this now either. She thought some of it was real. She thought she would be a good mother. Every woman, probably, except self-centered freaks like Alexandra, wanted children so she could prove she was a woman—physically and also emotionally. But such desires, such thoughts, were latent ones. They didn't explode. They didn't boil over in fierce quarrels and bitter, humiliated feelings, such as she had had today.

Alone in the cool early evening with the air of the summer night around her, she tried to peer into herself and find out about all this. Wasn't the need to have a child combined with the need to have a greater hold on Brad, to bring him back and tie him to her inextricably? No doubt of it—yet she had failed to see this. She had turned Brad away from her just when she wanted him most.

She had been wrong. She must acknowledge her mistake. She must blot out the quarrel as if it had never occurred, get back to the status of "two against the world"—Brad's career and happiness her one objective.

Through the French windows of the living room she could see him folding up his papers. The secretary was leaving. He smiled at the secretary, sharing some thought with her that was concerned with work—always the project nearest his heart. Oh, it would be terrible if work ruled out herself, his wife, as it would and could quite easily sometime, if she let it. To hold Brad she must go on being invaluable. She must be a part of his public presentation of himself. She must give, work and plan. If selfish desires plagued her she must subjugate them to a higher purpose—their nearness, their closeness.

Inside the house, Brad left the living room, escorting the secretary to the front door. When he re-entered he sat down a little wearily. The light from the desk lamp spilled into his face at an angle that showed its bones and hollows. He looked older than usual—middle-aged, almost. It was the first time she had ever seen him look that way and a feeling of protective love passed through her. She stepped quickly through the French doors and went up to him.

"Brad," she said, "I'm sorry. I was stupid today. Can you forgive me?"

9

So THE COMPACT implicit in their marriage was reaffirmed. It was a workable arrangement, even a happy one—and proof that it was workable and happy, if you needed any proof, lay in the fact that the retitled and streamlined column, "Iverson," by the estimates of the Audit Bureau of Circulation reached a public of four million readers.

One of Brad's prized possessions was the original of a *New Yorker* cartoon: a clubman ordering his breakfast, saying to the waiter, "I take a cup of coffee in the morning. A cup of coffee and Brad Iverson is all I need." Another treasure, also framed, photostated and enlarged, which made the yearly hegira from Burlingame to Bethesda, was an editorial pointing out that he had brought social consciousness to the mass audience which had once read him just to be amused. The fact that the editorial had appeared only in papers serviced by Hurd-Hudner syndicate did not detract from its value in his eyes, any more than the fact that he'd been paid to pose for it diminished his fondness for a framed copy of a whisky advertisement in which he could be glimpsed in hunting pinks standing in front of an open fire caressing a fine, pure-bred beagle hound.

The physical process of getting out the column had been brought together under one roof. Commuting to an office was a nuisance and, in view of his solidified position, quite unnecessary. Brad soon completed the executive bungalow he had conceived as an addition to the Burlingame house. His own sanctum was cork-lined to keep out disturbing noises. From it, stretching down a long hall, were—in that order—a file room, a reference library, another office in which sat the secretaries—Miss Malone, the column secretary, Miss Kohler, the correspondence secretary, and Miss Finch, who answered the telephones. There was also a room for the AP and UP teletypes.

Brad liked to get his column done by noon. At this hour the Hurd-Hudner office called and Miss Malone read the typed pages over the telephone to a secretary in New York, a method which had been found less expensive and more accurate than wiring. Brad, meanwhile, would be on his way to a luncheon date. He kept appointments until late in the afternoon. Between six and seven-thirty he attended cocktail parties—there were usually several to choose from—and he liked to have Sharon go with him. Cocktail parties were a working period for Brad—he was gathering material—nor did his routine vary much when he left Burlingame to work in Washington. He didn't encourage late dining: he could pump the news out of an ordinary group and be in bed with the light out by midnight. He was up by eight. One of the most valued periods of the day, to Sharon, was breakfast, a meal which by long habit they took together. No matter how rushed he might happen to be, Brad had never let business wholly encroach on this interlude; however, for a number of months, he had been bringing mail and newspapers to the morning table, giving his attention to these while he gulped down his food, then jumping up suddenly with the statement he had to go to work. Sharon made no comment for some time on this change in their relationship, but finally one day, following an evening when they had been out unusually late, she let it be seen that she wasn't too happy about it.

"Brad," she said mildly, "couldn't you sit down and chat for a minute?"

"Something, kiddo?" Brad said genially. He smiled at her but remained standing.

"Only that I never seem to see you any more," Sharon said. "I take a cup of coffee in the morning. A cup of coffee and Brad Iverson is all I need—but all I get is a cup of coffee. Don't you think we could talk things over sometimes, the way we used to?"

Brad now sat down as requested but he looked ready to get up again.

"Well, yes, kiddo, we could," he said, "only maybe not right at this time."

"There never seems to be any right time," Sharon said.

"There are lots of times," Brad said, "only you and I don't always hit on subjects for discussion. Subjects that are fascinating, that is, at eight-thirty in the morning."

"Well," Sharon said, "we could talk about something, I think. Once in a while. Or if all else failed, you could read me some of the better cracks from yesterday's column."

"That's not a very brilliant remark, Shar," Brad said with no show of rancor.

"No," Sharon said, "I suppose it isn't. I've been incommunicado so long I may be losing the knack for making brilliant remarks."

"But not," Brad said, "for making mean ones. Are the old nerves jumping around this morning, kiddo?"

"Yes," Sharon said, "they are and have been for quite some time. I've been wondering about a lot of things. Such as, for instance, what use I am to you."

Brad looked once more, this time despairingly, at the gold clock.

The moment had come for him to go out to the bungalow suite, but it was obvious that for today this moment would have to be deferred.

He settled back and lighted a cigarette. "If we have to go into it, you're a whole lot of use to me and you know it. So why go into it?"

"Because I'd like to know, that's all. You used to talk over your work with me; now you haven't time. Sometimes you used to come home early and we'd make love in the afternoon. Remember? But we haven't got time for that either."

"We'll have it," Brad said, "we'll definitely have it."

"I'll bet," Sharon said, "provided I can get myself appointed a Presidential aide. That, or steal a State Department file! Something that would make me worth your while."

"Kiddo," Brad said, "I'll be honest with you. Right now I don't know what you're driving at or what this conversation is expected to accomplish. If you're trying to tell me that you haven't had enough attention, that's something that can be changed, but not, as I say, just when I—"

"I'm no use to you," Sharon said; "I just feel that I'm no use to you at all."

"That," Brad said, "is, if you'll pardon the expression, crapola."

"I'll pardon the expression," Sharon said, "but I'll be damned if I want to go on being miserable and lonely. It doesn't make any sense. I used to think you valued my opinion. Then I decided you just needed me for an audience. It's obvious now that neither is true. So what am I hanging around for? Of course, I can still entertain for you and I don't embarrass you when you take me out; but let me tell you something—you embarrass me when I'm trying to be a good wife and you're playing footsie with the wife of some Congressional Committeeman. I wish I knew what the score is, that's all."

Brad removed specks of tobacco from his lower lip. He said, with no alteration in his composure, "It's a foul situation all right. Something has to be done about it."

"Something certainly has," Sharon said; "and if you won't do it, maybe I'll have to."

To her surprise she felt tears rising in her eyes. She blinked them back, but the tears grew larger and coursed down her cheeks. She was sorry for herself and at the same time furious with Brad because he'd kept his temper: he wouldn't waste on her the emotional energy he needed for his work.

"God, you can be irritating," she said.

"I'm sure of it," Brad said. He put out his cigarette and strolled around the room as if looking for a means of escape.

"Brad," she said, almost pleadingly, "I didn't mean to be tiresome. Perhaps you're right, my nerves are jumping, but it's not only that. Maybe it's stupid but that's how I've felt—and it's been getting worse. Couldn't we take a holiday, just the two of us? Couldn't we go somewhere and let me get over it?"

Brad poured some cold coffee in a cup and swirled it around; he peered into it like a soothsayer into a fowl's entrails. "Well, I don't know," he said reflectively; "that's not a bad idea."

"I think it's a good idea," Sharon said; "you don't know how much I'd like to do it. I think it's what we both need, I really do."

Brad drank the coffee. "Not a bad idea at all," he said, "but where should we go? And when? Those things have to be considered too."

"Anywhere at all," Sharon said feverishly, "I don't care. But I think it should be right away. How long has it been since you had a vacation? Three years?"

Brad shrugged. "About that, I guess. Vacation, schmacation. In this business you don't get vacations."

"Pegler gets them," Sharon said, "Winchell and Pearson get them. The syndicate just prints a line—Mr. So-and-so has gone fishing or something. Column will be resumed when he returns. Oh, Brad. It would be such fun. Can't we go?"

She got up, her hands on his arms, her face tensely raised. She could see he was tempted; she felt that much of the future, perhaps their whole life together, swung on the decision.

"Can't we, Brad?"

He held her closely for a moment. "We'll go," he said; "only I tell you what. I'll have to get a few columns ahead. You know H-H. He's a stickler for operational procedure, but I'll speak to him about it as soon as I get back to Washington."

"You don't want me to go back to Washington with you?" Sharon asked, a prescience of danger skidding down her spine.

"Well, sure I want you to," Brad said, "but on the other hand, what would be the use—making a big move out of it if we're going on a trip? You can get us cleared away here and read some travel folders. I'll have Miss Finch get them for you. . . . Now, kiddo, don't look like that. Being separated for a while may sort of relax us, make the trip more fun. Then the first minute I can get away, off we'll go to Shangri-la or maybe Acapulco like a couple of insane honeymooners. We'll get terrific tans and wear those cut-down French bathing suits and lie around all day swilling champagne and making love, just you and me on a tropical isle. How will that be?"

"It sounds nice," Sharon said.

10

"HASN'T HE said anything more about the trip?" Alexandra asked.

"Not a thing. He never even mentions it. I'm still supposed to be looking up planes to Mexico. Or making plans to canoe up the St. Lawrence—by myself. Not that I really mind. This is the sort of thing that does harm—" Sharon laid the clipping on the table between their respective cocktail glasses, now empty.

It was a Monday in the spring of 1945 and the sisters were lunching together in the St. Francis. Long ago, in some dim moment of the city's evolution, wives and daughters of the better sort had set aside Monday lunch in the St. Francis to prove—by conspicuous food consumption on a day ordinarily set aside for laundry work— that they no longer tubbed their own clothes. Sharon had called Alexandra early in the morning. She had been much disturbed by an item which had appeared that day in Letty Meeker's column; though she had assumed (correctly) that her sister had already seen it, she had read it to her on the telephone, then cut it out and brought it with her. She wanted its wording subjected to further analysis.

> *Burlingame's* INDIAN PIPE SET [Letty Meeker had written, using her own quaint system of italics] *are worried about the* PROLONGED SEPARATIONS *of the Bradley Iversons. Well, dears, we can report there's nothing to worry about*—AS OF NOW. *It's just that there's still a war on and Brad is an* AWFULLY BUSY MAN *with all the high-powered writing he has to do, and all* . . .

"What a foul bitch!" Alexandra said.

"Isn't she, though?"

"Now you may have an idea of the kind of thing she's been doing to me for the last ten years," Alexandra said. She took out of her purse a bundle of clips, soiled and creased as if by long possession and wrapped in two bits of yellow paper.

"I thought we might compare notes," she said, "because I have an idea about that woman. I'm going to get her fired, if it's the last thing I ever do."

Through the large oblong room the maître d'hôtel could be seen approaching, herding ahead of him the waiter carrying their second round of drinks. The maître d'hôtel bowed before them—two bows —one for each.

"Madame," he said to Sharon. He took the martini from the waiter's tray and set it before her.

"Baroness!" he said to Alexandra, giving her the double daiquiri. Earnest never forgot who had ordered which drink.

"Thank you, Earnest," Alexandra said.

"Are we ready to order something to eat now?" Earnest inquired.

"Not quite yet for me, Earnest," Alexandra said. "I'll finish this and then I'll see if I want just one more little drinkie."

"And you, Madame?" Earnest said to Sharon.

"I'll have the chicken patty," Sharon said. "I suppose that's all that's any good."

"The chicken patty is very nice," Earnest said. "We have also the Crab Louie."

"Is that nice?"

Earnest's face reflected nothing but approbation for the Crab Louie but he allowed a suggestion of regret to color his voice. The crab was nice, but out of season. He was sorry that he had no steaks. Soon, if the war news stayed good, there would be plenty of steaks, God willing.

He whipped the menus off the table and gave the drink and food order to the waiter standing just behind him.

Sharon raised her glass. It was fine being with Alexandra and having a chance to talk about things she couldn't discuss at the same level with anybody else. She had been looking forward particularly to this lunch, their first since her sister's return from her honeymoon with the Baron Nicholas Alexis Drobny. Alexandra, she thought, certainly looked well. She and Nicky had bought a ranch near Sonoma—or Alexandra had bought it, Sharon suspected, as a present for her bridegroom, as well as a joint residence, the point of a ranch being that Nicky needed horses to ride.

The switch to an outdoor life was something new for Alexandra, but it evidently agreed with her. She had a wonderful tan, and if her skin had coarsened somewhat, this wasn't true of her body. She had lost weight and there was a new suppleness and muscular toughness about her that seemed just as effective in its way, though possibly not quite so flattering, as her former voluptuous, indoor beauty. She did seem to be drinking a good deal, but perhaps that was a habit one got into when one lived on a ranch.

"You mean to say you've *kept* all that stuff?" Sharon looked incredulously at the soggy mass of clippings. It was unlike Alexandra—

particularly this new, ranchy Alexandra—to preserve mementos of any kind. It was clear that she must hate Letty as much as, if not more than, Letty hated her.

"It all goes back to your debut, of course," Sharon said. "Did I ever tell you about the scene she made?"

"You didn't, but Mother wrote me about it! How she came pounding on the door, yelling that I'd ruined her 'exclusive.' Then she had the gall to make it look as if I'd eloped with Schuy because I was dead drunk. 'Midnight Troth Follows Gay Champagne Party.' I telegraphed Anchy. Do you want to see what I said? I kept a copy of it—and of his answer. I want to rub his nose in both of them someday. And I know how to do it, believe me."

Alexandra seemed about to say something more but instead compressed her lips. While Sharon examined the clippings and the two telegraph forms in which they were wrapped, she stared out sullenly into the room as if she could see hanging in the smoky air the components of some Florentine plot, hatched by herself—a plot whose seductions might leave rapiered bodies in canals and courtiers rotting in dungeons. Come to think of it, there was something definitely medieval, whether Florentine or not, about Alexandra: her power for decisions, her melting beauty with its reserves of stamina that would wear down a horse, not to mention a man; the hungers and the ruthlessness that made common cause with an accountant's practicality. No one knew Alexandra who didn't know this about her, the conjoining of many imps within her, all schooled to pass unnoticed except at such shadowy moments as the present when, in silk doublets, daggers in hand, you saw them peering like assassins from the corners of her eyes.

The first telegram—a carbon of one that had been sent—was sent from Reno in 1934 and addressed to Anchylus Saxe, 8 The Day Building, San Francisco, California.

ONLY THING I HAVE EVER ASKED OF YOU OR WILL ASK IS DISMISSAL OF MEEKER WOMAN FOR INSULTING AND DEGRADING REPORT OF MY WEDDING WHICH APPEARED LAST MONDAY. OTHERWISE AM VERY HAPPY. SCHUY SENDS HIS BEST. THANK YOU FOR A WONDERFUL DEBUT. LOVE ZAN.

Anchylus had wired back:

MUCH AS I WOULD LIKE TO CONCUR IN YOUR EVERY REQUEST CANNOT TERMINATE LONGTIME TRUSTED EMPLOYEE ON GROUNDS OF PERSONAL IRRITATION. GLAD YOU LIKED DEBUT. MY BEST

171

WISHES TO YOU AND YOUR HUSBAND FOR A PLEASANT HONEY-
MOON AND MUCH HAPPINESS THROUGH THE YEARS TO COME.
LOVE FATHER.

The wishes expressed in the last line had an ironic air when considered with the items which followed—Letty's comments on the
progress of the marriage. Letty had kept track of all developments,
and her reportage made up in accuracy whatever it lacked in cordiality. Since Alexandra had spent most of the period in Europe it was
hard to say offhand where Letty had got her information. Part of it,
no doubt, had come from columnists such as Cholly Knickerbocker,
specializing in the doings of the international set; by the late thirties
Alexandra's Continental capers had made her eligible for this kind of
coverage. Another source, Sharon guessed, had been travelers willing
to trade a scandal about somebody else for a favorable mention for
themselves. Letty was a power; her dislike was feared, her favor
sought even by individuals so situated that they could well have
afforded to remain indifferent to her. Her memory was as accurate in
recalling an obligation as in avenging a slight and her perpetual
harassment of her enemies had become an important part of a journalistic technique designed to give a sense of superiority to those
whom she flattered.

> *Marry in haste, repent in Monte Carlo, we always say.* TOO
> BAD *that the repentance of the charming* SCHUYLER CUTTINGS
> *took the form of such* BAD LUCK *at the tables and such an un-
> fortunate* PUBLIC QUARREL *in the Casino bar.*

There were other notes of the same sort. San Francisco of the
period must have found them amusing. When Letty couldn't use
Alexandra as a target, she could use Schuy—and she did.

> *Schuyler Cutting won't get a State Department job in Eu-
> rope.* TOO BAD. *He'd told his friends he was so* SURE *of one!
> His lovely Alexandra (nee Saxe) was very* GAY *at a party in
> Fouquet's attended by the Maharajah of Jodhpur and
> F. Scott Fitzgerald, the* DRUNKEN *American writer.*

After the Cuttings had moved to Berlin, Letty wrote:

> *It could be that the Cuttings are* RUNNING OUT *of countries
> to play in, particularly the sort of play at which* MONEY

172

CHANGES HANDS. *Some of his checks have been so* RUBBERY *they have bounced* CLEAR *across the Atlantic, where his mother has had to make them* GOOD.

The divorce coverage which came later had an I-told-you note, unpleasant to the subjects, diverting to the reader. There followed a series of observations on Alexandra's career in New York and points east, few of them flattering; from Letty's accounts it would have seemed that Alexandra's choice of escorts had been limited to men who were wanted (a) by the police, (b) by their wives or (c) by nobody. As for example her description of Nick Drobny, her bridegroom, as a man with "one of the highest-priced titles in Hungary."

None of Letty's paragraphs were, it seemed, false enough to go to court over or unsavory enough to offend *The Day*'s readers. Yet all, taken together, added up to a curious hellbox of spite, as timeless and destructive as the hate which had made Alexandra keep them, plotting her revenge.

"Now," she said as Sharon finished, "if you think she's treated *you* badly, look what she's done to me. Do you blame me for feeling as I do?"

"I don't, Zan. I don't at all, only—"

Alexandra squeezed her arm. "You must help me," she said. Vaguely, but with great emotion, "Help me, Chicken."

"But I don't see, Zan," Sharon said shakily, "how I *can*. I mean, what we can do about any of this."

"We can do a great deal," Alexandra said firmly. She watched, as if from another planet, the approach of the waiter with their lunch order. "Not now, perhaps," she amended, "but someday. We can and, if we're smart, we will—"

"You mean, you have it all planned?"

"Well, not planned exactly, but someday we'll own *The Day*. You seem to forget that. Mother gets all of Grandfather Fabian's stock, plus half of Anchy's. It's all really ours, it's in trust for us, and when you get to own stock you can run a company. You can fire anyone you want, even the boss. Keep in mind what I'm saying."

"You mean, our beloved father?"

"I cross-examined George Dudley on this. Here's what he told me. Most companies today are controlled with far less than fifty-one per cent—some with only small percentages. Look, Anchy only kept twelve and a half per cent for himself. Each of us girls has the same —twelve and a half. If any two of us get together against him we'd have twenty-five per cent. That would sew up the situation, wouldn't it?"

"I suppose it would," Sharon said uncertainly. This type of thinking was new to her. It wasn't too complicated, but it was hard for her to get her mind on figures.

Alexandra pressed on. "He might be the one who winds up without a job himself. Wouldn't that be marvelous?"

The Florentine courtiers were laughing. Heads thrown back, mustachios pointed at the sky, they enjoyed their illusionary triumph; the blades in their hands glittered in the moonlight while the waiter served the plates of chicken patty.

"You'll see, Sweetie," Alexandra said, "what fun we'll both get out of it. So you will help, won't you? Please say you will. I'll feel so much better."

"Of course I'll help, dear," Sharon said. "Just tell me what I have to do."

Sharon was later to recall that lunch and the emotions it had set churning in her. She was to recall them on a day when, due to accident more than anything else, she found herself the only member of the family present at Jessica's deathbed. She was also to recall, even in the helplessness of her grief, the decision she had made at that luncheon, a decision which, for good and sufficient reason, she was not fated to keep and which, as a matter of fact, she took considerable pleasure, when the time came, in recanting.

For herself, she had accepted her fate. She was lonely much of the time, even when Brad was in Burlingame, but there was no more talk now of a second honeymoon. She had stopped reflecting on how different her life might have been if Brad had wanted children. Several times in the next three or four years she decided she was pregnant; for a week or so she would laugh or cry without any reason, she would experience an imaginary but effective type of morning sickness, take naps in the afternoon, find herself without the strength to make plans—a condition which lasted only until the pregnancy turned out to be a mistake and she would return to her normal level of adjusted restlessness. Wasn't it better, perhaps, to be a little unhappy rather than wholly bored like so many of her friends? At least she had the satisfaction of being married to a man who, when he didn't shut her out of his life, could command her entire attention. He had one weakness—he couldn't love "for keeps." She could love no other way. At least the house on Floribunda Avenue was charming, and they gave some splendid parties there. Nor was love, even on her own terms, entirely ruled out. Tenderness came through sometimes, hope came through. And Brad's writing was going marvelously. He was not a monster, not that at all. He was a brilliant man who in the throes of his career had naturally become a little isolated, a little self-centered.

It was an old, familiar story. She had married a Success.

V

Vital Statistic

"*First Stranger:*   Where was you born?
Second Stranger: Out of wedlock.
First Stranger: That's mighty pretty coun-
            try around there."
                              —RING LARDNER

1 ANCHYLUS had lived alone a good deal in the months before General MacArthur signed for peace with his five pens. Jessica had been advised, for the sake of her health, to stay in the country. He missed her, and to make up for it worked harder than ever, got out the paper, messed around in politics as usual, sat late in restaurants discussing how, when the chance came, the people of the United States could get the Democrats out of the White House. He hadn't the slightest inkling that trouble might be brewing with one, and possibly two, of his daughters. When his mind tracked back into the past to consider family hurts, he was solaced by one development which took place at this time: the heartening revival of his relationship with Pamela, that one of his three daughters whose behavior had most puzzled him.

It was good having something nice happen just then. A new world—and not necessarily a good one—was in the throes of being born. It was a world that took some getting used to.

2 THE SHIPS coming in stood high in the water due to the lightness of their loads—the supply ships homeward bound, the
transports in their tattered war paint, cut loose from their con-
voys at last, the hospital vessels still splashed hopefully with big red
crosses. Many of the wounded could not come up on deck but there
were always ambulatory cases who could; they stood at the rail
smoking and staring, and in their faces when seen closely there was
a bemused, guarded expression of attentiveness and unbelief. Most
of them had at some time abandoned hope of ever seeing this again
—the gray harbor, the big bridges, the prison island, the hills and
the docks, the shore, the lights of home. Seeing it was a miracle, but
with it went another, even stranger: there was a welcomer for each
man in the city just as if the hills, the water and the stony houses
had been streamlined into a woman's face.

Sometimes the face was known and dear and sometimes feature-
less and undefined—a Possible. But some woman was always the
welcomer. She was the beckoning shore.

Statistically, it is interesting to note that the woman was more
often real than imaginary; if not real at first, she rapidly material-
ized. In the Marriage License Bureau, that worn, ink-stained jump-
ing-off place, many young campaigners with old faces were busy
crystallizing their welcome. Thus one summer afternoon shortly before V-J Day in 1945, *The Day* included in its column of Vital
Statistics under the subhead *Marriages* an interesting item:

Harper, Clifford F.; Saxe, Pamela

The groom was a big, light-haired fellow in brand-new civilian
clothes. He had just been honorably discharged from the United
States Marine Corps, Third Division Reinforced. His discharge,
which he had with him when applying for his marriage license,
affirmed that he had participated in actions in Okinawa, Saipan and
Pelelius; under the column headed *Remarks* it contained the words
Service Honest and Faithful. This observation was in general an almost complete biography of Bridegroom Clifford Harper except
that he was twenty-three years old, that he lacked any well-established trade or profession, except soldiering, and that for him the
city of San Francisco was not merely a port of arrival but his
home. He had once won an Ivor Johnson bicycle in a *Day* circula-

tion contest, had taken and passed a lifesaving test at the Berkeley YMCA, and had been a high-school letterman in football and basketball. These situations and achievements had been highlights in his life. Also at one time he had owned an old Dodge roadster which had twin pipes and was tooled to look like a hop-up even though it wasn't one. It had *Here Comes Cliff* painted across the hood and *There Goes Cliff* on the rear. Also the words *Pass with Care* and *No Horns, Please, Driver Sleeping.*

Cliff had always been a good boy. He had been a wonderful son, his mother said. Yet he had always had a mind of his own. In spite of his popularity and his liking for sports and a good time there had been days when Cliff seemed moody and would lie around the house or go out to his workbench in the garage and make things with tools.

Asked by *The Day*'s City Hall staffer what pursuit he planned to follow after marriage, Cliff said that he was going to settle down in San Francisco. He had sometimes thought about going in the photography business. Or he might do garage work. He wasn't dead set. He'd have to see.

The bride wore gray. She was a well-built, medium-sized girl with red hair and grayish green eyes and a habit of slightly compressing her rather full lips before she spoke or smiled. She was several years older than the groom. In addition to the tight-fitting gray suit and small white hat, she wore black pumps and a white corsage and carried a black patent-leather purse. She gave her occupation as nurse and her address as Treasure Island Naval Hospital. *The Day* staffer never thought to connect her name with that of Anchylus Saxe, boss of the paper which employed him. He hadn't worked for *The Day* very long and didn't know much about the boss's family. When Matt Brody ate him out later for goofing, the staffer said he just never thought about a daughter of Anchylus Saxe going down to the City Hall and getting married to a gyrene.

Experience is an imponderable, no two persons receiving the same impression from a shared event. Nevertheless, it can be said broadly that to both Mr. and Mrs. Harper the steps leading up to their marriage seemed to have been arranged by friendly, possibly divine forces, and to have been inevitable and simple. This was, of course, a silly idea. While a certain amount of argument could have been brought up to support the notion of the friendly forces, nothing that had made the Harper-Saxe item a vital statistic, except maybe the love that had gone into it, was what you could have called simple.

3　Two wars had, to start with, helped to shape up this statistic—
the first one no less than the second. In that first war one particular day was important. For George D. Harper, later to be
the father of Cliff, the day was the one on which two regiments
of the First U.S. Army under Maj. Gen. Carlton Tate Morse attacked
the German forces holding the wood and village of Dortmont, in
the St. Mihiel salient. By four o'clock that afternoon the German
command had fallen back and in the evening, their supply having
caught up with them, the Americans dug in. The rain, which had
lifted during the attack, set in again; a southeast wind was blowing
steadily and at dawn the Germans counterattacked across a vineyard.

Private George D. Harper knew what had happened to him all
right. After one whiff of the stuff smelling like newly mown hay he
crawled out of the shell hole because the stuff was heavy and always
sought a lower level. He got his gas mask on before he passed out.
He spent four months in a base hospital at Lille, France, and close
to a year at the VA Hospital in Sawtelle, California. The doctors
told him when he got his discharge that if he was careful he'd have
nothing to worry about.

George Harper was careful. He was careful working in the Black
Cat Mine in Climax, Colorado, where he went after leaving Sawtelle. He was careful then and he was careful later when he found
the dust in the mine made his wheeze worse, and he and his wife,
Midge, moved to San Francisco, where there was said to be possible jobs and not much dust. Here he went to work for a garage, and
in San Francisco his children were born, all four of them, between
the years of 1922 and 1930, Cliff being the oldest.

"Wrap up your chest," his wife would call to him on foggy or
windy days, and George would wag his head as if Midge bored him
with her worrying, but he would wrap up as she told him to.

The wheeze was always there. You had to put your head against
George's chest to hear it. It was buried way inside of him out of
sight, quiet, rapacious and patient. It was one day one hour one second of that war not lost in peace or hushed by victory but living on
alive inside George Harper. It had made no armistice.

Cliff thought the far-off wheeze was fascinating. It was one of the
many things that made his father a worth-while person, more interesting than other people. Cliff liked to crawl up on his father's lap
when company was at the house. Curled in a comfortable position,

he would listen to the second voice that rustled, oh so gently, inside George Harper. While George's real voice was laughing or talking, the second voice continued to repeat its perpetual story about the shot-up vineyard and the men in the holes and the corpses under the bare trees and in the ditch in front of the hedge and the rifle fire and the grenades and the stuff that smelled like hay.

Few people would have ventured to say then, or even believed, that the war—and at that time still innocently called The Great War—was alive in those years, hidden away, not in the armories where the dusty flags were stored, but in the People, in the living structure of the world, just as the deadly sound of its drowned-out whisper had a life inside George Harper.

There was no sound warning anyone of war in those days. There was prosperity. Before the Harper family had been in San Francisco very long, they too had a piece of this prosperity, made specific by George's ownership of half the garage and half of the two-family house in the Mission, both garage half and house half being purchased on time payments. Peace was, of course, a permanent arrangement. When Lindbergh, the daring aviator, flew across the Atlantic, writers pointed out that with planes shuttling around the globe countries would be brought closer together and thus war made impossible.

George Harper didn't read much that the writers said. He had prosperity, of course, he knew that, but the trouble with it was he had such a tough time making a living for his family. After Cliff came Tracy; Denis Harper was born in Lindbergh's year and Sue-Ellen the year a politician, supposedly Herbert Hoover—although people were already starting to blame everything on Herbert Hoover, and he may have never said it—made the claim that in the U.S.A. there was a chicken for every pot.

George Harper didn't get to eat much chicken. He had to sell his interest in the garage but worked steadily as a night repairman for another garage specializing in highway emergency work—the Ajax, out on the El Camino Real. One night George got up a sweat getting a wreck slung in the hoist of the tow car and drove back without putting on his windbreaker. Next morning he was running a high fever. Two days later he was dead.

It was his own fault. He hadn't been careful.

Several months later with the help of her grocer (to whom she already owed a large bill), Midge Harper opened a soft drink and hamburger stand on the Harding Municipal Golf Course.

Cliff helped his mother at the stand. He was a good-looking, healthy kid. Though not big for his age, he was a husky and willing worker. He was the least rowdy of the Harper kids and the quickest to learn anything; at the stand, he would lift the cases of soft drinks that were too heavy for Midge; and when a couple of foursomes came piling into the stand all wanting food at once, he would take the sandwiches his mother fixed and put a relish or some pickle on the paper plate and serve the customers while Midge opened the bottles of coke, cream soda or near-beer. Always Cliff looked at the customers he served with great anxiety, to make sure they were pleased and if, as it often turned out, they were, his face would light with pleasure. Patrons of the stand treated him in a friendly way, especially if they had boys of their own; on the other hand, some of them flirted with Midge as if she, mother of four children, were still a young girl. Midge couldn't stand such talk. Her dark eyes would flash and she would smile warmly and beautifully and tell them to go on about their business.

One of the most pleasant men who played golf at Municipal in those Prohibition days was Peter V. Palermo, a businessman. He told Midge frankly he was in the liquor business, but, as he said, what difference did it make? There were no businesses what didn't have illegal aspects. Mr. Palermo numbered among his customers some of the finest families of the city. (It was he—although he did not think to mention this to Midge—who supplied the beverages served at the annual outings of the Bohemian Club, of which Mr. George Dudley, attorney for the Saxe family, was a member.) That was the way it was and if Mr. Roosevelt did what people thought he would do, why, pretty soon Mr. Palermo would be a legal merchant instead of a bum, he said, and Midge pretended to be shocked and asked who would dare call him a bum?

Midge got engaged to Mr. Palermo and the Harpers moved out of the old Mission house (where they had lost their equity and were living as tenants) to a better one. There for the first time the girl and boys had separate rooms. Mr. Palermo had the guestroom and he always visited the Harpers when he was in town. The grocer who had loaned Midge money told her what some of the old crows who traded at his store were saying about her, but Midge told him if that gave them fun, okay, let them go ahead and talk. She had her family to keep and she couldn't lie awake nights worrying about that jabber jabber jabber.

One April morning, Mr. Palermo was found dead in his car near Pier 27, his body punctured by a number of slugs from a .45 automatic pistol. The killing obtained a split-column, page-one story in *The San Francisco Day*, with equivalent coverage in the *Chronicle*, *Examiner* and the evening papers. Juvenile authorities sent a woman to inspect the house where Midge and the children had been living. At the next session of the Juvenile Court it was decided that since Mrs. Harper had no means of livelihood and since the children had been found living in undesirable conditions, it would be best for their own sake to take them down to the Otis Street Detention Home and later perhaps to a welfare home until Mrs. Harper could prove herself able to support them, and until she could show that conditions were desirable, or in other words, that she was not living with anybody, and above all with anybody like Mr. Peter V. Palermo.

It was the most awful thing that had happened since the beginning of the world. It was the end of the world. It was as if a huge snake, with coils stretching all the way from their house to the Welfare Home had slid across their lives, engulfing them with its evilness, tearing them apart from each other, breathing a curse on them with its foul breath and a witchcraft doom out of its staring eyes. Denis and Sue-Ellen were too little to know what was happening; they thought they were just going for a ride until Sue-Ellen began to sob and then Denis started too. Mrs. Harper had tried to make it seem all right to the children, but the day the car came for them she lost control of herself and ran out of the house and stood there cursing the woman from the Welfare Home, and when the door of the car shut Midge began to scream. Cliff had got in and sat there quietly looking for the last time at the happy house and his mother standing with her face all twisted and her mouth open. Cliff was yelling too, but only inside.

That Welfare Home, the place they all were taken to! That place. Oh, how Cliff longed for the day when he would be rich, when he would get the Governor or some great man to write an order and would go back there and put an end to it. He would drive up to the door in his car and make an end of it. Mr. Meggs, the principal, could get down on his knees and it wouldn't help. Cliff would throw him out and all the rest of them; he would have the place burned. The empty whisky bottles in the closet of Mr. Meggs's office wouldn't burn but the canes would and the mattresses they'd had to sleep on, full of bugs, stinking and rotting because any child was whipped who got up in the night to go to the john. When everything was burning he would tell people about Mr. Meggs and what he did when he had whipped an older boy in his office and he would have him put in prison.

Cliff made a friend while he was in the home—a freckled, frisky Jewish kid named Kim Borg. Together they had planned how they'd run away. They tried it twice but each time they were caught. That was when Cliff was eleven and had been in the home for thirteen months.

All the time Cliff and Sue-Ellen and Denis and Tracy had been in the Welfare Home, their mother, Midge, had been making plans. She had been trying to get them out, she had been writing to them about it and promising. They never doubted the great day would come. And it did come! Midge got them out. She was married now to another Latin-American type man, Rafael Vargas, one of *The Day*'s district circulation managers—the same person who later got the circulation route for Cliff. Once more all the Harpers were together, living in a small house in Berkeley, going to a real school, really alive again.

Every winter, spring and fall Cliff went to school and studied hard. He got the best marks in his class, especially in history and English. He had the circulation route in summer, a full-time job bossing the other fellows who distributed *The Day*'s home-delivered edition for Mr. Vargas. He got the Ivor Johnson and the car and the high-school letters and went in the Marine Corps, and all of this seemed in retrospect most satisfactory, particularly since it had led to the best thing of all, namely, getting married to Pam.

4   It was a warm and sunny day, full of twinkling windshields, hurrying people, excitement and city smells, like the day of a parade or a football game. Cliff and Pam walked away from the City Hall holding hands. Both were silent—Cliff out of contentment and the sense of having settled a most important issue; Pam because of a problem of conscience. Though Cliff had told her so much about his life, he knew little about hers. During the short period of their acquaintanceship she had told him briefly about her family—that she had two married sisters, that her real mother was dead but that she had a father and stepmother living in San Francisco. She implied that her family was well-to-do but she wasn't sure from Cliff's reaction whether or not he believed her. Probably many girls, casually met with, tried to assume importance by alleging family status later discovered to be false. It was quite clear that he didn't care what sort of family she came from—and this delighted her—but he was her husband now and it was time she got busy and

told him about herself. A wife had to establish her identity in her husband's eyes even if the problem of establishing it in her own eyes had always been so puzzling that even now, on her wedding day, it had not yet been solved to her full satisfaction.

A child, especially a female child, knows when she is being treated differently from other children. It is perhaps no less true that a child senses when a special effort is made *not* to treat her differently. Her instincts tell her that, under normal circumstances, she would be treated differently at times—either favored or discriminated against. To be dealt with at all times in a manner visibly equated with the manner in which one's sisters are treated can become, by paradox, a highly suspicious form of differentiation. Anchylus and Jessica had been vigilant to see that she was always given her share of presents (just like Sharon's and Alexandra's, particularly in such prized trade goods as jewelry, animals or clothes) or parties (attended by your own friends, dear . . . you know that Sharon and Alexandra have *their* own friends and you have yours, so you may invite whomever you wish. . . .) of picnics and theaters and trips to the country when the Saxes were living in the city and to the city when they were living in the country and to the White House or the City of Paris for clothes-shopping and to Blum's for chocolate malts or banana walnut cream parfaits and to movies and symphonies and the circus.

There was too much consistency about it all—a consistency which developed its own submerged threat. If such care had to be taken to give you the same things as others, yet separate from theirs, what was wrong with you?

Pamela had been reasonably happy growing up in the California Street house and the house in Atherton, but she had had the problem all the time and it had resulted in her strange action, which no one had understood, of going back to Oregon that time, trying to find her mother. Her personal ties with Jessica and Anchylus were firm and she didn't disown or disrespect them, yet she knew that before she could ever know who she really was she would have to go through this process of making a separate life. She would have to smooth herself into the churning yet sharply rhythmed life of the city and be lost among the streaming but secret, individually owned faces until something stopped hurting and a quiet ensued out of which a new identity with her name could be born and be hers. She had made up her mind to take this step and nothing could turn her from it. She had made it up long before the coming-out party and Alexandra's elopement, but she had put off action, not because she had wanted the party but because Anchylus and Jessica had wanted her to have it. So she'd had it. After the party she'd started talking about the job, and finally they had let her go and look for one.

Jessica had understood about it better than Anchylus. He wanted things to be the way he'd planned them, and the plans hadn't included a daughter who lived alone in a walk-up apartment and worked in an office. What was the sense of the expensive schools and the fine clothes and manners and all if your daughter was going to wind up doing that? He'd tried to talk her out of it just as he later tried to talk Sharon out of marrying Brad Iverson.

"The lonesomest thing in the world," he said, "is turning on your own lights."

He hadn't added that in his own case this form of loneliness had been avoided because he'd lived with Red Margaret Tighe or O'Boylan, as the case might have been—a precaution which, since other precautions had been lacking, had resulted in Pamela's arrival in the world. He added nothing, suggested no alternatives, but he made it clear that he disapproved.

"I'll be all right, Daddy," Pamela said. "I'll come home to see you all the time."

He opened his mouth to say it was stupid to pay rent when, if she insisted on working, she could still live at California Street. Pamela could see the thought passing through his head and she could sense, and be grateful for, the fact that he had decided not to say it.

"Living alone!" he said.

"It won't be nearly as nice as being here with you, Dads, but I feel as if I have to do it. Lots of girls live alone, you know, and I guess they get used to it."

Anchylus rubbed his cheek with his mashed knuckles. "Lots of them get to be old maids, too," he said bodefully.

Pamela laughed. "I'll be married sometime."

Anchylus snorted. "Why don't you let your mother give some parties for you, so you can meet a few decent fellows?"

"I don't want to meet any right now, Dad," Pamela said, "but I'll be home a lot. I'll try to find an apartment that's not too far away."

She found one on Telegraph Hill. It had one room with a window that tilted you out over the harbor so you felt you could spit into Alcatraz. Anchylus gave her fifty a month to pay the rent, but he still didn't understand and he hadn't liked the fellows she occasionally brought to the California Street house. The result had been that, first, she stopped bringing fellows there and, second, she stopped going there herself so much. With Jessica she'd always kept up warm, daughterly feelings, but Anchylus hadn't understood and he looked at her, on the rare occasions when they were together, with an obstinate, baffled coldness. She was already a stranger, coming home with tales of working in a drugstore, a department store, a library, a dentist's office, with kisses on the cheek, presents in a paper bag, and young men who did not amount to much. He hadn't forgiven her. That was what made it hard to explain her life to Cliff.

How could you explain nine years?

The years had laid a trap for her. You picked a year and made friends with it. You strolled down the street arm in arm with your buddy, the year, taking everything very easy, watching where you put your feet. Then—*wham*. Your buddy wasn't there any more. You got your last look at him as he ran around the corner with your purse in his hand.

The search was still going on for the person she was supposed to meet right off: Miss Identity; she has red hair, she could say, freckles on the nose. Built like a tennis player. Doesn't look too well in clothes, all right without them, I suppose. Very anxious to be in love. Trying that, too. Knowing all about the Mother Bit and the Sigmund Freud Bit, but no answer there either. Told at the desk by the woman in charge that they remembered perfectly, oh, yes, the person who had brought her in, but the card hadn't been filled out, and while she changed her clothes and took a bath they had phoned Anchylus Saxe.

When she walked into parties given by the young couples, married or living together in the rooms on Telegraph or Russian Hill with the sky for wallpaper, right away she took a quick look around to check. Was this the place? She checked in the bottom of the glasses that had been filled with the wine each guest brought as a house present, dragging the half-gallon jugs up the sixty-nine steps from Broadway. She checked among the voices, the men infinitely talking, eyes flashing, using intellectual words, particularly toward morning, and the bit about art and the integrity of it all. (Bill Saroyan had gone hungry up these same steps to the attics with too much light.) She searched also, later, among the cigarette butts dying with slow sizzling among the empty cartons that had held potato salad, chow mein, spaghetti, Marx and Steinbeck, the chains you had shed, death on the barricades, Madrid besieged, Daladier kissed for Munich, photographs by Bob Capa, the execution of Federigo García Lorca.

Where was the girl?

Nobody knew.

Awake in the night, she looked tenderly at the sleeping heads of lovers who would be strangers in the morning but whose sealed brows and quiet breathing held, after the pleasures of a temporary madness, a small investment of trust, the faith of princes and children. Finally the easy jobs which could be obtained without family influence and the one good one she let Jessica get for her, drawing ad layouts for a famous store (herself, of course, the artist's recreation of the wanted woman, sketched in the flared or the sheath skirt, the muff, gloves, the adorable sandals, the negligee, the cloche by Mainbocher, the fur by Magnin's). All the various jobs got boring eventually, whether good or bad, fun or not fun, and none of them were real; somehow they weren't what she'd been looking for. When the war broke out she took a course to learn to be a nurse's aide and went to work at Treasure Island. Here she fell in love with a doctor.

Her feeling for Dr. (now Commander) Don Helm was the most important experience of her life next to her adoption by her father and Jessica and until her meeting with Cliff Harper. Dr. Helm was a married man. He was almost sixty years old. He didn't make love to her but they had coffee together twice a day and, by his comments on people, situations, the work they were doing, doors to new understanding began to open, as they can only open when one suddenly accepts religion or achieves the friendship of the great.

Great was the word for Don Helm. True greatness, yet of such a special kind nine people out of ten would miss it. No bedside manner was his, no big, drippy chunk of good will. He wasn't even kind, not in the ordinary sense. He was a surgeon—a slender, gray man, made of bone—his hair, skin, fingers and operating gown the soft, aged color of gray bone or driftwood polished by the great storms. His eyes were a little darker gray, but his beard, when he hadn't shaved, came in white. It was only when he had a beard that he looked old. In addition to being bone-colored, everything about him was square—fingertips, face, brow and chin. This look of squareness and grayness and the slow, cold burning of a spirit purged of self was what gave him ruggedness. Slender as he was, he appeared stronger in every way than the two-hundred-pound flatfoot corpsmen who wheeled in the stretchers. To be with him made Pamela realize that this searching for a "new self" or "independence" or a "mother" was a mirage. Already, through Dr. Helm, her eyes were opened and she could wait for the next thing and be equal to it when it came. She was, within her own compass, the self she needed to be or to have.

What soon gave this self extension and application was her meeting with Cliff Harper. If she hadn't known Dr. Helm, she might not have been ready for Cliff. She might not have known what to do about him.

The meeting happened by accident yet in a natural, convincing manner which was pleasant to look back on later. She had come over to the city in the Navy bus after work with another nurse, Mabel Hill, whom she had known before, when she was doing ads and Mabel was a buyer for a department store. Neither had a date that day, and the errands they had to attend to were the type that could be skimmed through lightly. First they went to the store where Mabel had worked and for which Pamela had done the layouts and they strolled around happily chatting with friends. They separated for the errands, met again, went to a movie and then to Solari's in Maiden Lane, occupying one of the booths close to the bar.

It was still early. The bar soaked in a winy midafternoon lull. Two men were talking to the bartender—one stocky, nearly bald; the other big, young, light-haired and shy-looking. The bald fellow, who was rather forward, kept glancing over to get the attention of the girls, but both Mabel and Pam remained elaborately indifferent to these overtures. The fellows, from their conversation, had just been discharged from the service. They were joking with each other about the way they looked in civilian clothes, the bald one talking rather loud so as to be sure the girls overheard and paid attention, while the younger, better-looking fellow tried from time to time to shush him. The bald fellow had unwrapped something from a brown paper package and was showing it to the bartender and the latter, impressed, called one of the waiters over to look at whatever it was.

Mabel got interested too. Pretending she had to go to the toilet, she walked close to the group and on the way back, at the bald fellow's invitation, she stopped and looked at what was in the brown paper and let out a squeal. "It's not," she said; "you're kidding." But the bald fellow kept insisting, and finally Mabel believed him and she too seemed impressed and brought him over to the table, the big, light-haired boy following.

What they had in the brown paper was a shriveled piece of skin with bristly short black hair attached to it. It was the scalp of a dead Japanese soldier.

Pam didn't much care what the thing was. A blackish hunk of something and the hairs growing out of it. If you had nursed in a Naval General Hospital for nearly two years, you were not going to whoops up your lunch because someone showed you a dried scalp. When the bald-headed fellow asked her to pick it up, she did so, putting it back in the paper and returning it to him. The big, shy-looking fellow seemed to feel that she had performed a smart and unexpected action. "Put it away, Herb," he said, not speaking in the least like the young boy that, in spite of his size, he looked to be, but with authority.

Pam now looked at him with attention. She noticed something else about him that didn't go with his youngness. His hands shook. They trembled when he went to lift his drink. He wasn't drunk. It wasn't that kind of shaking. It must have come from being over-seas.

"Okay, okay," the bald-headed one said. He put the scalp back into his pocket as his friend had told him to.

Pamela turned to the other fellow. She faced him squarely for the first time and smiled warmly, the wide-lipped, curling smile that was one of her greatest charms. "Thank you very much," she said.

The big, light-haired fellow looked shy. He said not to mention it.

Somehow they had become a double date. Introductions were ex-changed. Now the first round of drinks was bought, Herb Cleary, the bald-headed fellow, paying. The light-haired fellow's name turned out to be Cliff Harper.

Herb and Cliff had straight bourbons, Mabel a Cuba libre and Pam a Scotch. She had never liked cocktails. When Herb asked rak-ishly what two beautiful women were doing all alone downtown on a fine Saturday P.M., Mabel told him how they had come over after work to see a movie but it hadn't been so hot. In a case like that, Herb said, why not take in another? Mabel said at once, quite primly, she was sorry, they had an engagement that they really ought to keep. But Cliff wasn't listening.

A pint-sized Italian newsboy went past the table selling papers and Cliff bought a *Day* and looked up the shows.

This would have been the time to tell him, Pam thought. She could call his attention to the newspaper and say casually, "Do you read this much? My father owns it. . . ."

In the first place, they wouldn't have believed her. In the second place, they wouldn't have cared. In the third, they would have thought she had flipped her lid.

Neither of these fellows had seen a new show in a long time, so it was immaterial what they saw. Mabel and Pam exchanged a high-sign and Pam gave a barely perceptible shrug. Then Mabel said they might have time to go, before their engagement, provided they left right after the show.

They settled on Lana Turner in *Slightly Dangerous*.

Ever since she was little and had gone to her first shows, Pam had liked sitting in the balcony best. It was more adventurous somehow. She didn't mind that there weren't four together downstairs. The main feature was just starting, and as soon as she and Cliff were seated in the balcony loge, such comfortable seats, the entrancement which she felt at all shows, good and bad, swept softly over Pam. She leaned forward, her lips moist and slightly open, her face rapt, feeling herself drawn into the oneness of the banked tiers of faces looking down, every face drinking in the magic which poured onto the screen in a soft column of metallic light.

The picture was a comedy. It was pretty silly; still, there were true parts. Right from the start Pam sympathized with the situation of Lana Turner, that seductive girl, working in a soda fountain. There she was just pounding along, day after day, so used to her job, bored with it, doing it mechanically, pounding along with no hope, no man in sight except some jerk that always whistled at her on the street, nothing in sight except that every three years she might get a prize (in merchandise) for being on time every day. Pamela laughed with the big laughs that went up from everybody at the screwy things that happened. Lana was supposed to be a lost heiress, but there was the feeling, the knowledge, of what she really was, of what (without the twist at the end) she would have gone back to: the job, the lonely pounding. As Pamela followed the flow of images across the screen, another film quite different and without pictures or beauty unrolled in the back of her own mind, a series of emotions and reflections.

She knew about this business of being a lost heiress. She remembered Anchylus saying that the loneliest thing in the world was turning on your own lights. She had been turning hers on now a long time, and she knew what he'd said was true. Also he'd said, "People get to be old maids that way. . . ." Was that to be her fate? You were close to it at twenty-nine. She could understand, hard as it was to believe, that many people lived and died alone, even in San Francisco.

5   DURING THE PERFORMANCE Cliff's closeness had been pleasant. Occasionally Pam had let him hold her hand; she had forgotten, almost, that she was with him. She remembered now. As they came down the heavily carpeted stairs into the lounge, they

seemed much better acquainted than they'd been two and a half hours earlier. Pamela put her arm through Cliff's in a comradely way and they stood close together in the lobby, watching the doors into the orchestra open and the people come out.

The four of them had dinner in a steak house near the theater. During dinner it was clear that Herb was making time with Mabel. Mabel was feeling rather high, and showing it, leaning her head occasionally against Herb's shoulder.

"Take it easy, sonny boy!" she cautioned him once, playing the part of a maiden sorely beset.

Herb grinned. "Listen to Grandma," he said, winking at Cliff and Pamela. He was eating and drinking prodigiously and looked red in the face. The two men paid the check, splitting it between them, and the foursome walked through the streets, two and two, half listlessly, not sure what to do next. Herb and Mabel dropped back a little, and Pam looked around a couple of times to make sure they were following. She was getting somewhat annoyed with Mabel. Finally she stopped and said decisively, "Where are we going?"

It was clear that the engagement to which the girls had referred earlier was either nonexistent or forgotten.

"What do you say we cut a couple of rugs?" Herb proposed.

Pamela looked at Mabel. It took no clairvoyance to discern what, in view of Mabel's current mood, the evening would be like if they took Herb's suggestion.

"Is that what you want to do?" she asked Mabel.

Herb was apparently now authorized to answer for his companion. He spoke up. "Me and Momma, we want to go places and do things. Eh, Momma?"

"I don't know why not," Mabel said good-naturedly. "How do you feel, Pam?"

The girls drew aside and talked together earnestly for a moment, the men doing likewise. Mabel insisted that she didn't care what they did. If Pam didn't feel like stepping out, she, Mabel, didn't either. Pamela told her to go ahead, she was tired, but Mabel and Herb could go. She wanted Mabel to go.

"So long, kids, don't do anything I wouldn't do," Herb said. He signaled a cab, which, although it already contained two passengers, swung toward the curb, obedient to the share-the-ride system then in vogue.

"I'll call you tomorrow," Mabel called to Pam. With a flash of plump blond leg she vanished into the cab.

"You musn't mind her," Pam told Cliff as they resumed their

stroll along the street, packed with a Saturday-night crowd. "She's a swell girl, really. She works like crazy; once in a while she cuts loose, that's all."

"She seems mighty regular," Cliff said.

A strangeness, now that they were alone, had fallen between them. They let themselves be carried by the crowd, sometimes pausing to look in store windows, so curiously light after the dim-out of recent months. Pam's feet were getting tired, though, in the high-heeled shoes. Cliff noticed her dragging steps and asked her if she'd like a drink. Pam said no, he might think she was crazy, but she'd like an ice-cream soda, and Cliff said fine, he could use a cup of coffee. Only it happened that the drugstore where they went was closing up and since the coffee was all gone Cliff had an ice-cream soda too.

Riding across town on the bus Pam was silent, fully aware now of this fellow with her and of all the things she'd noticed about him during the evening which in the past couple of hours had come together to make a person: his shyness, bigness, the youthfulness which didn't fit in with the harsh man's voice in which he'd told Herb Cleary to wrap up the scalp, and then the way his large bony hands shook when he handled things and his embarrassment at this. God, he was young, younger in years than she and younger in experience also in spite of all that had happened to him. He needed somebody all right, maybe just as bad or even worse than she did, but he was strong too.

With a fellow like this the proposition wouldn't be entirely one-sided. It wouldn't be all giving.

They had three blocks to walk when they got off the bus, then the steep side of the hill to climb. Pam knew every paving stone in those three blocks; she ought to: she walked them twice a day, on her way to and from work. She knew how the raw façades of the houses looked at morning and at night, in spring, summer, winter, fall. The houses and the windows and the paving stones were repetitions of the steps she took in passing them. They were Yesterday and To-morrow, her fight to make a life for herself, the dark face of memory and the blank face of the future. This was her street but she was alone, a stranger here; the mood of bitterness that made her identify herself with the imaginary struggle of the sodajerk in the movie came back now, and she thought while her heels clicked on the pavement and this fellow's footsteps, not quite grooved to hers, kept pace beside her, how does it pay off, what's in it for me or for any of us? They were at her door now, in the entry, with names written and

195

printed in the little slots above the bells surrounding them like people, all familiar names to Pam and all the names of strangers: Miss Kilkenny, Mr. and Mrs. Dian Body, Mr. Koslavsky, Elmer Kirkwood Sanger . . .

A thought went through Pam's mind: the flight from home and then the war and lonely search and the work and the names of the strangers in her doorway had brought about a possible benefit and handed her this fellow, Cliff.

Maybe the war stopped with fellows like Cliff. Maybe he was the victory or maybe the two of them together, that might be the victory.

"If you want to come up," she said softly, "I could make you that cup of coffee."

6 LEAVING Civic Center, now man and wife, Mr. and Mrs. Cliff Harper turned down Market Street. Here, in small soiled store fronts, interspersed with more imposing buildings, a succession of transient, hopeful enterprises bid for the diversion of the passers-by—novelty counters where souvenirs could be bought, pennants with the city's name stitched on them, penknives that wouldn't cut, watches that wouldn't keep time, and so on. Also tattoo parlors, fortunetellers, slot-machine burlesque shows, treasure hunts among bubble-gum marbles, and places where one's picture could be taken on a donkey or at the controls of a PYU or with one foot on a Gold Rush bar rail. Fellows who had recently spent their time handling weapons of government issue could, and did, pay money to plink with .22 shots at moving ducks, clay pipes, and ping-pong balls sustained on jets of water. Once such establishments had done a rousing business, but recently trade had fallen off. Nobody wanted to play war with peace breathing down his neck. Barkers attired in the raffish jubilance of a lost boomtime cried their wares with a shrillness induced by desperation.

"Have your picture taken, soldier? You and the Missus on the biggest day of your life."

Cliff looked in a puzzled, inquiring way at Pamela. It baffled him to know how a dwarf with a huge camera slung on him could detect that his past included military service or that the girl with him had in the last hour become his bride.

What he didn't realize was that the dwarf, catering almost exclusively to military personalities, had trained himself to recognize the type, or that Pamela was carrying in plain sight—in the easily identified envelope—the marriage certificate with which the city of San Francisco had presented her.

"Wise guy," he said.

"They see a lot of people," Pamela said.

They strolled on, but the hunchback kept along beside them with a waltzing, sidelong caper, already ramming a plate into the lopsided brown box of his camera.

"You and her, soldier," he said, "right on a train step. Leaving for your wedding trip. Two poses for a buck. Special to you, fifty cents."

"That kind of picture fades, I guess," Cliff said in a low voice, not with complete conviction.

The dwarf sensed success. He switched his attack to Pamela. "Two beautiful poses, lady. One for the memory book and one for the folks."

The bride probed Cliff with a look, rapid but penetrating. She said gently to the dwarf, "We'll let you take the pictures, if my husband wants them."

Cliff's expression relaxed. "We can't lose much for four bits," he said. "Maybe they don't fade, if you're careful."

"Captain," the dwarf said, jumping Cliff five grades and battle-field-commissioning him, "keep them in a slightly dark place, you can hand them down to your kids. That's the train step. So you want an ocean liner, four bits more."

During the picture-taking Pamela posed beautifully, smiling her wide-lipped smile. She stood, once, on the bottom step of the sawed-off bit of fake train, leaning back against Cliff, and again at the rail of the liner because what could you lose for four bits more? She was very happy. She had wanted the pictures. Having them taken was a proper feature of their wedding day. However, in spite of certain assurances, the touch of fingers and the quick looks with which she renewed for herself the reality of Cliff, she was gripped by nervousness. Not by the placing of a ring or taking pictures or even by making love did one person's identity merge with another's. A certain amount of information also had to be conveyed: who was who, and so on. It was usually the first step. Cliff, certainly, had seemed to think so. The first night he'd told her about his dad's death, the golf course, the Welfare Home, the paper route, the Dodge, the football letter and the Marine Corps. But what did Cliff know about her? When would she tell him and how would she tell him without making herself seem—as for a while she had once seemed even to herself—a freak of nature, an inheritor of nothing, a fake and a phony? And tell him anything or—as she certainly would have to sometime—take him to California Street, where she wasn't quite sure any longer whether she herself was welcome?

Cliff seemed absent-minded. As they left the photographer's he still luxuriated in the wonder of the day. But he was thinking about something now.

"Where are we heading, Mrs. Harper?" he said at length.

Pamela drummed up her courage. It came to her like the gift of a good saint. "I want you to see the house where I grew up."

She spoke with the bridge-burning decisiveness of one alluding to a shame, long-hidden, which was better owned up to now than later—a confession made in the manner of some brides and grooms who, on their wedding night, blast their own happiness by compelling their partners to read diaries recording their affairs with other people or disclose that until now they have made their living as spies.

"Why, sure, fine," Cliff said. "Let's go there. What street did you tell me it was on?"

"California Street," Pamela said.

"Let's grab a taxi."

"No," Pamela said, already protective of their communal finances, "we don't have to do that. We can just take the cable car, we're almost at Powell anyway, and then walk. It really isn't far at all."

The cable car was on its turntable, the gripman and conductor engaged in turning it around. When it started forward, Pamela and Cliff rode on the open seats, parallel to the tracks, sitting tight together; they got off at the top of the hill and walked on with deliberation, the bridegroom watching the bride to see if he could tell, by her expression, when they approached her ancestral home.

He could tell, all right. Her steps slowed down; she looked long and searchingly along the block, then up at him.

"There it is," she said. She pointed at a house across the street, an opulent house—larger, more ornate than the other residences close to it, though these also were large and imposing. Cliff, hardly glancing in the indicated direction, nodded casually. His refusal to regard the house as a curiosity was part of an already proved inclination to accept as natural whatever she presented to him—even the idea of coming up Nob Hill on their wedding day to look at a house.

"Quite some castle," he said.

His attention moved to a black limousine standing in the forecourt, the trunk lid raised as if to receive luggage.

"Looks as if somebody's home."

"It's my father," Pamela said; "that's his car. I don't know if Mother Saxe is here or not; I hope she is, though. Then you can meet both of them."

She hadn't planned on this, the finality of confrontation, the three people most important to her in the world placed before one another. Just looking at the house could have been a preliminary step toward this, with the commencement of the actual relationship put off until another time. Suddenly, however, she couldn't wait to have the meeting take place; only when it had would her two worlds meet, the long process of her self-identification finally completed.

"All right by me," Cliff said.

Arm in arm they entered the forecourt, crossed to the front door. Pamela felt in her handbag for the key she'd been given when she left and which she always kept with her. She didn't want to ring; it wouldn't seem like a homecoming not to open the door.

The chauffeur who belonged with the black car was nowhere to be seen, nor was there anyone on hand inside, where, over the stairs, the artificial constellations installed by Fabian Rupke stood fixed in their orbits, steadfast and changeless as the genuine, unseen galaxies in the sky.

In the center of the hall were several suitcases.

"I guess," Pamela said tentatively, "Dad's going on a trip. That's what it looks like anyway." She paused, composing a plan of action. "I tell you what," she said, pointing to the library, "you go in there while I run upstairs and find out what's what."

"Okay," Cliff said.

He peered with some apprehension into the large room, full of leather, books and studious gleams of light.

"Only you better come back quick," he said, "before somebody finds me there and tosses me out in the street."

"When they start to toss you out," Pamela said, "just show them this." She handed him the marriage certificate. Then, with an encouraging smile, she started up the stairs.

7 REVIEWING her wedding day later, Pamela wished she'd had a picture of the way Anchylus had drunk to her health and happiness, and to Cliff's, the three of them standing in the library beside the tall brass champagne bucket with the neck of the magnum

sticking out of it and Reuben—the butler who had replaced Temple—in the doorway, watch in hand. They had that round and then another, and she and Cliff toasted Anchylus in return and wished him a good trip. Then it was time for Anchylus to go.

He was leaving for New York on a business trip. Jessica was in Atherton. If Pamela and Cliff had come to the house a half hour later they would have missed him. Pamela had found him in his bedroom making last-minute phone calls while Reuben packed his toilet kit—the morocco case of Sheffield straight razors, one for each day of the week, the bottle of bay rum she remembered from childhood, the monogrammed silver flask of brandy for his nightcap. He'd put his hand over the mouthpiece of the telephone and looked up at her with the bearish look of love and bafflement and wariness with which, for a long time now, he had greeted her arrivals.

"Hi, baby," he said, "what are you doing home?"

Pamela had stood before him suddenly shaking, wondering if everything was going to go wrong now, and said, "I got married this morning, Dad, to a wonderful guy. I brought him to see you."

Anchylus hadn't properly ended his telephone conversation, whatever it had been. He had just hung up the phone. Then he had stood up and taken her in his arms.

This was it, as far as he was concerned—the suspicion that she'd gone over to the enemy, somehow, wiped out in a dozen words. She had come home indeed if her first act on getting married had been to bring her husband to him. Not like Alexandra, fleeing over the mountains in the cold Sierra dawn. Not like Sharon, marrying a man he'd asked her not to.

He still had one daughter left, out of the wreck of things. If he were going to have one, this one might be best. Over all, she had cost the most, if you were going to rate daughters by any such measures as that.

"Well, congratulations," he said.

Pamela held onto him. She knew something big had happened. Coming to the house had been exactly the right thing to do. She hadn't planned it that way but that was how it was turning out. She was very glad she'd come.

"Thank you, Daddy," she said.

"Where is this character?" Anchylus said.

"Down in the library."

"Well, then," Anchylus said, "let's go down and meet him."

He'd started out of the room with his arm around her, then turned back to tell Reuben to bring some champagne.

Possibly it had also been lucky that the only champagne Reuben had on ice had been a magnum of Veuve Clicquot. A magnum had a regal air about it. Also it was more than any three people could drink under ordinary circumstances, particularly if one of them had shortly to catch a plane.

They had drunk all the proper toasts. Cliff, in Anchylus' presence, had seemed younger than ever. As for Anchylus, the first clue that he really liked Cliff had been a suggestion he'd made as they were all walking out to the car.

"Look, why don't you people make yourselves at home? The place is yours—regular damned hotel, no charge. Cook off till Monday, but sure to be food somewhere if you look for it, I guess."

Pamela perceived the flattering nature of the invitation. However, she treated it reservedly, not knowing what Cliff would want to do. "That's awfully sweet of you, Daddy, but I don't know. I'm not sure that we can."

"Think it over," Anchylus said imperiously, stage-managing the honeymoon. "Go back and finish the wine, anyway. It's good wine."

"Thank you very much, sir," Cliff said. "It *is* good wine. I had champagne once in the Pacific, but this is better. It's the best wine I ever tasted."

This speech, like the champagne itself, buzzed in Pamela's brain. When they were back in the library working on the considerable remnants of the magnum, she said suddenly, "Darling, how did you get champagne in the Pacific?"

"Made it," Cliff said. "Navy compass alcohol the fellows stole. We made every kind of drink with it. For champagne we mixed it with cider. We had a sarge, he'd been a pharmacist's mate, he carbonized it, only not like this, of course."

"This ought to be better," Pamela confirmed. Then, her thoughts taking a new direction, she said, "Dad liked you. I know he did or he wouldn't have asked us to stay."

"Think so?" Cliff said seriously.

"I know it."

"Well," Cliff said, "that's okay then."

"Did you like him?"

"He's a great guy. A real, bona-fide Wheel."

"He is, though I never think of that. I want you to meet Jessica. She's terrific too."

"You call her Jessica? Your mother?"

"I always called her Mother Saxe when I was with her," Pamela said, "but in my thoughts I called her Jessica. Dad was never married to my real mother. I guess I never told you that. It was a romance."

"You're kidding."

"No," Pamela said. "I suppose I should have told you. I married you under false pretenses, in a way."

"The hell you did."

"Oh, yes, I did. I was afraid if you knew what I was you'd walk out and leave me."

"You don't even want to say the word, do you?"

"No, I don't. I hate that word."

"Why you little—"

"Don't say it, Cliff; I hate it."

"Can't I ever call you a little red-haired bas—"

"Not on our wedding day. Besides, I'm not."

"Yes, you are. You just said so."

"That's how I started, but I was adopted. They adopted me by taking me to live with them. But you know when you were telling me about the Welfare Home? Well, I was in a home too. My mother took me to one when she was sick, maybe dying. That's how I knew so well what you were talking about. I knew we belonged together before that, but that made it certain."

"Were you in the home a long time before they adopted you?"

"No, only a few days. But you know, every minute of those days I've lived over in my mind. It's as if they were still going on and the clock that measures them ticking off the minutes very slowly, each minute a month or a year, while the other clocks I live by go whirling at the normal speed. I go back there when I dream. I start off from there. Not that being there was so terrible, but it became a hinge between two versions of me. I can't explain it. Do you know what I'm talking about?"

"I guess so. Like me planning to go back and burn the other place down. So I could get rid of it. Only I guess the only way to do that would be to burn my brain."

"Exactly."

"Do you figure you'll still go back there?"

"I don't think so. When I met you I stopped needing the hinge. I slammed the door. But I'm kind of an artificial person, all made up of little pieces, not what I seem at all. And timid, at least about some things."

"Everybody's timid about some things. Everybody."

"Not you."

"I'm no different."

"I couldn't imagine you being timid about anything in this world."

"I was, though."

"In the Service?"

"I was plain scared to death in the Service, half the time. But that's different from being timid. I was timid in the Welfare Home. They made you that way; it was protection. If you didn't get timid you couldn't stay alive. I was timid in Berkeley, too, in school. You know what of? Being a teacher's pet. I knew I was one, and it came in handy, but I tried to let on I wasn't. I had lots of fights about that."

"If you had fights, then you weren't timid." As if this settled the discussion, Pamela seated herself on her husband's lap. After a few moments she said, "I guess I'd better go back to where I was sitting."

"If you do, then this marriage is a total bust, a flop."

"Don't say that."

"You're mighty particular about what I'm supposed to say."

"That's the way brides are. They're particular and they're screwy because it's the biggest day that will ever happen to them and I'm the screwiest, most particular bride that ever lived."

"You're only a bride on paper so far. We could still have it annulled."

"Want to?"

Cliff gave this some thought. "No," he said. "Not right now, anyway."

"Is that your final answer?"

"Yup."

"Good. Cliff," Pamela said, "do you mind if I get just a tiny little bit plastered? Not that I intend to, but do you mind if I do?"

"You can't get plastered on this stuff. It's too mellow."

"Shall we send out for some compass alcohol?"

"Later, maybe. Let's see if we get anywhere with this first."

"I'm getting somewhere with it," Pamela said. "I can feel every swallow of it pulling up through me. Does it affect you that way?"

"Let's go back to your apartment," Cliff said.

"Wait," Pamela said, "not when we're having a serious conversation. This is a conversation we should have had days ago, but all we did then was make love."

"You were the one that started it."

"I only said I was going to get a little plastered."

"You said you could feel the champagne pulling you."

"Well, it is pulling me. What I meant to say was, I'm ashamed of telling you this, such an important thing about myself that way."

"What way?"

"Just letting it come out as if it wasn't anything. I'd had it planned exactly how I was going to tell you if you asked me a question about myself, but you never asked me a single question."

"You don't have to ask questions," Cliff said, "when you start out with the answers."

"And you're still sure you don't want it annulled?"

"I don't want it annulled."

"I'm terribly glad."

"What do you want to do now?"

"I want to get some more champagne," Pamela said, "and then I want to show you the house, including the ballroom where my sister Alexandra and I made the most fantastic debut ever made in San Francisco, after which she eloped and I got myself a job selling hairnets."

"Have some more champagne," Cliff said, "or wine, as your father would say."

"Did you really like him, Cliff?"

"Sure, I liked him," Cliff said. "He's a terrific guy. It was swell of him to suggest we stay in the house."

"Would you be very much against our staying?"

"Not if you'd like to. Is that what you want to do?"

"It would kind of bring things together. If you're sure you don't mind."

"Any place is all right with me," Cliff said.

"Then we'll stay," Pamela said decisively. "And in the morning, I'll cook you breakfast. A really gorgeous breakfast. We might even invite some guests. Herb and Mabel, if we can locate them, and the Third Marine Division and some people who can sing. No harps. That smacks of funerals. I can't stand harps, only beautiful singing. Is that the kind of breakfast you want too?"

"Perfect," Cliff said. "Just turn mine over easy."

8   THE FIRE they had lighted in the small marble fireplace glowed softly in the room, its coals throwing an uneven, flawed glow on the curves of the heavy mahogany and cherrywood furniture. Sometimes a knot in the coals would flicker up bright for a second, bringing into relief the cherubs holding up the mantelpiece and the

wallpaper with its rose design and the slow curve of the bed's footboard where the mahogany swelled into a pair of sleeping serpents.

It was warm in the room. Through the walls there came the pulse of the city, locked out here. Time also was locked out. There were three clocks in the room, one on the mantelpiece with gilt shepherds and shepherdesses, a big wall clock, and another, a small gold one, beside the bed, but the first two didn't synchronize, and the gold one had stopped.

Pamela lay on her stomach. Her hair was mashed sideways on the pillow and her cheek and nose were pressed against Cliff's shoulder. Now that she was awake, this position made it hard to breathe. She moved her nose an inch or so to one side, then swerved it pleasurably over a small area of her husband's skin.

Her eyes were open now. She had remembered where she was and with this memory came a quick jolt of happiness and triumph; she tightened the muscles of her belly and pressed down on the bed as if to confirm its reality. If possession was nine points of the law the bed was hers, just as the husband was, though Jessica would hardly think so.

She tried to picture how Jessica would look and what she would do if, by some chance, she walked in now.

Carefully, taking pains not to wake Cliff, Pamela disentangled herself from his embrace. She slipped out of bed and crossed the room to where her clothes and his were piled in an amiable tangle; she felt in his pockets until she had located the marriage certificate. This she unfolded. She propped it against the gold clock on the night table and got into bed again and lay looking happily at the piece of paper with the great seal of the City and County of San Francisco and the signature of the Judge and the names Mr. and Mrs. Clifford Harper.

Well, she said to herself, I made it. Bastard or not, I'm a statistic now, praise be to God.

Oddly enough this matter of becoming a statistic wasn't really as important—as it turned out—as the impulse which had brought her back to California Street. The reunion with her father, effected on her wedding day, was to be a source of strength to both of them in the series of events which later made the split-up of the Saxe family a *cause célèbre* in San Francisco.

VI

The International Belle

"*Coelum, non animum mutant,*
Qui trans mare currunt."
                    —OLD PROVERB

1   NICKY was restless at the ranch. For a year he'd seemed content
     to school his jumping horses and play cowboy and make love to
     Alexandra, but early in 1946 he lost his peace of mind and
started writing letters to Hungary. Every morning he went down
impatiently to the mailbox to wait for the answers to his letters
and for the paper which came out RFD. When the paper arrived,
he would sit on the terrace and read it gloomily, smoking cigarettes
and shouting to Alexandra to bring him cups of coffee.

His trouble was the Russians. They weren't behaving the way
he wanted them to in Hungary. Also he was worried about his
mother, who still lived there on the family estate near Lake Balaton.
She was almost eighty years old. Her husband, Nick's father, had
been killed fighting for the Germans in World War I and her oldest
son, Fefi, had been killed fighting against the Germans in World
War II. Then she'd lost all but 150 acres of the estate when the
land was partitioned by the Smallholders' Government. She'd had a
very hard life and Nick felt she should have been excused from

further trouble but she was in for more of it now because of the Russians.

Alexandra dutifully read the paper after Nick was through with it. She read the whole of it, not just Letty Meeker, the headlines, the White House and City of Paris and I. Magnin ads and the society news, as she used to. She read the reports from foreign countries more than once and memorized the pronouncements of George Catlett Marshall, so that she could use them in arguments with Nicky and thus appear intelligent in his eyes. Apparently, however, she might have saved herself the bother; she didn't get the same impression from the reports or from General Marshall's statements and notices that Nicky did. As far as she could see, the news was quite all right. Everything over in Europe was hunky-dory outside of some food shortages and some fussing about control zones and about elections.

"But they haven't done anything too bad yet, have they?" she asked Nicky, meaning the Russians.

"They are showing their coalition sentiments," Nick said.

"What does that mean, Nick?" Alexandra asked.

"It means that when they shoot a collaborationist, they permit a Mass to be said for his soul," Nick said.

"What's wrong with shooting a collaborationist?" Alexandra asked. "I thought this was open season on them."

"To a Russian," Nick said, "any Hungarian of whom he is afraid is a collaborationist. Except those, like me, who were Resistance fighters. We are fellow Communists. Or so they think."

Alexandra could see that he was making plans. She was not disturbed but she wanted to be in on them.

"Are you going to try to get your mother out, Nick?" she asked him one day.

Nick cocked one eye at her through a boil of cigarette smoke. He seemed amused by her question, but it was hard to tell. Because of a need to accommodate himself with the least possible trouble to a variety of social circumstances, often those which placed his own life at stake, Nick's face was permanently set in an expression of sardonic amusement. If he had been walking to the gallows, you felt he would have worn the same expression. It was almost impossible to tell whether he was laughing at you or not.

"Of course," he said.

"Then I'm coming with you," Alexandra said.

"Perfect!" Nick said. "We will get passports."

"Will they be hard to get?"

"For you, an American, a passport is no problem," Nick said.

"What about you?" Alexandra asked.

"For me, a hero of the Resistance, only a very small problem. I shall talk to some friends of mine. Then we will see."

The first friend he had to talk to was a cousin who lived in Miami, Florida. Alexandra and Nick flew to New York and took the Orange Blossom Special to Miami. It was very hot in the train since the railroads were using their air-conditioned cars elsewhere, and you only had a choice of two entrees, both dull, in the diner; but Alexandra had never been in the South before, and she enjoyed the trip. She was happy being with Nick. She had bought a number of books in Brentano's dealing with foreign affairs and so forth. However, most of the books didn't share Nick's views on the character of the Russians but took a line more in keeping with the views of General Marshall, and Alexandra failed to get much out of them that would make her appear intelligent where Nick was concerned. Half the time she would sit with her book on her lap and stare out at the low-rolling, piny land and the red clay roads with old jalopies riding slowly over them and the small wooden houses with the tramped-down yards and the thin-legged, puffer-bellied children and old people, black, white or brown, standing big-eyed and solemn watching the train go by.

In Miami it was very hot, being off-season. Alexandra and Nick went directly to the house of his cousin, Mrs. Ford. Mrs. Ford had left Hungary in 1939. She was a rich woman, and to make it all the better, she'd married a rich American, a partner in an advertising agency with offices on Madison Avenue, New York. Mr. Ford seldom came to Miami, but Mrs. Ford remained in touch with him. Her main pastime seemed to be keeping in touch with people. She kept in touch with them all over the world and had helped a great many fellow citizens to leave Hungary before and during the German occupation. She had continued working at this job during the Russians' display of coalition sentiments, and Nick thought she could help get him a passport of the kind which would not be limited to entering his native land. That, to a former hero of the Resistance, would have been quite simple, but for Nick there was also the problem of getting out and of getting his mother out. Alexandra would, of course, get out; she was an American, like Mrs. Ford.

The lawns of Mrs. Ford's pink house rolled right down to the Channel. Here a few yachts were berthed for the summer, and on the biggest one, the Sirocco, you could see sailors hanging over the sides in boatswains' chairs painting or standing on the deck smoking and looking at the shore. Mrs. Ford went swimming every day and had a wonderful tan and a very svelte figure, remarkable in a woman who was sixty if she was a day. Little gold specks floated in the bottom of her eyes like grains of sand picked up in the backwater of a clear green wave. She had a wonderful European-sounding laugh, *"Tscha, tscha, tscha,"* ending on an upward note. Her hair was blue. Men were mad about her, particularly an Italian who ran a gambling house down near the Causeway and who dropped in to see Mrs. Ford on his way to work, about 9:00 P.M. Gambling was the only kind of business besides yacht painting which went on in Miami off-season, but even this wasn't doing too well. Mr. Pachetti, Mrs. Ford's friend, explained that peace was ruining the people. He carried a pistol in a shoulder holster on the chance that some personal type of war might break out with reference to his gambling operations.

Mr. Pachetti would never have had his dinner when he dropped in so Mrs. Ford would let him finish the hors d'oeuvres left over from hers and give him a cup of coffee. No liquor. She said it was ridiculous to give hard liquor to Italians; they never could hold it. She treated him rather badly. Alexandra would have liked to see his gambling house but Mrs. Ford wouldn't hear of it. No decent woman, she said, should set foot in a place of that type. She was very nice to Alexandra. She said she had always been afraid that Nicky would get hooked by some ugly, stupid woman; your handsome, sporty men so often were. Mrs. Ford was glad that Nick, a true hero of the Resistance, had shown better taste. She looked fondly and gaily at Alexandra as she said this, and the gold grains stirred in the deep, lazy bottoms of her sea-green eyes. She put her arm around Alexandra, filling her nostrils with Matchabelli perfume and laughing the wonderful laugh low in her throat, *tscha, tscha, tscha.*

2   THERE WAS a great deal of telephoning and writing to be done about the passport. Mrs. Ford did the writing with a pen which had a number of small diamonds embedded in its shaft. Sometimes Nick was called to talk to someone she had contacted by telephone and he would talk in Hungarian, his voice leaping out deep and friendly, with a tone Alexandra had never heard in it before. At such times she knew that he was talking to one of the men whom Mrs. Ford had helped out of Hungary—usually someone with whom

he had worked in the Resistance. Some people were discouraging about the passport; others held out hope.

Finally all possible contacts had been made and results promised. There had been nothing to do but wait. Mr. Pachetti invited the Drobnys and Mrs. Ford to go over to Havana as his guests, on board his boat, but Mrs. Ford said this was ridiculous—Mr. Pachetti's boat was only good for fishing, it would never make it to Havana and if it did they would all be seasick. So they went on the steamer. Alexandra was sick anyway but she enjoyed the trip. Just as they were getting close to Cuba a storm built up. Steep dark seas slanted out of a twilight-colored sky and the waves sent spurts of foam into the air as they smacked into the rocks below the lighthouse. The harbor itself was smooth and the sun poked through scoops of clouds and lighted up the white and pink and orange and cream-colored houses on the slopes above the water. Nick had been playing cards. He came out on deck in a silk tropical suit and a panama he had bought in Miami and he and Alexandra and Mrs. Ford and Mr. Pachetti stood at the rail while Mr. Pachetti pointed out Morro Castle and other landmarks. Mrs. Ford already knew them. She showed her boredom with Mr. Pachetti by contradicting him about details which he described. Now the ship was steady. It came on smoothly past the freighters at anchor and the line of fishing boats and the long wooden piers. The whistle let out a blast. Alexandra took Nicky's arm and went down the gangplank feeling like a bride.

Mrs. Ford took a room at the Nacional for Mr. Pachetti and a suite for Alexandra and Nicky. She herself planned to stay with some transplanted Hungarian friends, the Feris. Mr. Feri, a soldierly-looking white-haired man, had been, like Nicky, a cavalry officer in Hungary. He belonged to a club out at Marianao where you could shoot live pigeons. Nick proved to be very good at this, as he was at all sporting activities. While the shooting went on a flunky in a white coat trundled around a cart from which whisky and rum drinks and beer were served and the members and their guests drank a good deal but Nick never touched a drop; he was too intent on the shooting. He shot in the finals of that day's go-round against a part-Irish Cuban named Domingo Nolan who had a withered arm and eyes so red from drinking they looked like balls of fire in his crook-nose, pale, tan face. He beat Nick by one bird, and Nick took Alexandra aside and explained apologetically that he had bet a thousand dollars on himself and had to have the money right away. Alexandra wrote the check and Mrs. Ford endorsed it and a boy went to cash it while they all had some more drinks. Then

Nick paid Domingo Nolan, but Domingo didn't even buy a round of drinks, being the kind of man who panicked when the check came around.

Night crawled up out of the ocean and spread over everything, a tom-tom Cuban night, moist and fever-hot. Mr. Pachetti took them all on a tour of the rumba joints ending at the Callejon de Noche, where he got quite drunk. He was furious because a good-looking Cuban boy with tightly brushed black hair kept dancing with Mrs. Ford. The boy was part of the Callejon's floor show and in the last act he turned out to be a girl and came out in spangled trunks doing a tap dance. He, or she, and Mrs. Ford later detached themselves from the party, and Mr. Pachetti was left to pay the check. He was not a good sport about it. He said he was going to kill the Cuban but Nicky got him calmed down and took him back to the Nacional to get some sleep.

Back in the pink house in Miami there was a telegram waiting, saying Nick's passport was okay. Nick had to pick it up in Washington. He was to travel as an attaché of the Hungarian embassy, a status made possible because he had been in the Resistance. He thanked Mrs. Ford with tears in his eyes. That night they dined on the terrace in the black Florida night and Mrs. Ford served champagne to celebrate his passport. It was one of the nicest evenings they'd had in Miami. Next day Mrs. Ford saw them off at the airport, and she cried when she said goodbye to Alexandra and gave her a big zircon dinner ring set with real emeralds. She said it was to remember her by. Alexandra didn't think there had been much to remember except the passport, but she let it go. She was very happy to be on the way to Hungary at last. She had always loved to travel and now she was going far—the farthest she had been yet from California Street.

3   ALEXANDRA and Nicky flew to Washington and Nick picked up his passport and Alexandra got one for herself, Brad Iverson helping to push it through. From Washington they went by train to New York and then took the Queen Mary to Cherbourg. Americans were just beginning to travel again. Paris was loaded with them, and the Champs d'Elysées looked like Market Street, with all the neon signs advertising U.S. products and the marquees with the names of U.S. stars on them. Alexandra didn't like it and kept away from Fouquet's and the Ritz Bar because they reminded

her of being so unhappy in Paris with Schuy Cutting, her first time around. She loved Vienna, though. She and Nick spent five days there, then took the Orient Express. There was no trouble about the passport anywhere, and they arrived at the Keleti Station in Budapest on a sunny August morning and went straight to a hotel Nicky knew about on Béla Bartók Street and along a great boulevard beside the Danube lined with the ghostly shapes of hotels that had been bombed during the siege and never repaired. Budapest was dark compared to an American city, but it had a different kind of darkness. Overhead a million stars spread in a big, bright drift across the summer sky. It was a clear night, warm and still, and you could smell the river and hear the rustle of leaves, and on all sides you could feel the life of the old, mysterious city and see the reflection of its dim, old lights like golden dust on the night sky.

Nick had many friends in Budapest. He kept pointing out their houses to Alexandra—some of these tremendous palaces, the upper windows often broken out and patched with boards and paper. To her surprise he didn't want to see the friends themselves. He explained that things changed. It was too hard to tell which of his friends were working for the Russians. Most of those he trusted had either been killed in the Resistance or had left the country. He felt like a stranger in Budapest and for the present he was satisfied to remain one: his main concern was to rent or buy a car so he could get to his mother.

There weren't many private cars around, it seemed. All you could see were military vehicles and coalition jeeps decorated with the flags of four nations. In these jeeps French, English, Russian and U.S. soldiers rode around demonstrating the close governmental co-operation of the Four Nations, but when one of these coalition jeeps went by, Nick said unpleasant things. He still took no stock in coalition. Finally he rented a car, though one too small for all the baggage they had to load on it. Alexandra had to sit mashed up against the door with her dressing case and biggest suitcase in the front seat beside her.

Nick relaxed as soon as they were outside the city. He lost some of his impatience to get to his mother and drove along slowly, telling Alexandra about the countryside and how the people lived. He had brought along a sack of cigarettes and candy, and when he and Alexandra stopped in a village for gas, he handed out presents to the kids who crowded around the car. These Hungarian village kids were thin but healthy looking and they seemed happier than the kids Alexandra had seen standing in the tramped-down yards of the little

215

houses in the Florida and Georgia and Alabama woods as she rolled past in the Orange Blossom Special.

The roads were good. Sometimes they were so overgrown with greenery that they were like tunnels or tubes through a world of soft green leaves. After traveling for a while in one of these green tubes the car would rush out into the sun and tear along between open fields fenced with stone walls. Nick would shout with joy. Sometimes he put his arm around Alexandra and sang songs in Hungarian, teaching her the words. When a shower caught them in an open space he wouldn't stop to put the top up. The big raindrops bounced around them like tennis balls and the wind bent the trees into witchlike shapes. As night fell the shower stopped. The earth steamed and the trees dripped; smells of leaves and grass and a feeling of lightness and goodness filled the air. They stopped at an inn and drank red wine and ate a fresh-water fish called fogas which tasted like salmon and came from the Lake Balaton, now only fifty miles away.

Next morning they reached Nick's mother's house. He had written that they were coming, and his mother was expecting them and ran out on the steps to greet them. She kissed Alexandra on both cheeks and made an affectionate speech to her in Hungarian which Nick translated.

The house was not as old as Alexandra had expected, nor was it constructed like a castle. It was made of wood, with bay windows and a lot of gingerbread scrollwork like some of the older houses in San Francisco. It stood on a hill above a cemetery. From all sides of it, on the banks of the hill, slanted rich, black land, planted with grapes. Nick's mother looked more like a small, spry, dried-out California farm woman than a baroness. She had tough, wrinkled hands and sharp, ironic dark eyes with the same mocking, joking wrinkles around them that Nick had. She made a lunch of pepper steak and many kinds of homemade jam and slabs of light, flaky pastry. After lunch she took Alexandra upstairs and showed her Nick's old room and his horseshow prizes and class pictures in cavalry school and a snapshot of him with his friends in the Resistance and the stern, bearded man in the center of the picture, who was General Miklos. There were many closets in the house, one packed with stacks of hand-loomed sheets, tablecloths and pillowcases and another containing a chest of silver service enough for a banquet of fifty, every piece heavier than sterling, and all stamped with the family crown. An old peasant woman who had been Nick's nurse lived with his mother and helped with the housework, the two old ladies waiting on each other and quarreling about the way to do things, as they had no doubt been doing since Nick's mother, Katy, had come to the house as a bride some fifty years earlier. Late in the afternoon Nick took a walk down the hill to inspect the vineyard. Entering the kitchen later, Alexandra found him sitting in a wooden chair with his breeches rolled up, smoking a cigar and chatting happily while his old nurse washed his feet in a basin.

Alexandra didn't ask when they were leaving or what the plans were about Nick's mother. That was Nick's department. She felt sure it would all come out all right. She wouldn't have minded if he'd decided for them to stay where they were. She could picture herself, the young Baroness, living with her handsome husband and the old nurse, Luisa, and the little, bent, beautiful old Baroness in the narrow, dark house on top of the vineyard. She would spend her time sorting the linen and silver and eating delicious meals in the dark dining room, with the ironic, slanting faces of Nick's Magyar ancestors looking down their noses at her out of the big picture frames. It would be pleasant in summer and in fall when the vines were stripped and the first storms came in and then in the winter when the snow brought peace and the peasants—surely there were still some peasants around—came to the house to sing Christmas carols. Did they sing carols in Hungary? She knew they did in Germany. She made a mental note to ask Nick about this.

It was all very satisfactory. She wrote Jessica and Sharon long letters about it, letting them know how different it all was from life on California Street.

One evening after she and Nick had been in his mother's house about a week, the old Baroness didn't come down to breakfast. Nick went up and spent two hours locked up with her in the bedroom. When he came down, he told Alexandra to pack the suitcases; they were leaving.

"What about your mother?" Alexandra said. "Isn't she coming too?"

"She's decided not to," Nick said soberly. He looked tired. For the first time she could remember, his eyes held no amusement at all.

"Good God, Nick," Alexandra said. "I thought she wanted to leave. Wasn't that what she wrote you?"

"She's changed her mind," Nick said.

"But why?"

"When it came to the point," Nick said, "she just couldn't do it. She says she's lived here too long. She thinks it's better if she stays."

217

Alexandra could see how worried he was. "Jessica's the same way," she said. "I don't think she'll ever move. She'll always live in California Street."

"It's different for your mother," Nick said. "Nobody will take her house away from her. She can live there until she dies."

"Will they take this house away?" Alexandra asked, surprised. "I thought your mother could keep it."

"One never knows," Nick said. "Anyway, there is nothing we can do about it."

"We can send her money, Nicky," Alexandra said; "at least there's that."

"Yes," Nick said, "there's that. We can always send her money."

He brought the car up and loaded their bags on it. Luisa and his mother were both crying. They came out on the steps to say goodbye. Nick kissed Luisa and she gave him a rosary. Then he kissed his mother, and after kissing her he knelt down in front of her and she made the sign of the cross over him. She said goodbye to Alexandra most affectionately and with great composure. Nick helped Alexandra into the car, burrowing out a place among the piles of luggage. Before he got in himself, his mother ran down the steps to him and held onto him fiercely with her crooked old hands, as big as a man's and hard as stones.

4 IN BUDAPEST Nick set about the job of arranging the trip out of Hungary. Everything went smoothly. The passports were issued and he got two second-class tickets on the Orient Express for the following Monday. The first-class tickets were all taken by Americans who had been in Budapest on business but were leaving because of strikes in the suburbs and rumors of trouble in the coming elections. On the sides of buildings and billboards in Bararos Square and on Dozsa Gyorzy Boulevard there were new posters of a square-shouldered man with thinning hair and bulbous eyes. This was Rakosi, Minister of the Interior and head of the National Police. Nick said he was a Russian stooge and that the Communists had him in training to be Premier.

On their last night in the city Nick took Alexandra out to dinner. They went to a place in a cellar called the Candlelight Club, and here Nick met several friends. One of them was a former Resistance fighter named Gero Bem. He was plump and apple-cheeked, with a small mouth and twinkling blue eyes like a youthful, beardless

Santa Claus. He seemed particularly glad to see Nick and was most deferential to Alexandra, ordering wine and special czardas songs and bringing his own party over to Nick's table. At first Nick behaved affably, but he was drinking more than usual and Alexandra could detect that Bem's friendliness annoyed him.

"We must go," he said to her several times, and each time she started to get up. But Bem wouldn't hear of their leaving. He had started drinking toasts.

"To the new Hungary," he said.

Everyone drank the toast quite solemnly, including Nick. When it was over, however, he sat down and did his trick of gobbling up the glass. Alexandra thought that he was very funny, but apparently the trick was not considered in good taste by those present. Conversation lagged and there was a feeling of discomfort at the table until Nick and Alexandra finally got up once more. This time Bem made no effort to stop them. Nor did he shake hands with Nick. He sat staring right through Nick with his merry little eyes while Nick said goodbye to the other people and escorted Alexandra outside.

"What was the matter?" she said. "Was he angry because you ate the glass?"

"To hell with him," Nick said.

"He seemed so glad to see you at first," Alexandra said.

"Regardless of what he seemed," Nick said, "he has become a cop. He's one of Rakosi's men."

"How can you tell?"

"I can smell it," Nick said, "but to hell with him."

"If he is a cop," Alexandra said, "I'm sorry you ate the glass. It really seemed to make him furious."

"Never mind," Nick said. "We have the visas. There isn't a damn thing he can do about it."

A taxi at least twenty-five years old was coming down the street and Nick hailed it. As soon as they were in it he began to kiss her and she kissed him passionately in return, pulling his hand inside her dress, the wine and the kisses making her dizzy and the czarda music still going through her head. Except for the wineglass incident, she thought later, they couldn't have had a pleasanter last night in Budapest.

Next day they arrived at the Keleti Station an hour before traintime. They were taking no chances on losing their places. Nick went to buy some cigarettes and Alexandra, with the porter who had ridden over with them from the hotel, was seeing to the luggage when a woman with a face like a bulldog came up to her and told

219

her in Hungarian that she would have to be searched. The porter translated this apologetically. Alexandra sent him to get Nick, who was standing by the tobacco stand talking to two men.

"This woman is some kind of lunatic," Alexandra said. "Nick, can you make her understand that we've been cleared, we are taking nothing out, and I am traveling on a United States passport?"

Nick looked sick. White lines crawled like worms into his handsome face. "There has been a mixup," he said. "If she wants to search you, let her search you. As a favor to me. It will not take long."

When she got back after taking all her clothes off in a cold john-smelling room and letting the dog-faced woman go through her handbag, vanity case and suitcases, and also poke all over her with a hurting, shame-making rubber glove, Nick was outside with the two men. He was standing behind a chain-link fence which divided the train platform. He spoke through the fence while she stood on the other side, shivering. He said he would have to be in Budapest two or three days longer. He wanted her to take the train and wait for him in the Emperor Franz Joseph Hotel in Vienna. He wouldn't let her argue. He spoke roughly and impatiently through the mist-wet links of the fence. She could see that he was in some desperate trouble, but there was nothing she could do except obey him, since that was what he wanted. There seemed some chance, at least, that he was coming to Vienna later, his personal luggage as well as hers having been placed on the railroad carriage. The last she saw of him, he was walking away with his long stride between the two men, both smaller than he, one wearing a felt hat, the other a derby.

5   BACK AT THE RANCH she tried to forget that night. The harder she tried, however, the clearer it became, in its nightmarish precision of detail. It was not the sort of sight that you forget, particularly if it happened to be your final glimpse of your husband on this earth. Nor was it easy to reconcile the safe, effortless life in Sonoma with the events leading up to the disappearance of the Baron Nicholas Alexis Drobny.

She had waited for him in Vienna for two months. She had gone twice a week to the Consulate to make inquiries, demands and protests. The Consulate advised her to take the matter up with the Hungarian Consulate. The Hungarian Consulate had nothing to say. She cabled Mrs. Ford and telephoned Anchylus, asking him to use his influence with the State Department. He could tell them all the facts. A man had disappeared, six feet two, with joking eyes, a rider, a shooter, forty-two years old, married to an American woman. He had walked away one foggy morning with two persons encountered at a railroad station.

Anchylus talked to people of influence. He wrote letters and made a number of telephone calls. That much he proved to Alexandra when she returned to San Francisco. He showed her his memoranda on the subject and the copies of his correspondence. He had made an effort. There was no doubt of it. But yet—yet somehow the thought lurked in her mind that Anchylus hadn't gone all out. This thought might have been inaccurate. She didn't know. Yet she felt that if his heart had been in it he would have come up with a miracle as he had done in the past when his own affairs were at issue. Anyway the thought persisted, and it had its influence on the course of action she took later.

The State Department couldn't act. The Hungarian Consul wouldn't. There was no reason to believe, he said, that the disappearance of a baron was the result of Government action. Possibly the Baron had enemies. Had Alexandra been in touch with the police?

Friends told her to go to Paris. There was *rapprochement* in Paris. Everything went more easily there. However, in Paris all the answers were the same.

Only one individual shed any light. This was the Embassy Counselor, not to be confused in any manner with the Consul. The Counselor was a man who advised the Ambassador on protocol and so forth, keeping him in step, as it were. Alexandra was referred to him by Embassy officials, as a means of keeping her out of their hair and because, when you came down to it, her husband's case was an inter-embassy affair.

The Counselor looked like a Peter Arno drawing. He had a blank-staring, courteous, old-man's face with lecherous, popping eyes, and his mop of white hair was so well curled Alexandra was sure he had it done at a beauty parlor. After kissing Alexandra's hand he sat down stiffly in a straight chair opposite and came at once to the heart of the matter.

"Was your husband at any time a member of the Communist party?"

"He hated Communists," Alexandra said, surprised.

"But he could once have been a member of the party, could he not?" the Counselor asked.

"I suppose so," Alexandra said; "though if he had been, I would think he'd have mentioned it."

"Nevertheless," the Counselor said, "he might not have mentioned it. He might not have wished to."

"No," Alexandra said, "he might not have considered it important. I'm sure he wasn't actively a member, though, if that's what you mean. But why do you ask, m'sieur?"

It seemed appropriate to call the Counselor *m'sieur*, he was so much more French than American in appearance.

"He was a Resistance fighter, you have told me," the Counselor said. "Many such men became party members. The party was the best-organized force working against the Germans during the Occupation. When the party created its own Occupation, in a military sense, the Resistance people renounced it. The party didn't care for such defections. A number of cases have come to our attention—cases in which the party sought to reassert its discipline, sometimes quite drastically."

"I see," Alexandra said.

"You understand," the Counselor said, "I am merely trying to arrive at an explanation. I am sorry I can't be of more help."

Alexandra discussed the Counselor's idea with several people. Some of them thought it made sense; others upheld her own opinion, namely, that it was ridiculous.

Nick was a Magyar aristocrat and a landowner. Resistance or no Resistance, what would he have had in common with the Communists?

If you had to have a theory it was better, and easier, to believe he had been made to disappear because he'd eaten a wineglass in a public place.

Only once did she have direct word bearing on Nick's fate. This was early in 1948, when a man with a thick Hungarian accent telephoned from San Francisco asking if he could come out to see her at the ranch. He said he had some information which might be of some interest to her.

Alexandra felt reluctant to have him come to Sonoma. She arranged to meet him in the city. He turned out to be a boy about nineteen years old who had recently made his escape from a Communist labor camp. When first arrested in 1946 he had been held in the AVH Headquarters on Balaton Street, Budapest, where Nick Drobny had been one of his fellow prisoners. Nick had told him about having an American wife and about his life in San Francisco. Before the transfer of Alexandra's informant to the labor camp Nick had been executed in the basement of the AVH building. The charges against him, publicized to the other prisoners, were that he was an American industrialist agent, a Fascist spy and a Trotskyite saboteur.

Alexandra wrote regularly to the old Baroness. At first she received answers, but after a while these stopped and she lost touch with her. It had not proved practicable to send her money, with any assurance that she was getting it.

In 1948 Letty Meeker published the following item:

> *There are rumors from Hungary that Alexandra Saxe Cutting Drobny's second husband, the* COMMUNIST, *has been* HANGED *as a traitor to his country.*

6 LETTY'S DISPARAGEMENT, no matter how vindictive, couldn't alter one fact: Alexandra was a genuine International Belle. Many San Francisco families, it was true, had produced International Belles, but no family after World War II had produced one as indubitably proven. Alexandra had done the European Bit twice—once with Schuy and once with Nick; she was still beautiful and she had a title. In some cities (more sophisticated or less lively, depending on one's point of view) these facts might not have meant much, but in San Francisco they were of significance. Furthermore, Alexandra's new status was all the more engaging in that it included both mystery and tragedy and in that she seemed to attach no importance to either. She spent most of her time in the country. And she lived alone.

Relatively alone, that is. A woman conditioned to a full, active existence couldn't resign herself to complete loneliness, regardless of her state of mind or the pleasure she took in the homespun activities on a ranch. There were times when, since no other company offered, she went out with men who would have bored her badly a few years earlier; she felt that what she did was her own business and that although country living might be dull at times, it had the compensation of being inconspicuous.

The ranch was, in a way, a legacy from Nick, as was her taste for outdoor pleasures. She helped brand, dehorn and castrate her own cattle: sometimes she was in the saddle eight or nine hours a day with no sense of boredom and little fatigue. She didn't dramatize what she did: it was hard work, and if she occasionally went out with a cowboy, it was not because she found cowboys glamorous. She had always felt contempt for women who, after a spell in the sagebrush, took up with its denizens—chic, perfumed women with grown children and $50,000 a year in alimony. None of that for her.

She was both infuriated and disgusted by an item of Letty's which ran in *The Day* in January 1949, just when she had been thinking that Letty had forgotten all about her.

> NUMBER THREE *for the beauteous Baroness Drobny may be a Sonoma County brand inspector. Can such things be? "Zan" Drobny, in spite of her unfortunate marriages, always seemed to shimmer in the tradition of the renowned Daisy Fellowes or England's Lady Duff-Cooper.*
>
> *But a* BRAND INSPECTOR!
> *Ye Gods! Say it isn't so!*

Alexandra didn't linger over the paper. She proceeded into a bedroom where the curtains were still drawn and a sleeper lay rolled in a sheet. Alexandra moved around the bed until she achieved a position directly over that at which it could be presumed the sleeper's head lay. She bent down toward the sheet and spoke into it; she spoke loudly, considering the fact that her voice didn't have to carry more than a few inches.

"Coley," she said, "I want you to get up. I want you to get up and I want you to get out of here."

7 ALEXANDRA rarely cleaned her own house. That job fell to Manuela Mena, a Mexican woman who lived in town and came out three days a week. This wasn't one of Manuela's days but it had been borne in on Alexandra powerfully, even before Coley was out of sight, that the place needed doing up. She wanted it scrubbed, vacuumed, aired and polished—not sometime later but right now. To have a tidy house, thoroughly put to rights, could be a great comfort.

Taking the breakfast things from the table, she rinsed them off, washed out the coffeepot and put away the liquor bottle—even sniffing it without the least temptation to take a drink. From the kitchen she bustled into the living room, dusting and sweeping, the sleeves of her striped riding shirt rolled up to the elbows. Women, she thought, didn't seem to realize what pleasure there was in sweeping;

it was so much more satisfactory than vacuuming, and with no gadgets to mess with. Instead of messing with gadgets you fought the dirt hand to hand. You called it out of hiding and stood it up in front of you. Then you pitched into it and destroyed it. How could she have let things get in such a mess? She rushed out to fetch furniture polish. Somehow the rings left by glasses on the night table must be gotten off. It was ridiculous, but she'd hardly ever looked into her own linen closet: she even had trouble remembering where it was. Once located, however, the closet's store of monogrammed pillowcases, towels, cloths, spreads and heavy linen sheets heartened her for the tussle of getting the bed made.

After an hour of hard work, the room looked quite presentable. Alexandra sat down and studied her sweaty, dust-grimed face in the bedroom mirror. Suddenly, for no reason, she burst into tears; she hurried to the liquor cabinet and poured out half a tumbler of bourbon, which she drank straight. She felt a little better. She couldn't imagine what was wrong with her, why she had exhausted herself like this.

She took another drink, a smaller one this time. Her pain was now smoothing out, her violent tensions relaxing. Returning to the bedroom, she took off her clothes, dumped them in the middle of the floor, quite heedless of the passion for tidiness which had obsessed her all morning; lightheartedly she ran into the bathroom and turned on the water in the stall shower as hot as she could stand it; she slid under the needling jets of spray, lathering her body, gasping with pleasure, at peace for the first time that day. No, she thought, no letting Anchylus off this time. Letty Meeker was his fault because he let her write whatever came into her head, no matter whom it hurt. Letty had counted on that. The insolent, lying bitch! She thought she was untouchable. All right! The moment had arrived to test that theory. Either the family meant something or it didn't, and if it meant anything it meant that Letty was through. *Fini!* She had gone too far at last.

Alexandra got out of the shower. Without waiting to dry herself, she dragged the telephone on its long cord into the bathroom and called her father's office.

"Miss Wilke," she said, not sure whether it was Miss Wilke or the other girl who answered, eager only to get her mission accomplished before her determination weakened. "This is Alexandra Drobny. I have to see my father right away, Miss Wilke; it's really important. Will he be there this afternoon? Because I'm driving into the city and I thought as soon as I got in I'd come up there."

8 SHE HAD NO PLAN for the interview: she'd simply put it to Anchylus that he had to fire Letty. Either that or— But her imagination hadn't reached beyond the basic demand.

It was difficult to conceive what excuse he could invent for refusing.

Suddenly she realized that she was hungry; she'd had several drinks and hardly any breakfast. A good lunch, with perhaps one cocktail, two at the most, would brace her up for what lay before her. She went to Jack's, ordered some food, and sent the waiter out to see if he could get a copy of *The Day*. It might be a good idea to have Letty's item with her; chances were that Anchylus hadn't read it. He always claimed he read everything in the paper, but she didn't see how this was possible. With the objectionable paragraph in hand she could simply plunk it down in front of him and ask what he was going to do about it.

The luncheon crowd in Jack's had started to thin out. Alexandra was—as she'd expected to be—one of the few women in the place. At lunchtime Jack's was like a men's club, each group with its special tables—Louis Lurie's bunch at their table near the door, and grading down from this, in a broadening money pyramid, the Montgomery Street crowd, the advertising boys, the law cases which had adjourned from the Hall of Justice. She had finished her second Manhattan and was attacking a broiled chicken and a heartening bottle of Krug Traminer when a man on his way out stopped at her table; she found herself looking up at the well-filled-out frame and friendly, suave, pink face of Timothy Wilkins III. Tim waved goodbye to his own lunch companions and seated himself across from her.

"It's been too long, Zan," he said by way of greeting.

"It certainly has," Alexandra said, "but you know, country life can pin you down. I'm just a ranch woman now."

"Can't say you look it," Tim said feelingly. "We've missed you around these parts."

"I've missed you too, Tim," Alexandra said. "How are you, sweetie? You look wonderful. How's Sophy and the wee ones?"

Tim had married Sophy Suell—rather indecently soon, Alexandra felt, after her own elopement with Schuy Cutting. She would have been more flattered if a man who had proposed to her at least a dozen times had waited a normal interval—say, a year or so—before tying himself for life to someone else. Still, Sophy was a good match

226

and very sweet and they had a slew of cute children, she'd heard; she didn't know exactly how many.

"Oh, fine, just fine," Timmy Wilkins said, "all fat and sassy. What's all this I read about a new romance for you? Or is that one of Letty's charming fictions?"

"It's a most uncharming lie," Alexandra said. "Quite typical, of course, of Letty. I suppose you realize she's hated me for years. That must be fairly obvious."

"Do you know, I've always thought she was an unpleasant woman," Tim said.

"That's the understatement of all time," Alexandra said. "She's a killer. If you want to know why I came down today it's expressly because I'm going to Father. I'm going to demand that he fire her."

Tim whistled softly. "Lots of luck," he said.

"I'm going to need it," Alexandra said, "but that's what I'm going to do. I thought you might be interested."

"Not only interested," Timmy said, "absolutely fascinated. I wish I could be there to see the fur fly."

"I wish you could," Alexandra said. "I could use some support. I'm terrified, Tim, isn't that silly? You don't know what that woman has done to me—and yet I'm scared to death."

"I'm betting on you, baby," Tim said; "give 'em hell."

"I will," Alexandra said, "but, of course, Letty is just part of it. The real person to beat is Anchy. And I don't have to tell you about him."

"A crocodile," Tim said. "An absolute dinosaur."

"You're so right," Alexandra said.

"Last of his kind," Tim said. "The species disappeared when they brought in the railroads. Huntington, Crocker and that bunch—he belongs with them. I've studied the old boy a little on my own account. I know."

"Well," Alexandra said, "I have nothing to lose but my brains. And the worst of it is I know just what will happen. He'll be so polite, so sweet and fatherly. He'll say the item is unnecessary and ridiculous—as it is—and he'll promise to bawl Letty out, and probably will. And everything will go along just as before till the next time she feels like taking a poke at me. The only real, honest-to-goodness way to throw her out would be to throw Anchy out first. And that's something nobody is going to do for some time."

"If ever," Timmy said. "He's rather safely entrenched, wouldn't you say?"

"Safely," Alexandra said, "but not perfectly. I've given a lot of thought to that too, Timmy, and while it's a long, long way home it's not beyond the bounds of possibility."

"Is that so?" Tim said quietly. His expression hadn't changed, but suddenly she felt he was regarding her with a new attention. Her own mind, following her train of thought, turned back to reveries of which, long ago, she had spoken to Sharon—spoken at a time when only a loose mass of half-formed schemes and thoughts had been kicking around in her. The idea was scarcely any clearer; Alexandra only spoke more positively now because the urge to make her wish come true was stronger.

"It can be done," she said; "and while this may sound undaughterly and all that sort of thing, I'm just the girl to do it."

"With your little hatchet," Tim said. He said it gently, not meanly, waiting to hear more. Since she had respect for Tim's intelligence, the fact that he was interested was a stimulus to her imagination. She went on as if presenting an idea which had definite shape and scope.

"With my little hatchet," she said, "consisting of a sizable stock interest. I've been told that stockholders are rather important people. They have certain rights."

"They most certainly do," Tim said. He signaled the waiter and asked for a cup of coffee.

"It all depends, of course, how they handle themselves. And what sort of situation they're confronting."

He spoke casually, but Alexandra could tell he was putting out a lead. She for her part was suddenly extremely glad she'd run into Tim. Their meeting seemed a most propitious accident. Tim had been making a name for himself as one of the best young brains on Montgomery Street. Instead of going into the Pacific Midland, as everyone had expected him to, he'd set up his own brokerage house, Wilkins & Shimenko. People who had been amused at his taking Leon Shimenko in with him had now stopped smiling. Wilkins & Shimenko were not by any means in a class with the big established firms in the street but they had done well; they were definitely on the way up. The thought came to Alexandra that her friendship with Tim Wilkins might prove to be an asset.

"You know all about these things, Timmy," she said. "What would we have to do, to have our way?"

Tim Wilkins noted the droop of the long eyelids and the way her fingers, holding a dessert spoon, began to tremble. She's not kidding about this, he thought.

"When you say *we*," he inquired in the same light tone as before, "what do you mean? You and your sisters, or just you in the editorial plural?"

"Well, at least Sharon and I," Alexandra said. "Anyway, I've talked to her a little about it. I don't know about Pamela. I suppose we'd have to leave her out of it. But we might not absolutely need her. Do you think we would?"

Tim looked reflective. "I couldn't say, offhand," he said, "or at least not till I know a good deal more about all this. That stock you mentioned—is it yours outright?"

"Oh, yes," Alexandra said. "I know it is!"

"And Pamela's and Sharon's?"

"Theirs too," Alexandra said with confidence. "Mother told me all about it once. It's all in her estate, so she gets her income, but we own it. I forget the details. We own it, but we can't vote until—that is, unless Mother died."

"God forbid," Tim said.

"God forbid," Alexandra echoed sincerely. "But tell me, Tim, if Mother agreed, if she said we could vote it, then couldn't we? I'm rather stupid about these things."

"That again," Tim said, "would all depend on how the trust was set up. And another most important point: do you girls, or you three plus your mother, if she has retained an interest, own more stock, or as much stock, as your father? That could be the nub of the whole thing."

"Yes, we do, Tim," Alexandra said.

"As much as?"

"More than." She tried to remember what Jessica had told her but was a little vague on this point.

"Well," Tim said, "I can tell you this much, speaking broadly: stockholders, and especially big ones, can embarrass the hell out of management. They can ask a lot of questions that are often very tough to answer."

"What sort of questions?"

"What's happening to the money? That's always the basic question. Then if you're not too happy with the way the company is being run, you boil that down to others—are the dividends being paid, for instance?"

Into Alexandra's mind, now thoroughly roused, flashed a picture of the last quarterly report—a printed statement always enclosed with a check made out to her by the San Francisco Day Publishing Company.

"They're not," she said, "or at least not enough. We have a little

229

stock that isn't in the trust, and my dividend checks are the same size they've been for years and years. That isn't paying proper dividends, is it, if the company has been growing?"

"Hard to tell," Tim said; "that would take some going into."

"Oh, Timmy!" Alexandra said. "I'm so glad I met you. Tell me more."

"Have to get back to the office," Tim said, "but I'll tell you what I'll do. I'll see what dope we have available and work up an analysis for you, with an opinion on what remedies to take. If remedies are what you're interested in."

"They are," Alexandra said.

"All right," Tim said. "Next, we ought to know how the family-owned stock is held—I mean, how it's divided among you and your parents and sisters. Can you write me a note about that?"

"Of course, Tim," Alexandra said. Her eyes were glowing. "Oh, my God, Tim," she said, "if we could really do this, wouldn't it be *something?*"

"Well," Tim Wilkins said, "we'll see. So I'll expect to hear from you?"

"You will, Tim," Alexandra said, "you certainly will."

Seeing him stop at the cash desk on his way out she guessed—accurately, as it turned out—that he'd had her lunch charged to his account. Timmy was really a very nice person and quite brilliant in his way; it was embarrassing to recall that when he'd been courting her, a dozen years earlier, she'd thought him rather stupid.

Now she could hardly wait to find out what he thought about *The Day.* So many exciting and fascinating channels of conjecture stretched ahead in various directions that, with the last of the wine still lurking in its bottle beside her empty plate, it seemed a pity to leave the restaurant. She had a few sips more, and then, on an impulse, signaled the waiter and ordered a small brandy.

9 MISS WILKE had set up Alexandra's appointment for three o'clock. This hour was, in Miss Wilke's opinion, the most comfortable time for Anchylus, the hour when he was best able to deal with difficult appointments. By three the bulk of the day's work would be well out of the way, the mail attended to and the editorial meeting over. The operation of the newspaper always came before anything else on Anchylus' agenda. Until all problems pertaining to it had been settled he couldn't give his mind wholeheartedly to

anything else; hence his power to defend himself was reduced. At three, on the other hand, he was relaxed, fortified by a good lunch in the executive dining room and, usually, by a nap. Anchylus always denied that he took a nap, but Miss Wilke knew better. She knew that he liked to sit in the big chair when he came down from the dining room and doze off. She never let any calls through at this time. He would wake up by himself after a half hour or so and buzz her, asking impatiently what was going on. He would be disappointed if there hadn't been any calls but if there had been any, and she'd held them over, he never reproached her.

Alexandra had no way of telling that her appointment was considered, by those around her father, as a threat to his well-being. She had no way of reading Miss Wilke's mind, nor, if she'd had, would she have been interested in using it. Nothing, to Alexandra, was more irrelevant to the main purposes of life than the opinions of office people or underlings of any sort. It was the opinion of one's friends that mattered—the specific level of opinion on which Letty Meeker had assaulted her. If the office girls had read Letty's item and hence were expecting some form of protest, even a violent one, from her, Alexandra, that was strictly their own business: she wanted no part of them. If Miss Wilke didn't like her, that went double; she didn't like Miss Wilke either, and it was just lucky for Miss Wilke that her tone was polite, even if no more than barely so, when she greeted her. Alexandra was in a mood to put up with zero from a stone-faced broad in front of a typewriter. It was certainly a comfort to reflect that if her plans went through some heads would roll around the office, and one of them might well be Miss Wilke's.

"You may go in, Baroness."

"Thank you," Alexandra said, walking past her into Anchylus' office. She found that she had to make an effort to walk firmly and not to sway. Having that last brandy in Jack's might not have been such a good idea. The room fell into a pattern of gently rising and falling planes in which her father's face was the only fixed point. She concentrated on this point, accepting the chair which he pulled out.

"Well, Alexandra, what brings you into town?"

"Oh, come on, Father," Alexandra said, "let's not be childish. And let's not waste time."

Anchylus looked at her a little anxiously. In the genial, interested regard which he kept on his face, as if for presentation to some other caller, she read his guess that she had been drinking—or the suspicion that she had. This angered her and the anger helped to clear her head.

231

"I trust you know why I've come. If you don't you ought to. Or is it possible you've stopped reading your own newspaper?"

Tears formed in her eyes. She forced them back. She had experienced a sudden feeling of pity for her father. He had so little idea of what she was ready to do.

"Anyway," she went on stanchly, "I brought this with me."

She had torn out Letty's column—she was sure she had—and put the offending clipping in her purse. Only now she couldn't locate it. Dredging around for it she brought up, first, the other Letty items, wrapped in the telegrams in which she'd placed them before showing them to Sharon so long ago; these, also, she'd felt she might need as ammunition. Finding today's item at last, she shoved the whole collection across the desk.

"There!" she said.

Anchylus searched the clipping carefully. Then he looked at the others. Something in the manner of his daughter's entrance—something not related to the fact that she was slightly tipsy—reminded him of the time when Sharon had told him to stay out of Indian Pipe. It wasn't a pleasant memory.

He pulled a pipe out of his pocket and stuffed it with tobacco. "Well, now, Zan," he said, "let's not get our guts in an uproar about this."

Alexandra sucked in her breath. "Father," she said, "my guts have been in an uproar about Letty since I was seventeen years old. I've put up with—God, I can't tell you! Somehow she finds out everything and she makes it all look stupid and horrible. I've had all I'm going to take—"

She was cold sober now. She wasn't yelling and her voice wasn't shaking; it was pitched down at a hard, quick level where the words broke and skidded and fell over one another like somebody reading aloud and skipping through a passage that could be slurred or hurried through because it was too familiar to bother about. Down in the big handbag from which she had produced the clippings she found a beat-up package of cigarettes and she lighted one with a kitchen match which she struck on her thumbnail like a cowboy.

"All right, all right now, Daughter. Not saying I blame you a hundred per cent—"

"Blame me!"

"Wait! Maybe you're right, I could have paid more attention to the stuff. I see your point—"

"Anchy," Alexandra said, "you don't. You don't see my point at all."

232

Anchylus looked thoughtfully at the intercom. "Tell you what," he said, "I'll get her in here, if you like. Then you tell her just what you've told me. We'll see what she has to say. You want me to do that?"

His hand moved toward the key labeled *Society*.

"No," Alexandra said, "I don't. What I want is for you to fire her. I didn't come here to . . . make scenes. If I saw her I'd probably tear her eyes out. I asked you once before and now I'm asking you for the last time. Just fire her. Right now. That's all."

"So that's the way it is," Anchylus said gently.

"That's exactly the way it is, Father," Alexandra said.

Anchylus nodded. He sat wagging his broad, heavy head up and down, his eyes almost invisible behind the hang of his eyebrows.

"You're my child, Zan. Grounds for complaint! That Letty! She can stick barbs on her words. Otherwise—" he chuckled heavily— "why, otherwise I wouldn't have her. What use would she be?"

"You're defending her?" Alexandra said. She had expected that he would, though it had seemed for a moment that he wasn't going to.

But Anchylus had resumed his serious, pondering air. "What I'm defending is a principle. Call it that—hate the word—but what do you suppose would happen if I fired a reporter every time some friend of mine came in and beefed he hadn't been treated right? Hell, Zan, I couldn't keep a staff."

"Is the principle you're trying to defend that your own family should be as defenseless as your friends?"

"I didn't say defenseless."

"Are you going to fire her or not?"

"I've got one measuring stick for a pink slip: accuracy! Are the facts right? Now let's look these items over and—"

"Oh, God, what's the use!" For a moment Alexandra's strength drained off—the strength of the good lunch, the two Manhattans, the wine and the brandy, and above all the strength of her rage.

It was hopeless. She shouldn't have come.

Anchylus went on, unperturbed. "Where do they hang the bass drum? That was what your Grandfather Fabian used to ask. Now you take this squib about the brand inspector. Consider it, step by step. Is it true or false? That's what we want to know, isn't it?"

Alexandra said nothing. She waited for what was coming.

"Step number one. Do you know such a fellow?"

"Yes."

"You been out with him? To a country dance or some such doings?"

"Yes."

"More'n once?"

"Yes. But does that give her the right to—"

"Hold your horses," Anchylus said. "So far, we can't send Letty to the gallows, can we? What I mean is, she's not *too* far off the facts. You are acquainted with a character like she describes. You been seen around with him. So—"

"That wasn't what she said—that I'd been seen around with him. She said that I—"

"Well, take it this way, Zan," Anchylus said, "she's *guessing*. She didn't say you *would* marry the geezer. She said might. It's here— right here in black and white. Mind you, a staffer on a copy desk, he wouldn't be allowed to say that. No ifs. No mights. But she's writing *gossip*, and the tune of wedding bells is all that makes such chit-chat bounce along. Now if—"

"You just said you didn't allow iffing, Father. Here's the terrible, the really awful part of it. She has a sort of evil power of knowing facts *before* they're true, of *making them come true*. That's what give me the creeps, and that's why I—"

"Gossip—" Anchylus said.

"It isn't even gossip," Alexandra said. "Nobody knows I know this man. Nobody but a few yokels. God knows how she ever found it out. As for marrying him—"

"No thought of that at all, eh?"

"Father, I won't answer that. It's simply too unthinkable."

"You want Letty to print a retraction—of a guess?"

"I told you what I want. If you don't fire her I'll—I declare total war. I mean it. And I think—I think I'd like a glass of water."

The strength which had come back to buoy her up had gone again and the vague intersection of remote planes had turned into a spin. Alexandra focused on the thermos carafe in Anchylus' hands as he poured out the water—but the pouring too became part of the depths spinning around her. As she leaned forward to get the glass she lost her balance and slid softly, luxuriously, from her chair and relaxed, for an incomparable moment of peace and triumph, with her face against the soft, thick office carpet.

Tim Wilkins watched Leon C. Shimenko read the memo he had sent him on the San Francisco Day Publishing Company. Leon read slowly, holding the memo close to the long nose which everyone had decided was so aristocratic once it had been established beyond doubt that its owner was a bona-fide prince.

"Well, Leon?" Tim said.

His partner put the paper down. "I'm not sure I know what you mean about this thing, Tim," he said.

"Well, it seems to me it's pretty obvious," Tim said. "If these figures are right, the old man owns less than an eighth of his own company. It wouldn't take much to dump him, once the girls start voting their own proxies."

"That is, provided he survives his wife," Leon said.

"I don't see how he can help it," Tim said. "I understand she's not in good health at all."

"You want to own a company," Leon said, "it pays fifteen cents, Tim, on a par value of five dollars? We'd do better with a few shares of P.G. & E.—or some school bonds, maybe."

"Quite so, Leon," Tim said placidly.

"So you want to be an editor?" Leon said. "What for? You running for Congress or what is it?"

"I'm surprised at you, Leon," Tim said. "I thought you learned something when you were with Dean Witter. Listen, I remember when this stock came out; it was subscribed around town in a couple of weeks. A little gets traded once in a while, but you'd have to have a microscope to detect the activity. Bet you we could find out who the owners are in two days, even without access to the registry; my old man probably knows half of them."

"So?"

"So," Tim said, "I call your attention to one item on that statement—the entry where it says the San Francisco Day Publishing Company has cash assets of one million dollars. So if we have to spend a hundred thousand, say, getting control—with the daughters' help, of course—we have a ten to one profit right there. Then we sell off the plant and real estate to an insurance company and lease it back. So we have another million, three quarters anyway. There's other equipment in addition to the plant—vehicles and stuff— enough to collateralize a loan. So we get back the hundred thousand we put in to start with. Leon, it's the first really great Deal that's come into this office since we opened up for business. How can you sit there telling me you don't see what I mean?"

Leon Shimenko laid the memo down. He tilted his chair back, staring into space.

"Remember the party the old man gave for the two girls, the

coming-out party? My God! That was the first San Francisco party for Leon C. Shimenko."

"You broke in good all right," Tim said. He was watching his partner narrowly.

"In one room, Tim, they had birds in a cage. But not real birds. Made of silver or something. You turned on a switch, they sang. That was a party."

"Look, Leon," Tim said, puzzled, "you want me to get choked up because we drank some champagne there, and now we might get to raid the old man's company? I drank wine with everybody in this city and I took out their daughters too. I'd still raid their companies, if I knew how. A deal is a deal."

Leon nodded. His air was sympathetic, but he sniffed with his flared-back, houndy nose as if he smelled something bad.

"Tim," he said, "I might lie to my mother, I might lie to my father, in his grave now, or my wife. But I won't lie to my partner, so I have to tell you, the deal is no good."

"Why not?"

"Because of the birds. The silver birds that sang. The old-time family. The big house. Everything of that nature."

"I'm afraid I don't get your point, Leon," Tim said.

"My point is that San Francisco people want what is here to stay. The cable cars and the ferryboats. The old houses. And also the old family business. If a couple of smart young guys start a money fight and dump an old man out of his company, people will hate the smart young guys. Am I right or wrong?"

"In this case," Tim said, "you're wrong. When you say that San Franciscans protect the status quo, you have something. But the Saxes don't quite fall in that category. They're the kind of family that almost made it but not quite. I think I'm accurate in that. There was some old scandal, the gal who was supposed to be adopted wasn't adopted. Or she was adopted but she was also a bastard. Pappy will remember what it was."

Leon C. Shimenko brightened up a little. "That I never heard," he said with a faint show of interest.

"It was before your time," Tim said, "before mine too. But that's not the only angle. There's the personality of Old Man Saxe. Take it one way, he's just the kind of guy you'd expect people here to go for, only they didn't go for him. Hard to tell why. Fifty years earlier he might have been another Hearst or Fremont Older or Mike de Young. As it worked out, though, his daughters are above him. He and Sharon don't talk. And Alexandra hates his guts. She was the one started me on all this, as I said in the memo. So if we come into this it won't be like a couple of outsiders muscling in. We'll just be taking sides in a family fracas that started before we got into it. Also, we're San Franciscans too, even if you're from Minsk."

"Pinsk," Leon C. Shimenko said. "How many times do I have to tell you?"

"Well, I wouldn't admit it," Tim said. "My point is that we're not a couple of hoods from Wall Street. Frankly, I don't think a deal like this could hurt us. All we can do now, anyway, is watch the situation. The mother's health might improve. It might be a long time yet before the girls get hold of that stock."

In this prediction—if it could be considered a prediction—Tim was wrong. This conversation took place early in 1949. And in the fall of that year Jessica was taken to the hospital.

VII

A Letter from Mr. Garber

"To explain the cultural barbarism they see in us, Europeans have an easy answer: it is the product of a business civilization."
—WILLIAM H. WHYTE, JR.

1 MATT BRODY sat close to his employer's desk. He had drawn a chair at right angles to Anchylus' and was not more than a foot or two away, so that, by leaning forward, he could speak almost into the latter's ear. There is something in the nature of death which invokes secrecy as a substitute for, or concomitant of, reverence for the deceased. Matt, like many people, felt that a reduction of vocal pitch was properly indicated in relation to the matters which he was discussing.

"The services at the Cathedral will be at ten o'clock on Saturday."

"I thought I told you to make it Thursday," Anchylus growled.

"I'm sorry, boss; it was a little tough."

"What was so tough about it?"

"There was a wedding there at noon, sir—Pomery-Mitchell."

"Must be John P. Mitchell's daughter. East Bay people?"

"I believe so. He's in the contracting business. Anyway, it's a pretty big wedding, and they're putting in some special decorations. Plan to start on them the night before, and since you wanted it in the morning . . ."

Most of this explanation, delivered in Matt's characteristic mumble, was ignored by Anchylus.

"Wednesday was out?"

"No, I wouldn't say out. They do have another service on that day. A much smaller one, of course, but I thought—"

"Wednesday might be too soon, at that," Anchylus said. He added, recapitulating oft-considered factors, "I want people there. I want 'em all there. The ones she knew."

"Yes, sir," Matt Brody said, and waited. He hoped Anchylus wouldn't make him change the date. Appleton Brothers had obtained special permission from the Health Department to hold Jessica's body beyond the five-day legal limit.

Anchylus rubbed his cheek. "Saturday. Well, I guess it will be all right."

Matt had been careful not to bring up—nor, he noticed, had Anchylus mentioned—Friday as a possible day on which to hold the funeral.

Friday was the day of the annual stockholders' meeting. As a director of the corporation, Matt was well aware of this. The date had been set at the last meeting, a year ago, and the notices duly mailed out. Matt Brody wasn't sure what steps, according to the terms of the corporation charter, had to be taken if an adjourned meeting were to be held. Possibly the directors would have to meet. He had thought of calling George Dudley and asking him but had decided to wait until, and if, he got word from Anchylus suggesting an adjourned meeting. No such word had come through, so it seemed evident that the meeting would take place as scheduled.

Anchylus had relapsed into thought. He sat hunched over, tapping on the desk with his busted hand.

"Where did they put her this time?" he asked.

Matt Brody experienced again the puzzlement he'd felt when he'd heard a similar question, two days earlier, addressed to the doctors in the hospital hallway.

"Appleton Brothers," Matt said. "Was that all right?"

"God damn it, Matt," Anchylus said, "I don't mean which ghoul house. I mean *whereabouts* there. What kind of place. *Where did they put her?*"

"They call it a Slumber Room, Mr. Saxe," he said.

"Where in hell did they dig up an appellation like that? Do they make up their own argot?"

"I suppose, like other businesses, they develop a trade terminology," Matt said.

Anchylus resumed drumming on the desk. His mouth worked and his jaw muscles flexed. He seemed infuriated by the nomenclature which had been quoted to him.

"Ghouls, all of them," he said. "Ought to be eliminated by legislation, slumber rooms and all."

Matt Brody made no comment, though it occurred to him to wonder how, if official action were taken to suppress the undertaking trade, people were going to get buried.

Anchylus' slabby face was full of misery. "Can a person . . . go to see her there?"

"Why, yes, sir. Yes, of course."

"Do you have to call up first, or anything?"

"No. I'm quite sure you don't. Of course, if you want me to, I can tel—"

"Never mind. Let it go," Anchylus said. He straightened up. He was looking at the clipboard in Matt's lap—the regular morning conference clipboard with its tear sheets from the Overnight.

"Get any more on that fellow that wanted to be strapped to the A-bomb?"

"Not yet," Matt Brody said, "but Shep Wheatcroft in Washington thinks the item is authentic. He's still trying to find out the guy's name."

"That could be a hell of a story," Anchylus said. He waved his hand to show the interview was at an end.

Matt started for the door but when he was halfway there Anchylus spoke again. "Thanks for half-masting the flags. I suppose you were the one who had it done?"

"Yes, I was, Mr. Saxe," Matt said.

"Well, thanks, thanks," Anchylus said. "That was just right. The proper thing to do. Tell Miss Wilke to step in here, on your way out."

2   Matt Brody relayed the message. Clipboard under his arm, he walked down the hall, past the lettered doors of production, circulation and advertising executives, to the newsroom and his own desk at the end of it. He still doesn't actually realize she's dead, he thought. I wonder how it will hit him when he does? And I wonder why he doesn't put off the stockholders' meeting? Doesn't he know he's not in shape to preside?

He braced his feet on the bar under his desk. He was glad he'd had the flags half-masted instead of waiting until Miss Wilke or somebody else thought of it. He was glad also that Anchylus had noticed the position of the flags and assumed that he and not somebody else had ordered them this way. The flags—two Stars and Stripes, two California Bears—decorated the four corners of the Day Building, and when Matt ordered them half-masted he had supplemented this with the further direction that all four of them be kept at half-mast until Jessica had been buried.

The half-masted flags told much to the people of San Francisco. Their somber tribute was by no means a routine one. Since the construction of the building in 1922, the year of Fabian Rupke's death, the flags had been half-masted exactly thirty-three times: for Fabian himself, for twenty-seven Memorial days, for the deaths of Woodrow Wilson, Calvin Coolidge, Warren Gamaliel Harding and Franklin Delano Roosevelt, and for King Tut, a racing stallion in whom Anchylus Saxe had owned a half interest and who had come to his end in a stable fire in the thirties, only a week before he was to have competed in the Gold Cup at Bay Meadows.

Anchylus sat at his desk just as Matt Brody and then Miss Wilke, in her turn, had left him. He was still trying to get it through his head about Jessica, as he had been trying, now, for more than forty-eight hours: he'd come nearest to getting it the first day, after the glimpse of her in the Repository—another ghoul name, though a slightly disinfected one.

This was no good. He'd lived too long not to know what happened when a person parted company with reality. He was too smart for that.

Death had never seemed particularly horrible to him; he'd taken it in his stride. He had understood it on the farm when his father had gone to war to have fun and hadn't come back and when his uncle had come back and sat dying and smelling in the rocker on the porch. He had seen Death, the quiet traveler, in saloons, in the street, under the freight cars and in boardinghouse rooms, in the cold and the heat, at night, at dawn. He had seen senseless, craven death and witless death and, a few times, the conquering kind of death achieved by the unafraid.

Death wasn't a bit like Jessica. Maybe that was the trouble.

He concentrated on the memorandum Angela Wilke had left with him. There were at least twenty names on it, the important ones underlined. Mostly people who had called to find out about the funeral:

no need to call them back, old friends though they were. The notice would run tomorrow, now that the time had been set.

Mr. Winkler is very anxious to talk to you.

It was the last notation on the memo. He pressed the intercom key and said, "Come on in, Dan." Ordinarily, of course, that was just what Dan would have done, even if Anchylus had been talking to someone else at the moment.

Everyone was treating him with kid gloves today.

Dan Winkler sat down where Matt Brody had been sitting. He had a black band on his right sleeve—his sorrow for Jessica made public and tangible, like the half-masted bunting on the building itself.

"How's it going, Dan?"

"Lousy," Dan said. "I couldn't sleep all night. You look better, though."

"I got some sleep," Anchylus said, "but I don't feel so good. I don't know why I came down. I can't seem to get my mind on anything."

"When Helen went," Dan Winkler said, "I couldn't get it through my head at all. I was that way for three weeks. I guess you remember."

"I do," Anchylus said.

"Believe me," Dan said, "it's the worst part."

"What's on your mind, Dan?" Anchylus asked.

"Nothing that won't keep," Dan said, "if you don't feel like talking."

"Spill it, you silly son of a bitch," Anchylus said.

Dan Winkler took a letter out of his pocket and laid it on the desk.

> Mr. Daniel Winkler
> Secretary, The Day Publishing Company
> The Day Building
> San Francisco, California
>
> DEAR MR. WINKLER:
> We, the undersigned, represent clients of record now controlling stock in an amount equal to 150,000 shares, or 15% of the outstanding common stock of the San Francisco Day Publishing Company. Since this holding constitutes a controlling interest I am hereby making demand on you, in behalf of my clients and their associates, for the nomination of certain persons, to be designated by them, to represent their interest on the Board of Directors, said nominations to represent a voting majority.

I am addressing this letter to you, as secretary, for discussion with your Board, in the hope that any differences may be discussed at a personal conference prior to the annual stockholders' meeting. I believe you will find that the demands of my clients are reasonable and will work to the future benefit of the company and the increased satisfaction of its share owners and if acceded to will save all concerned the labor and expense of a voting contest.

Will you kindly advise me whether such a meeting is acceptable to you, and if so, what date and place would be convenient?

Sincerely,
MORTIMER GARBER

Garber, Macleish, and Smith

Anchylus read the letter with care. When he was through he got his glasses out of his pocket, put them on, and read it again. He had crumpled one side of the paper by gripping it too hard. His face had a mottled, patchy look.

"What in hell clients is this jackass talking about? Why doesn't he come out and say who he represents?"

"Don't ask me. That's his idea of playing it cagey, I suppose. This town's too small for that stuff though—"

"And?"

"Wilkins and Shimenko. Young Tim, that is, and that Russian what-not he's tied in with. Anyway, that's what they say down in the Street. W and S had an analysis made of us six months ago. Showed it to some of their customers—confidentially, of course."

"Young Tim! Why, he's a snot-nosed punk."

"That's right. But it's him, all the same. I guess he wants to wipe the snot off on our sleeve."

"Has George Dudley seen this?"

"Nobody's seen it. Except me, and now you."

"The finks," Anchylus said, "jumping on a man when he's down!"

"They didn't waste much time," Dan Winkler assented grimly. "This was mailed yesterday morning, but you can bet your boots it's been planned for a long, long time. That's what makes it look sort of peculiar, from where I sit. The timing, I mean."

He paused, looking at Anchylus significantly, but whatever he wished to imply about the timing of the letter, in relationship to Jessica Saxe's death, seemed to have escaped his listener.

"Wilkins and Shimenko," Anchylus said. "Hell, we bank with Pacific Midland. What does this little prig Tim Wilkins think he's doing? Get his old man on the phone. Wait, I'll get him myself. I'll tear the hide off him."

He reached for the telephone. Dan Winkler put his hand on it.

"I wouldn't do that if I were you," he said.

Anchylus looked at him somberly. "You don't think his old man's in on it, do you?"

"No," Dan Winkler said, "I don't. I think it may be just young Tim and that Russian partner of his, and certain others they've pulled in."

Again he paused. He had given the words *certain others* a most pregnant emphasis. This, however, was bypassed by Anchylus' steadily rising anger.

"The letter's a stinking lie, of course," he said. "They haven't got fifteen per cent of the stock. They're waving an empty gun around, trying to scare us."

"I'm not so sure," Dan Winkler said.

"What do you mean, you're not so sure, Dan?" Anchylus said. "You know how the stock is held, what the girls and Jessica and I have. No one could buy a control. And I mean no one."

"I hope not," Dan said.

"I *know* not."

"There's been some activity, though," Dan Winkler said. "Remember when I told you three, four months ago our listing was up pretty near two points then? It's a point higher now. That's a lot of points for a low-price issue in that space of time. It sure looks like someone might be after our hide. I checked some of those transfers. Half of them were handled through Eastern brokerage firms—firms that don't even have offices in San Francisco."

"What does that prove?"

"All right," Dan Winkler said, "suppose you were an individual who wanted to get his hooks on a small, rich, family-owned and -operated company like, say, *The San Francisco Day*. Let's leave out the inducements. To me they're fairly obvious. Let's concentrate on the technique of the operation. What would you do, if you were that individual? Would you publicize your intention, before you had made your position? Would you go into the San Francisco Stock Exchange, for instance, and bid up the stock until the price was out of sight? Or would you try to keep the matter under wraps? Naturally, you'd do the latter. You'd buy under street names and so on. Using Eastern brokerage houses would fit in with that sort of situation, wouldn't it?"

"It would," Anchylus said, "but isn't it a little farfetched?"

"Anything that's dangerous is farfetched or it wouldn't be dangerous."

"You trying to tell me these punks have me whipped?"

"You know better than that. All I'm saying is we don't want to let it go. If we met with them, we might know where we stand."

"I don't want to meet with them. I don't want to have anything to do with them."

"Is that what you want me to tell Garber?"

Anchylus considered this. "Just tell him—politely, of course—that we refute his claim of a majority of interest in *The San Francisco Day*. We won't let him nominate anyone for the Board. Meanwhile, send his letter to Dudley, just so we can have a legal opinion on it."

"All right," Dan Winkler said.

"And don't look so glum," Anchylus said; "quit worrying. I own *The Day*—or the Saxe Trust Estate owns it, which amounts to the same thing—and we're not just about to sell out. Not now and not ever."

He looked belligerently at his friend, as if ready to fend off a new attack, but *The Day*'s secretary-treasurer didn't rise to the challenge. He seemed to be weighing his next words carefully.

"Are you sure, boss?" he said at length.

"Of course I'm sure," Anchylus said. Then, as some overtone of his companion's question caught up with him, he rasped, "Sure of what?"

"Sure that you and Saxe Trust are interchangeable terms," Dan Winkler said.

Anchylus let that one go by. He didn't catch the drift of it. He was puzzling over it as Dan Winkler stood up.

Dan took the lawyer's letter off the desk. "I'll write an answer to this," he said, "and I'd like you to take a look at it before I send it. Why don't you take a rest now?"

"I'm feeling okay," Anchylus said. "Maybe it did me good to get riled up. Was that what was in your agile brain, roweling me with all this chatter just to see if I'd snap back to normal?"

"I wish it had been, Anchylus," Dan Winkler said. "Honestly I do. I don't feel as happy about all this as you seem to."

"Well," Anchylus said, "you go and find a wall to wail on or a telephone to use. Me, I'm going to have my lunch."

The lunch was pleasant. Not so the nap which followed it. Hardly had Anchylus' head nodded, his body comfortably settled in the big chair, than his head jerked up: into his mind had come the thought of Dan Winkler's remark about the timing of the letter—that it had been "peculiar." In what way peculiar? Anchylus had hardly noticed the remark when it was made. Now it suddenly seemed the most significant part of the conversation.

". . . certain others they'd pulled in . . ." Dan had said that, too. And his hint that the Saxe Trust Estate might have sold stock to Garber's bunch.

Sold stock! No, that wasn't what Dan had been trying to get over. The Trust couldn't sell its holdings, without the most elaborate fiddle-faddling. What Dan meant was that the girls—or at least one of them, or two even (he knew Pamela would never go for the idea) had put in with the Garber bunch. That the girls were going to vote with them.

The girls!

God, it couldn't be! But if it was? What if that was at the bottom of all this, the family split he'd never quite admitted to himself, the very existence of which he'd always denied in spite of the break with Sharon, the trouble with Alexandra over Letty Meeker.

Then the fat was in the fire, sure enough. Then the Garber bunch were not exaggerating their power. They might be *underplaying* it. The stock had been bid up. It had been rising for months, as Dan had pointed out. Someone had obviously been accumulating it, or some combination of persons.

Fifteen per cent, Garber had claimed. Why, hell, if even one of the girls was in with him they'd have almost that much without any additional buying at all.

Why, if this was so, had Garber claimed so little? In a negotiation like this the logical move would be to claim more, not less, than you held. Here, again, there was something that didn't add up, something that called for more thought. . . .

He was awake now with a vengeance. All this must be gone into at once and thoroughly. No use saying it couldn't be—that the girls wouldn't turn on him like that, the moment they had power in their hands.

The moment! Hell, the very second! Hold your horses, now, he said to himself. Do you need to learn a lesson in human nature from your own kith and kin? People were like that—and it went for men and women equally. The law of fang and claw—that was what people lived by regardless of the trappings they borrowed from their tailors and preachers and librarians and couturiers. If they wanted something they went for it, all out.

Over my dead body.

That was an expression he had often used himself, meaning it down to his toes. It was just as true when the body was someone else's, even their own mother's.

Yes, it could be. That must be faced. Could be, and chances were ten to one it was. Even with the unexplained moderation of Garber's claim (moderation, of course, only if all this new thinking proved to be correct) the girls were in it somehow. Why hadn't he foreseen the possibility? He, who always kept his guard up? He'd made his first mistake setting up the Trust that way, going along with the tax men's suggestion that Alexandra, Sharon and Pamela take outright ownership of the stock to save inheritance taxes. Why, for awhile he'd considered putting all his own holdings in the kitty, instead of only half. He'd have done it, too, if it hadn't been for George Dudley. George had been skeptical of the whole operation. He'd wanted to keep the voting powers where they belonged, and to hell with taxes. But even then people regarded George as old-fashioned. George had probably been born old-fashioned. That kind of bachelor lawyer always was. But how right he'd been, damn it all, and how smart!

Anchylus shoved himself out of his chair. His left foot had gone to sleep, a foot which, as his reverie ended, he'd been thinking, longingly, of planting on the backside of that fink Garber. Limping, he walked to the desk and pressed an intercom key.

"Ask Mr. Winkler to come in, Miss Wilke," he said, "and get George Dudley on the telephone."

3 Anchylus' reluctance to believe his daughters had turned against him was based on a sort of sentimentalism, the general kindliness and the deep, solid feelings of family loyalty which lay under his outward roughness and acquisitiveness. This reluctance or unbelief handicapped him even while he cast about for a means of defending himself against this sudden, strange attack.

It might, he thought, all be a mistake. He would believe that, anyway, until proved wrong; he would go on hoping that the girls weren't in it.

His doubts would have been dispelled quickly enough if he could have eavesdropped on one conversation—an early-morning chat between Sharon and Alexandra on the morning of the day Mortimer Garber sent his letter. The letter itself, unwritten as yet, had been the subject under discussion.

Alexandra had brought it up. She had gone to call on Sharon at the Mark, finding her sister in a negligee, about to order coffee. Alexandra also had a tray sent up, and the two breakfasted in front of a window affording a fine view of the city.

"It's just a matter of form," Alexandra explained, "a way of putting him on notice."

"I know," Sharon said.

"And besides," Alexandra went on, "our names won't be mentioned. This will just be a request, on behalf of certain unnamed clients, for some places on the Board. I don't see what's so horrible about that."

"It isn't horrible," Sharon said. "All I mean is—this doesn't seem the time to send it."

"There's no use waiting," Alexandra said. "What would we gain by that?"

"We could at least wait till after the funeral," Sharon said.

"It isn't *us*," Alexandra said, "it's—other people. Tim and Leon and this Garber."

"We're involved, though," Sharon said. "Why pretend we're not? We are most definitely involved, and I just think—"

"Sweetie," Alexandra said, "we could wait a year or two years. Would that make it any different? It wouldn't. Sending the letter will probably mean that the stockholders' meeting will be postponed —holding an adjourned meeting, they call it—and that *is* important."

"Well, all right," Sharon said. "Not that I care, as long as we aren't mentioned."

"We won't be," Alexandra said. "Garber was definite about that. He said there would be no point in mentioning us."

"I've said all right, Zan," Sharon said. "I can't concentrate on this. I still feel too terribly about Mother, I really do. Do we have to go on talking about it?"

"No," Alexandra said, "we don't."

"Then, let's stop," Sharon said. "Would you like some more coffee?"

Alexandra allowed herself to be helped to the coffee. She added cream and sugar and took a thoughtful sip. "I feel terribly about Mother, too," she said with feeling. "Please don't think I don't. And it was a bit of the Old Gruesome, getting there and having Letty be the one to break the news. She'd been hovering around, I swear it, waiting for the chance, just absolutely drooling for it. It was ghastly."

"I know how you must have felt, dear," Sharon said. She shook her head pityingly. "Letty, of all people!" she said.

"Well, at least she won't be around much longer," Alexandra said.

"Don't let's talk about it any more, please," Sharon said. "I'm going to help you. That's all I can say. And truthfully, Zan, I'm not going to do it to get rid of Letty. I don't hate her the way you do. I just feel that if the paper's run as badly as you say, and all that, Anchy should retire."

"He should and must," Alexandra said, "before he ruins everything."

Alexandra put down her cup. She looked at her sister in the blazy, inspirational way which Sharon remembered from their childhood. "Shar," she said, "I just want one promise from you. That you won't back out on me."

"When have I ever?" Sharon said. "You know I don't back out. What makes you say that?"

"Because this is unusual. We've never been in anything like this together. Will you give me your solemn word of honor that you'll go through to the end, no matter what happens?"

"I said I would, didn't I?"

"Yes, you did," Alexandra said, "but I want you to promise."

"Oh, good God, Zan," Sharon said, "you can be tiresome sometimes. What difference would a promise make? Do you want me to swear on the Bible or something?"

Alexandra considered this. "No," she said, "but I want it to be definite. I want you at least to shake hands on it. Will you do that?"

"On what?"

"On our agreement that we're in this together. And neither one of us will back out on the other, ever, until it's all over. All right?"

"All right," Sharon said. She held out her hand, smiling a little mockingly. "Is that what you want? Do you trust me now?"

"I trust you, sweetie," Alexandra said. "I just wanted it to be definite, that's all."

In the morning sunshine, in front of the window, with the plunge of the vertical city as a witness, the two sisters solemnly shook hands.

4 "Pass the letters around, Matt, that will be quicker than reading them out loud," Anchylus said.

From his chair in front of the fireplace he looked at the group gathered in his library—Jacob Rupke's library, originally, then Fabian's, now his own. There many matters pertaining to *The Day*, more of them constructive, stimulating ones, had been discussed—

252

how different from those which would be discussed here tonight.

This time the library meeting had been called at his orders in an effort to fend off *The Day*'s dissolution or, at least, its seizure by wreckers and looters.

"The letter designated Number One, gentlemen," he said, "explains itself. The letter designated Number Two is an answer to it prepared by Dan Winkler and sent out this afternoon. It represents my position, taken at my own initiative, and one which I'm prepared to maintain, subject, to some extent, of course, on what we decide here tonight. Does anybody want another drink before we begin?"

Nobody did. Matt Brody took the letters from the desk and distributed them—copies mimeographed less than two hours before by Miss Wilke herself, who had stayed overtime to do it. She had volunteered for this duty. She'd felt, and Anchylus had agreed with her, that in view of the confidential nature of the letters it was much better to have her do them than to send them down to the mimeograph department in the circulation office. Miss Wilke herself, notebook open and pencil handy, sat in a corner, prepared to take notes, just as if the gathering, so informal in appearance, had been a Board meeting, and it was clear to everybody in the room that Miss Wilke's presence, though any woman's presence tended to tone down the freedom of the language used, if not the ideas exchanged, was appropriate and necessary. The deliberations of the men present would be well worth recording.

The group packed power. Four of the six men in it were Board members—young Winterhalter, who had come with George Dudley, and a man named Haskell, brought in turn by young Winterhalter, being the only exceptions. In the chair which balanced Anchylus' beside the fireplace sat Oakleigh Donovan, heavy and tweedy, a cigar clamped in his large coplike face. He had been one of *The Day*'s presiding counselors for almost twenty years, and his daughter, Gertrude, had been in Alexandra's class at Burke's.

Across the room from Oakleigh, directly facing him and at the same time as far away from him as he could get, George Dudley perched like a trim little white-headed bird. George didn't like Oakleigh Donovan: he had always been vaguely surprised that he hadn't taken a bundle of investment funds, at some point in his career, and headed for Tahiti with a chorus girl. Oakleigh was the type that would.

George Dudley had opposed his election to the Board when his name had first been put in motion and he had opposed him again later, with no better results, in the matter of floating *The Day*'s first listed stock offering, an issue which Oakleigh's firm, Donovan & Bean, had underwritten.

From the seat of his stiff chair, extending straight down, George Dudley's legs barely touched the floor. He didn't mind; he needed alertness if he were to give Oakleigh his comeuppance tonight. He would have preferred, to be sure, a daytime conference, particularly since this one was sure to last past nine-thirty, his regular bedtime, but on the whole he enjoyed all conferences, even those convened to deal with emergencies. Conferences were the nearest thing to courtroom operations which fell to a lawyer whose temperament had made him choose to deal with people in nonadversary relationships.

Anchylus had put the "palace guards"—Matt Brody and Dan Winkler—on his left and slightly behind him, side by side on a two-seater couch. He felt somehow safer with them there even though recalling how someone had once pointed out that the little couch, when occupied by a pair of henchmen at a session like this, suggested a bellhops' bench in a traveling man's hotel. At that time he'd answered, "There's a place for bellhops."

Come right down to it, if there was nothing wrong with having a few bellhops around, there was nothing wrong either with being a bellhop—or with somebody's being one, that is, as long as it wasn't you. Bellhops made money. They were useful members of society, a damn sight more so than many a company director.

He glanced around to see if everyone was finished with the letters. They hadn't, quite, but there was already a new feeling in the room, a growing tension.

"Well, gentlemen?" he said.

Oakleigh Donovan set his drink down. As the man with the best qualifications to pass judgment on stock operations, it was fitting for him to be the first to speak.

"I should like to ask one question," he said.

"Go ahead, Oakleigh," Anchylus said.

"If this man Garber's claim has anything to it, how could his group have gotten the position he says they have without our getting wind of it?"

"I asked myself the same question this afternoon," Anchylus said, "and I asked Dan Winkler. You may think we were asleep at the switch. All I can tell you is we weren't. Not much stock has been traded, a little more than I'd estimated as the minimum, but not much. I believe Dan has a rundown of all the transactions, as shown by the registry. What was the figure, Dan?"

254

"A hundred and thirty-three thousand shares, as of Monday," Dan said. "It might be a few days before we have the figures on the trading since then, but the price has remained steady. I wouldn't guess it had been much."

George Dudley was looking fixedly at Oakleigh. "The sale of a hundred and thirty-three thousand shares," he said, "should hardly reduce a first-class company to desperation if some errors had not been committed previously, somewhere along the line."

Anchylus motioned for him to shut up. "I may as well put it to you as I see it, gentlemen. I have reason to suspect that the group represented by Mr. Garber has reached some sort of understanding with two of my daughters. Under the terms of a trust set up some years ago—George Dudley can refresh us on the terms of it—the Trust in its entirety represents three hundred and ninety thousand shares, of which the two girls in question would control two thirds."

He lighted a cigar, letting the announcement sink in. Without turning, he could imagine the shock and dismay on the faces of Brody and Winkler. He'd talked to each of them with reference to the Garber letter but he'd been careful to keep his suspicions about the girls out of his talks, partly because that was what they'd been— suspicions.

Now they were conclusions.

"Are you sure of this, Anchylus?" The question came from Oakleigh Donovan. He took a healthy swig out of his highball, finishing it. He looked as if he could have used another, and Anchylus didn't blame him. He felt like a snort himself.

"I am," he said.

"You mean," Donovan said in amazement, "the girls admitted it?"

"In effect, yes," Anchylus said. "I wasn't able to reach my daughter Alexandra. She has a ranch in the country and she's apparently either not there or not taking calls. I did reach my daughter Sharon Iverson. While she didn't make an open statement of her position, she said that she had been asked to vote for changes in the Board. I'm having lunch with her tomorrow and I'll know more then, I hope. But from other information I've obtained—" his eyes met George Dudley's, who nodded affirmatively—"I think it's safe to assume that Alexandra was the one who asked her. I won't try to fill you in on the family aspects behind all this. I'd prefer, for the purposes of this meeting, to accept it as a fact and to go on from there."

Once more a silence fell. Haskell, the outsider, was making notes on the mimeographed letters. Young Winterhalter, who had refused a seat and was leaning against the wall near the orchestrion, looked at George Dudley as if for permission and then spoke up, rather nervily, at such a juncture as this, since his voice and opinion carried less authority than those of anyone in the room. Practically, you could say, no authority at all.

"Mr. Saxe! Can we assume that the third trustor, participating equally with the other two ladies named, will vote her shares with management or against it? Or is such information considered classified at this time?"

Where did they get expressions like *classified*, Anchylus wondered, these punks around law offices, as if they were talking about want ads? From the army probably, though young Winterhalter, spindly and round-shouldered, facially handsome in a dyspeptic sort of way, looked too juvenile to have served in any organization more formidable than the Cub Scouts.

"The information is not to be considered classified, as you call it," Anchylus said, "nor is anything else that anyone here in this room would like to know. Everything said here, on the other hand, is considered classified to anybody not in this room. Is that clear?"

"Yes, sir," young Winterhalter said.

"Then, to answer your question," Anchylus said, "the third trustor, my daughter Pamela, will vote her shares with mine."

He made this assertion with a thrill of pleasure. He hadn't asked Pamela. He knew he hadn't needed to. She'd be with him. She'd be with him all the way.

"Well, that's good news, anyway," Dan Winkler said.

Donovan raised a polished toe. Sighting over it into the air and speaking as if to no one in particular, he said, "Well, well. Could there have been some looseness about this damned Trust, a certain lack of foresight, shall we say, from the legal angles?"

George knew at whom this thrust had been aimed. He put in quickly. "The Trust was set up in accordance with decedent's wishes— in an effort to relate these with the anticipated demands of the various taxing authorities."

He seemed about to add more, rubbing his woolly hair cap, but once again Anchylus silenced him. "If you want to tangle with Oakleigh, George, do it later. . . . To sum up our position," he went on, "my own holding is one hundred and twenty-five thousand shares. With that, and the other holding mentioned, we can count on voting not less than two hundred and fifty thousand shares."

"With maybe twice that much against us?" Donovan's tone was incredulous.

256

"Maybe," Anchylus said. "You never know how many ducks are roosting in a pond, Oakleigh, till you go to count them."

"All right," Oakleigh said, "but it's a son of a bitch all right. A real son of a bitch."

"It could be," Anchylus conceded.

He gave Dudley the floor.

"I'd like to say," Dudley remarked, in his precise, high-pitched voice, "that all this seems bad. Black indeed! But aren't we forgetting a few things? I still think that many of the shares recently transferred have been bought, not by conspirators aligned against us but by the public who may very well be for us—not out of a desire to oust management but as an expression of confidence in it! The recent buying, in other words, might be the normal effort to take advantage of a depressed price to make a good investment. We should keep in mind that a lot of people own stock in *The San Francisco Day*—have owned it for a long time. They've always supported our Chairman's policies; it would be stupid and wrong to jump to the idea that they've suddenly changed their minds. If we did that we'd be doing exactly what Wilkins and Shimenko—granting they're the real opposition, and not just a front or façade—want us to do. If even a reasonable percentage of the shareowners vote the way they've voted in the past, *The Day* is safe and the interests of Management are safe. What we ought to do, here and now, is figure how to make sure that they vote that way. Does that make any sense to you gentlemen or not?"

Anchylus swiveled around in his chair. "Thank you, George," he said. "I've been waiting for somebody to say that."

"Hear! Hear!" Matt Brody said.

Dan Winkler looked at him with surprise. To Winkler, Dudley's speech (though it had a hopeful, prissy logic in it) was just so much whistling in the dark. He shook his head, staring dismally at the carpet. "All right," he said, "it makes sense, if the next move makes sense. What's the next move? I believe that's what we'd all like to know."

"That's what we're coming to right now, Dan," Dudley said.

He turned to young Winterhalter. "Irving," he said, "will you take it from here?"

"With your permission, sir," young Winterhalter said, "I'd like Andy to do that. You gentlemen have all met Mr. Andrew Haskell. I happened to know Andy was in town, so I blasted him at his hotel and he very kindly canceled out of a plane to let me drag him over here tonight. Naturally, he has to be filled in on Day Pub, but I think if we give him a few minutes' listening time we'll get a notion whether or not the SOP we used for Amalgamated Wineries, which Andy handled for us, fits Day Pub. Gentlemen, Mr. Andrew W. Haskell."

"Thank you, Irv," Andrew Haskell said. "I would like to repeat, gentlemen, that as Irv says I have *not* been briefed on this. I'm talking simply off the top of my head."

He paused, looking around pleasantly. His voice had the accent of one associated with an Eastern prep school and an Ivy League college rather than a Chicago law firm. He was a big fellow with a narrow, ascetic face and the tall, bony body of an oarsman or a basketball player. In clothes and poise and condescension he was, Anchylus decided, one of the insiders—the wellborn ones, the policy-makers of the eastern side of the continent, the cities where San Francisco was regarded as a frontier town. He disliked Haskell on sight but couldn't help admiring him for the very qualities he found so irritating.

"As Irv has kindly mentioned," Haskell went on, "I've been in a couple of these things before. As a rule, I try to ask Management a bunch of questions. So I hope you'll bear with me, will you? At times these questions—well, they hurt a little, but it pays to ask them, just among ourselves, before shareowners get to asking them on the floor of a meeting. Get what I mean?"

"Quite so, quite so, Andy," Winterhalter declaimed heartily, glancing around for further support. No one else, however, said anything. Those present were fixedly regarding Haskell, waiting for him to go on.

"Can you give us an idea what sort of questions you mean?" Winterhalter cued helpfully.

"Well, yes, Irv, I think I can," Haskell said. "They're more or less routine. They pop up somewhere along the line in every proxy fight. What is the earnings history of the company? What relation does it have to dividends? How do you stand with your bank? Have you got a public-relations department and if so what releases has it put out that tell Management's side of the story? If there isn't any public-relations department, then we try to set one up. That's one of our functions. Also, circulars have to be written and advertising placed— sometimes a lot of it. Among local advertising agencies, I can suggest a splendid outfit of hard hitters—Minott, Grubb and Stash. They were with us in the Wineries Thing Irv mentioned. Tell the story. That's what it boils down to. You must realize the opposition will be doing it, so why not you? Seize on anything that could be used against you and correct it or, if it can't be corrected, explain it in a manner that will seem favorable. Once the literature is printed and mailed and the ads are out we send crews around the city and solicit proxies door to door. Not many raiding groups have the facilities or know-how to do that. That's where we have it on them."

He paused. Anchylus had his head lowered, glaring at him. Oakleigh Donovan hid his face, rubbing his cheek in his hand; Brody and Winkler, on the bellhops' bench, looked drugged; George Dudley fidgeted.

Public relations! Circulars! Advertising and door-to-door canvassing directed at people always credited with being your friends—people who had invested in you. It was strange talk for the ears of men representing an entrenched power, the might of a newspaper whose status had never been questioned. Strange indeed, but nothing to what came next.

"Now," Andrew Haskell went on, "let's glance at the personal ledger. I hope none of you will take this too much to heart, but if I may mix a metaphor it's well to leave no stone unturned. Skeletons in anybody's family closet? Has an employee on the executive level or, God forbid, gentlemen, a member of the Board ever been in jail? That question for Day Pub is hypothetical, of course; I use it merely for the purpose of an illustration. Expense accounts. Ah! Often some soreness there. Have they been out of line? Any European junkets, company limousines? Club dues paid by the company treasury? Has anyone been keeping a mistress? Best to check over all that sort of thing."

Andrew Haskell smiled modestly and lighted a cigarette. He seemed to be inviting questions from the floor.

"You understand, Andy," Winterhalter broke in, "time is of the essence. It's unfortunate. The annual meeting takes place Friday afternoon."

"So I understand," Haskell said, "but couldn't you hold an adjourned meeting?"

"What about that, George?" Donovan said, addressing Dudley.

The latter, surprised at having his opinion asked, said with no great amount of decisiveness, "Why . . . er . . . I should think that would be up to our chairman."

Dan Winkler was nodding. "The meeting should certainly be postponed, Anchylus," he said.

He spoke in a voice for Anchylus' ear alone, but not so low that Donovan failed to catch the remark.

"Anchylus," he said, "there's a quorum here, I believe. We could put through a motion of adjournment at once. I don't know what period of notification is stipulated in the charter, but—"

"Thirty days, Oakleigh," Dudley said. "That could be altered by a resolution of the Board and telegrams sent to all the stockholders."

Oakleigh took the cigar out of his mouth. He crossed to Anchylus' chair and leaned over it. "You have every reason," he said. "Good God, man, everyone will understand. We don't have to hinge it on the struggle for control. You've had a grievous personal loss. It's all the reason you need."

Anchylus lifted his head. "I will not postpone the meeting," he said in a loud, clear voice.

Donovan leaped to one side. Anchylus' sudden shout, as it amounted to, after his long silence, came like a clap of thunder. The six other men in the room stared at him nervously. He ignored five of them, addressing himself to Haskell.

"I wish to thank you, my dear sir, for your suggestions. I also wish to inform you that we're not grafters on *The Day*, we're not taking bribes or running a whorehouse or any of the other activities you were courteous enough to bring up—"

"Take it easy, boss," Matt Brody said.

Dan leaned forward to put a hand on his arm. Anchylus, however, stopped only long enough to blow his nose. Then he went on. "Mr. Haskell," he said, "I believe that's your name, you were very kind to come over here and give us the benefit of your experience. I'm sorry we can't use it. We're not a winery or any similar enterprise; we're getting out a newspaper. I'm confident that we'll continue to get it out without publicity agents or canvassers or advertising. That happens to be just what the schemers and plotters who want to grab my company expect me to do. Time is what they need, gentlemen; they're the ones who want the campaign, they're the ones who need the advertising gimmicks. I don't. I'm going to make them win their battle by Friday, ten A.M. If they can't win it by then I'm going to make them lose it for keeps. I've got a few ideas myself on how to proceed. I'm low, gentlemen; I lost my wife the other day, it's true, and as a result of that I'm lower than a bull's ass in heelfly time. However, I'm going to win this fight if it's the last thing I do. Angela," he wound up, wheeling on Miss Wilke and addressing her by her Christian name for the first time that anybody could remember, "you can go home now. Matt and Dan, I'd like to talk to you upstairs. And now, if the rest of you will excuse me, I'll declare this meeting at an end."

5 MIDNIGHT. The carillon of Grace Cathedral struck its hour chime, then sounded twelve. The slightly flawed but pleasant notes spun through the air from the hill above the city and spread out, wavelike, into a slow, metallic silence. Thus the big G bell (called by theologians the "St. Paul Bell") would, on Saturday, deliver its heavy beat, fifty clangs, one for each year of the life of Jessica Saxe, according to the Episcopal custom.

Anchylus listened. He shivered, trying to think of Jessica being lowered into the ground. Jessica nailed up in a box! A bundle of bones, this incredible thing that had been a living, breathing woman. Jessica, dead, who had walked up the dark street ahead of him, holding her father's arm while he came after with the pistol in his pocket. Jessica, the light-footed, the long strider, proud and wary and generous, who had said when the call came through from Oregon, "We must get her at once. . . ."

He could understand about the daughters but not about his wife. No use coming back and back to that thought. Leave it be. It would get to him soon enough. Not having it in him might be a good thing now. He knew that Matt and Dan, good friends though they were, hadn't approved him. They'd gone away annoyed, thinking ill of what he'd done even though, at the last moment, the meeting had reached a compromise plan of action. Together they'd sketched out an advertisement—mild enough in all conscience—pointing out to stockholders that a "fly-by-night outfit" was trying to seize control of *The Day*, and warning them to be on their guard.

He'd lost his temper. That was always bad. After all, he'd called the conference. The men there had been trying to help. He shouldn't have shut them up and turned them out. Not that it mattered too much where Oakleigh Donovan and George Dudley were concerned: they were used to him. But young Winterhalter had looked at him as if he thought he'd gone crazy. Maybe he had, almost, for a minute or two—but that fellow Haskell! God, what a fool! He could never stand the type, superior and plausible. If his own plight was so desperate that he had to have pleaders like Haskell around him and the scavengers from advertising and allied fields that Haskell had wanted to bring in, then the jig was up. He might as well telephone that fellow Garber and tell him to come over and wrap up *The Day* and take it home.

Pipe in mouth, he undressed, put on pajamas, slippers and a bathrobe. Maybe, he thought, he'd read for a while. He studied the books in the little shelves on each side of the coal grate: most of them were Jessica's—a leatherbound volume by Thomas Love Peacock; was it the one she'd quoted from that day at the Exposition? He put up his hand to take down the book, then drew it back because he'd heard, far away in the still house, the ringing of the front-door bell, an eerie sound at this hour. He went out quickly to the head of the stairs, then down to the landing. He had intended to answer the door himself if Reuben hadn't heard, but Reuben was there, also in night clothes, letting in Hugo French, who looked up at once and saw him peering down.

"Am I disturbing you, Anchylus?" he called up in his clear doctor voice, and Anchylus said, "For Christ's sake, Hugo, of course you are. I was sound asleep, God damn it. What do you want?"

"You were *not* asleep," Hugo said calmly, handing his hat and coat to Reuben. "I saw a light in your bedroom. I was passing and I wondered if you were all right."

He went up to the landing and shook hands.

"Naturally I'm all right," Anchylus said testily. "I'll buy you one drink, but only one. Come on up."

He led the way to his room, the route his companion had taken so often when Jessica lay ill there. Here Hugo sat down at once in the best chair and said, "I came once before to see you but you weren't home. I wanted to tell you how heartsick I was about Jessica —but then words seem worse than inadequate. I think you know how I felt."

Words only seem inadequate, Anchylus thought, when you throw them around like buckshot.

"That's all right, Hugo," he said.

"What I particularly regretted," Hugo went on with great precision, "was our meeting in the hospital. I'd had no intention of imparting the news to you in that fashion. It was . . . unfortunate. Actually, I'm sure Dr. Immelman felt the same way. He's a fine chap and a magnificent surgeon. If anyone could have saved her, Anchylus, it would have been he."

"So you said at the time," Anchylus said shortly.

Hugo shook his handsome head in a restrained, stricken way. "It was one of those completely unpredictable situations," he said.

"Hugo," Anchylus said, "I'd rather not talk about it."

The victim of the road accident, he thought, shouldn't have to give first aid to the ambulance driver. Suddenly be became conscious that two of Hugo's fingers had fallen on his wrist. They remained there, accurately propped against the vein, while his eyes held the sweep second hand of his own wristwatch.

"Do you realize it's been four years since you've been in for a checkup?"

"I haven't needed one," Anchylus said.

The doctor put his watch away. He took a sphygmomanometer out of his pocket and slipped the cords around Anchylus' arm.

"I hope you're having a good time," Anchylus said.

"This is something you should have done at regular intervals," Hugo French said. He pumped the bulb, releasing the compression slowly as he studied the meter.

"If there's one thing I can't stand," Anchylus said, "it's a stupid, nosy sawbones, using his profession as a means of jamming his way into a man's house."

"But not, apparently, into his confidence," Hugo said.

"How high is it?" Anchylus asked.

"Too high," Hugo said, "but no higher than it's been for the last eleven years."

He retracted Anchylus' right eyelid. From somewhere in the folds of his clothing, which seemed to have more pockets than a magician's frock coat, an ophthalmoscope had appeared. With its help Dr. French examined the conjunctiva and the distension of the eyeball's flood vessels.

"Without your bedside manner and your wife's dinner parties you'd still be checking compensation cases for the Matson Line," Anchylus said. "Did you ever stop to think of that, Hugo?"

"Often, old boy," Hugo said. "Stretch out on the bed and slip off the top of your pajamas."

"I'm sorry I let you in," Anchylus said. "I take back that offer of a highball."

"Breathe deeply," Hugo said. He pressed the stiff rubber ear of the stethoscope to Anchylus' chest below the left nipple, then moved it an inch or so toward the sternum. After listening for a moment he moved around to check the lungs. "Cough," he said.

"I feel great," Anchylus said, "so don't start telling me I'm developing a fatal disease. I won't believe you."

Hugo French put the stethoscope away. "For your age," he said, "and the type of life you've lived, you're in remarkably good health. If you'll listen to a word of advice, though I suppose you won't, I would suggest your taking it a little easy. I know there's no use pulling punches with you, so I'll put it this way: you've sustained a massive emotional shock. I consider it a great misfortune that this stock fracas should hit you before you've had time to adjust to that shock."

"What the hell fracas are you talking about?"

"You forget," Hugo French said, "that I take care of George Dudley and I see him almost every day. We're all old friends, Anchylus. It was quite natural that he should tell me you're going into a proxy battle for *The Day*—just as I believe it's natural, and indicated, for me to tell you to spare yourself all you can. I'd much prefer to see you go away for a while and rest, let the chips fall where they may."

"Oh, that's what you'd prefer, is it?" Anchylus said. "You know, Hugo, you mean well, but you're the most irritating son of a bitch I know. If I took your advice, or anybody else's, on how to run my business, I'd have been bankrupt thirty years ago."

Dr. French sat looking at his patient grimly, or perhaps just wearily —but wearily enough for his professional tact and personal good will to have worn thin.

"We all go bankrupt in the end, one way or another," he said. "The thing to do is to put it off as long as possible in the only way that counts, the physical way. That is, unless you figure on the soul. And Osler said, as I recall, that he'd dissected a great many human bodies without ever finding just where the soul fitted in."

"Well, it fits in someplace," Anchylus said angrily. He hadn't planned to make this statement, but now that he had made it he felt that it was true. "It fits in, all right, though I don't expect a sawbones would know that much."

"I hope it does," Hugo French said, "but for the purposes of this emergency I wouldn't rely on it entirely. That's perhaps all I meant to say."

"Don't worry. I'm not relying on it," Anchylus said, "or on you either. I'm relying on myself, the way I always have. It was kind of you to come in and all that, but if I give you a nip it's got to be a quick one because I'm getting damned sleepy. And I haven't any ice up here."

"I don't need ice, old boy," Dr. French said. "A small straight Scotch would be just fine. For old times' sake."

"For old times' sake, then," Anchylus said. He went to the wall cabinet to get the bottle and glasses.

Grace Cathedral's chime struck one. Anchylus knew what he was going to do. When, two days previously, he had gone to the place called the Repository he had done so in obedience to a certain need. Ever since then the pressure had grown in intensity until he knew that if he didn't get release from it he couldn't think straight or even sleep. Somehow the nip of whisky he had taken with the doctor—which would ordinarily have made him drowsy—had caused all inclination toward sleep to vanish. He dressed quickly, putting on the clothes he had taken off an hour earlier. Then he called a cab. He gave the driver the address of the Appleton Brothers Mortuary.

6 INDIRECT LIGHTING of a delicate, rosy hue lighted up the entrance of Appleton Brothers. The façade was colonial, large white pillars framing a cream-colored door between two clipped potted cypresses. On the right of the door a well-polished brass plate bore the legend NIGHT BELL.

Anchylus pressed the bell. He stood staring sullenly at the door. It was impossible to him that Jessica, even the reduced version which was all that now existed on earth, could have lodgement in such a place—a commercial lying sort of place, smugly hypocritical. He should have come before. He should have done something about it. But what? He struggled with this problem; he was so immersed in it that he was not aware when the door first opened. Suddenly he found himself face to face with a pale, wavy-haired young man of about college age, slender and graceful in build, wearing a black suit and tie and a white, button-down shirt.

"Can I help you, sir?" the young man inquired.

Anchylus merely grunted. He resented the young man's tone—a polite, self-effacing tone, actually, yet one which assumed that he himself, demanding entrance, had no business here. No business in the house which now contained Jessica! He walked past the young man into the hall beyond.

"I'm Anchylus Saxe," he said. "I came to see my wife."

"Just a moment, please, sir," the young man said.

He turned to consult a large letterboard which flanked the hall. Twin angels supported the board on which, in removable letters, was printed a list of names and dispositions. The dispositions fell under two headings—Chapels and Slumber Rooms—the chapels being numbered from one to five and the slumber rooms from one to ten. Evidently a considerable population of the dead was housed in this building, their type of accommodation being determined by some law known only to the management. Well down on the slumber room category was the name Saxe, Mrs. Anchylus, and the number 6.

"This way, please, sir," the blond young man said.

He led the way down a hallway illuminated in the same discreet, soft light as the building's façade, past a double row of half-open doors. None of the doors in Appleton Brothers were fully open, but, on the other hand, none were fully closed: a compromise between these two states seemed to be the one desired, as if to provide access to those within without loss of privacy on their part. Subdued organ music filtered through the hall—a phenomenon which impressed Anchylus even though he realized the music came from a record. There was also a smell of flowers in the air, though no flowers were visible, and under it, or combined with it, another smell, so faint it resembled an illusion, yet stubbornly perceptible, ancient, dark, remote and unmistakable—the smell of the dead.

"Number six, sir," the young man said. He had stopped beside one of the half-open doors to which, deferentially, he gave a slight push. Anchylus stepped inside. There was a lectern near the door and on the lectern a blankbook about the size of a school exercise book. This book bore the name *Jessica Rupke Saxe*. Under the name, traced in a stencil made to look like handwriting, was the subhead *Friends Who Called*.

Anchylus opened the book. Nothing had been written in it, though a freshly sharpened pencil, held in a clip beside it, made writing easy. Anchylus took the pencil and wrote his name in the book. While it seemed absurd to denominate himself as a "friend" he was under a strong impulsion to write something on the blank pages. He felt as if by this act he could keep Jessica, if she were really here, from seeming so alone. Also, here in Appleton Brothers, one felt the need of doing what was expected. The blond young man watched him sign the book, then turned and left, Anchylus moving forward toward a casket resting on a dais at the far end of the room. Masses of flowers flanked the casket and trailed over its top and sides in brilliant sprays and somber, brooding wreaths. Part of the great lid of the casket was hinged so that it could be raised without raising the rest of it, and this part was now propped open. Inside was the doll-like corpse of a middle-aged woman, frail and inert. The face of the corpse corresponded roughly to that of Jessica but its expression was utterly false; it had been so dissembled with wax and colored with cosmetics that any real identification was impossible. The woman had dyed black hair and a weak, retiring smile. A crucifix rested between her clasped hands. She didn't look in the least like a dead person but rather like a healthy person who, just as she was ready to go out for the evening, had been drugged into unconsciousness.

Anchylus sat down on a chair beside the casket. He felt a kind of relief: finding a stranger in the coffin freed him of the obligation to mourn. He could let his mind wander at will, recalling (as he'd hardly had an opportunity to do till now) the Jessica he'd actually known and loved. For a while, this train of thought proved satisfactory. Then the immediate worries centered on *The Day* intruded. He found himself communicating them to his wife, or at least to the image of her which lived in his mind.

"I guess it was Alexandra started it," he said; "Sharon would never have had the getup. Not that she isn't smart; I'd never call Sharon a dumb sort of girl. But she's never been the same since she married Brad. I should have stopped her."

"You tried, dear," Jessica said.

She spoke as she often had in the past, when they had been getting dressed to go out somewhere and he could hear her but not see her, the half-open door of his dressing room standing between them.

"Tried, yes," he said, "but trying was no good. I should have clamped down. I'd had him on the payroll, damn it all. I knew. Never was a good reporter, even if he could throw words around. She drove her ducks onto the wrong pond."

"It's absurd to fret about that now," Jessica said crisply. "Never inquire why somebody marries someone else. There is never any reason. Still, in this case I believe you're right—Alexandra must have been the one."

"Some hucksters got hold of her," Anchylus said. "They're using her. Penny-ante little bastards, trying to steal my paper. Oh, she's sore at me, I know that. Sore clean through, but I wouldn't fire poor old Letty just to suit her. Letty is a real newspaperwoman. She's always done her best."

"Perhaps you should have fired her, just the same, dear. It might have helped. Still, I'm puzzled that Sharon would side with her. Sharon is not vindictive. Now please don't go back to that Indian Pipe thing; that was certainly in bad taste, but it was not vindictive, she was not looking for revenge, and you weren't free of blame, dear, either. You must see that. You'd embarrassed her."

"Embarrassed her!" Anchylus burst out. "Jesus Christ, I love that. I spent thousands educating her and dressing her up and getting her married off and all of a sudden her own family isn't good enough for her. Let me tell you something, Jessie—"

"You can tell me nothing," Jessie said severely, "until you lower your voice. I will not be shouted at."

"All right, all right," Anchylus said, "but if I'm that embarrassing I wish I had the money back we threw away on her. It all went down the sewer, if you ask me."

"You are stubbornly refusing to see my point, Anchylus," Jessica said.

"Well, what the hell is it?"

"The characters of our three girls. Their contrasting natures."

Uncomfortable as he was on the hard mortuary chair, Anchylus' exhaustion had been getting the better of him. He snored lightly.

"Anchylus!"

His head snapped up. "Excuse me, dear."

"Did you hear anything I said?"

"Every damn word of it."

"You did not," Jessica said, "but I will not repeat. All I want you to keep in mind is that our daughters, with the possible exception of Pamela, are self-centered women. Self-centered and luxury-loving and a little spoiled. I'm forced to admit it, and I think it is my fault."

"Well, I don't know about that," Anchylus said quickly. He never liked Jessica to be blamed for anything—even if it was she who fixed the blame.

"It was, though," Jessica said. "I was the one who raised them to be such ladies. That may have been my mistake. Fabian set a great store by cultivation and I, as many people do, may have confused cultivation with manners. Sharon and Alexandra could have done with more of the first and less of the second; they were never quite ladies, not in the finest sense. However, since they are self-centered it must appear extraordinary that they find a cause to get together on, even a cause like this. I fail to believe that they'll co-operate with each other very long. They'll end looking at this in different ways—or they could be persuaded to without much trouble. Does this thought mean anything to you? Don't answer hastily; you're usually much too hasty. Think it over for a minute and then tell me."

Anchylus thought it over. He almost dipped into sleep again, but the thought was strong in him and after a short interval he raised his head. His eyes were shining under the hairy snouts of his eyebrows. He rubbed his cheek with his mashed knuckles.

"By God, Jessica," he said loudly, "that's it. Why didn't I think of it myself? You've got it. Yes, you have. You've hit the nail right on the head. Divide—and win. That's what you mean, isn't it?"

"I hope I didn't put it in those terms," Jessica said, "but at least you've got the general idea. I should hate to see anything happen to the paper, particularly if the girls brought it about. Nobody can run

The Day but you, dear, and I hope you run it for a long, long time."

Anchylus felt tears in his eyes. "I just don't know how I'll run it without you, Jessie. Sometimes I just don't know how I can go on."

"Of course you can go on," Jessica said with spirit. "All you ever got from me was companionship, not direction. And, mind you, if what I've said has put any notions in your head, please act discreetly. I can't bear another scandal. Will you promise to be careful, and not lose your temper?"

"I promise, Jessie," Anchylus said humbly.

The blond young nightman, who had not been long with Appleton's, stepped into the lab and bummed a cigarette from the technician working there.

"This job gives me the creeps," he said.

"What's wrong with it, boy?" the technician said. "You're getting paid, aren't you?"

"The people is what's wrong with it," the nightman said. "There's an old bastard in Slumber Room Six talking and jabbering to himself. He's been in there an hour. What will I do?"

"Think nothing of it, boy," the technician said. "Sometimes they put ashes on their heads and roll on the floor."

7 ANCHYLUS KNEW, in a hazy sort of way, that the conversation with Jessica had never actually taken place. During her lifetime he had formed the habit, when away from her, of chatting with her mentally. This habit had continued after her death—or at least in these days immediately following that event. The talk in the mortuary had fitted naturally into the category of such conversations, yet it had been of a deeper sort: whether the words and thoughts exchanged had welled up in his brain alone or had issued also from hers, he wasn't prepared to say. It didn't matter. Out of the chat with Jessica, whether unilateral or not, had come the notion of dividing Sharon and Alexandra in their plot to take the paper away from him: this was a sensible idea. Once it was put into effect, his course of action would be much simpler.

He already had a luncheon date with Sharon, scheduled for today; thus the means of approaching her was ready at hand. How to go about the job was, however, ticklish: one wrong move and she'd see what he was getting to and, most likely, turn him down. She could be a rough customer, as she'd proved in the past.

Anchylus gave thought to this problem on awakening that morning. He thought of it while he shaved and dressed and while driving to the office; once at his desk, other matters pushed it into the background, and with lunchtime approaching, still not having solved it, he decided to feel his way along. He would try to appraise her attitude and then, if he saw any chance of success, try to improvise the right approach.

He had ordered lunch sent down from the executive dining room. With an immediate bereavement in the family it would not be in good taste to lunch in a public place: also, the executive menu was very good and Malcolm, the waiter, adept at serving. By 12:45, the time appointed, a table for two had been set up, cocktails mixed, and the hot dish of the day was keeping warm in the servidor. Sharon looked very trim in a black fitted suit and a sable stole; she was polite but not, at first, too friendly—evidently on her guard against some appeal on his part.

She ate three eastern oysters with a frown as tight as the one she'd worn when she'd come to tell him about Indian Pipe.

"I can't understand," she said, "why you've put off Mother's funeral almost a week. It's, well, excuse my saying so, Father, but it's barbarous."

"Why?" Anchylus asked.

"Because a person should be buried right away."

"Your mother will be laid to rest in the proper manner," Anchylus said stiffly. "I'm seeing to that. She would want her friends to be there. Many of them haven't come in from the country. They need a day or two to make their plans."

"I don't like it," Sharon said, "and then, all this *business*. While she's—I mean, before she's even *buried*. That's indecent too. And shocking."

"Dragging the family into a proxy fight wasn't exactly my idea," he said.

Sharon let the waiter take her plate.

"I didn't say it was," she said, "but at a time like this! What will people say? I understand you've even refused to postpone the stockholders' meeting."

"I certainly have," Anchylus said.

Malcolm served chicken gumbo in Staffordshire cups. When he had left the room Sharon said, "I think that's ridiculous."

"I don't know," Anchylus said. "I just don't know what we're coming to. Worked for forty years to put this paper on the map—and now, by God, a shyster writes in and says it isn't mine any more. How would you answer a letter like that, Daughter? What would you do in my shoes?"

Sharon looked at him with frank surprise. "Was that really what it said?"

The surprise related to the content, not to the existence of the letter. She knew about it, probably had known even before it was written. This was the time to make his move.

"What's Zan up to, Daughter? You going to stand by and see her stab me in the back?"

Sharon evaluated his question calmly. "I don't think anyone is stabbing anybody," she said. "Certainly not Zan. I believe she does want certain things to be different; she seems to have talked to some people and—well, I suppose she's gotten some advice."

"Stinking advice, if you ask me."

Sharon took a sip of *vin rosé*. "That remains to be seen, Father," she said. "After all, would it be so awful to have some new people on the Board? You've had it all to yourself for a long, long time."

Anger rose in Anchylus. He fought it back. "Well, now, baby, that might be true. Yes, I suppose you might have something there."

Choosing his words carefully, he forced onto his large face a wheedling, temporizing leer so palpably false it gave him a maniacal expression. "You might be surprised," he said, "how quick I could agree with you. If *other matters* were straightened out. I'm not as young as I used to be, you know. What would you say if I told you I might go a hell of a way with thinking of that kind? Stockholders should be heard. They should, by God. I'm tired of slaving. I might—mind you, I'm only saying I *might*, that would depend on circumstances—I might consider putting my own stock on the auction block with yours, if I could get real newspaper people in here."

"Do you honestly mean that, Father?"

"And how I mean it! Maybe there's no fool like an old fool, as the fellow said. But I've been thinking. Could be I haven't kept up with the times a hundred per cent. Could be some new blood would help out, people with savvy, even—" he gasped, forcing himself, in agony, to bring out this sacrilege—"even *chain* people."

Sharon wiped her mouth carefully. It was clear that he deserved attention, though none of this sounded right.

"You mean," she said with hesitation, "you would consider *stepping out?*"

"Now, now, don't let's go too fast. Not *out*. No, I wouldn't say that. But I'd go a long way to meet the *right bunch*. You want to know what has got under my skin worst of all about this whole mess? Hurt me worst of all, you might say?" He bent toward her, breathing hard in his determination to make this sound pitiful. "Well, it's this—you putting in with Alexandra. You, a daughter who knows newspapering! Married to a newspaperman yourself. These people are burglars—two-bit bandits trying to get their paws into the kitty. They've got Zan bamboozled. And you know why she let it happen? Because she hates Letty Meeker. So help me!" he added earnestly. "She's willful; nothing ever fazes her. Now isn't that an awful reason to break up a corporation and make mock of a family's love, just to get one old lady reporter fired from her job?"

Malcolm served small apple turnovers. Neither father nor daughter spoke until he had left the room once more.

"I hardly think that's all that Alexandra wants," Sharon said.

Anchylus snorted. "Don't let her fool you. I suppose she's talking about dividends and so forth. Alexandra! Can you imagine it? She never gave a flying frig about money and she never knew anything about it, either. If she burned every share of *Day* stock we put in trust for her she'd still have enough. Letty's head is what she wants, only she isn't going to get it. I'm not just about to fire a reporter to suit a beautiful, obstinate slut like Zan. I hate to use the term, but it applies —you know it does—even if she is my daughter. Could you find something out for me?"

"I could try," Sharon said. Stirrings of a new idea were now making themselves felt in her own nerves, as her father had been hoping they would.

"Then, listen," Anchylus said, "and get this. Once a long time ago Hurd-Hudner put out feelers. Wanted to know if *The Day* was for sale. Well, it wasn't—at that time. I'm not saying it is now. But, could you find out if they're still interested? Would Brad put his ear to the ground?"

Sharon avoided his eyes. She busied herself pouring out the coffee. "And if they're interested," she said, "what then?"

"Well, then—this is confidential, you understand."

"Of course, Father." Her fingers, holding the coffee spoon, were trembling very slightly.

"Then," Anchylus said, "you can tell them from me. Tell them a deal could be worked out. I'll show you what I mean."

Sharon left the Day Building an hour later, walking fast. In her purse was a memorandum slip with certain figures jotted down— figures on circulation, street sales, advertising, liquid assets and a welter of other things she didn't understand, although the gist of them was clear, namely, that *The Day* was far from moribund, or even infirm, but that it was, on the contrary, a superb newspaper and (barring one or two minor and of course, temporary setbacks) a financial prize of the first order. And this prize, this package bursting with great possibilities, wrapped in the glory of an historic past, might be disposed of under the table, in utter confidence, to the proper, carefully chosen recipients and providing, of course, that the necessary although reasonable and advisable conditions of sale were met: Anchylus' conditions, naturally, the chosen recipient of all this being, also quite naturally, Hurd-Hudner.

It had all been logical when he explained it. Now, though hardly any time had passed, it was becoming vague. The trouble was she didn't know enough about business: she could sense the handling of situations involving people, as she'd often proved for Brad's benefit, but the cold arithmetic of operations, mergers and so forth was out of her field. Never mind. Clearly there was a chance here to do something highly important, bring two titanic interests into alignment, and grow mightily in stature thereby.

She, the go-between in such a deal as this. It was a little dizzying, but why not? Who else was available? And even if somebody else had been available, why shouldn't Anchylus properly have turned to her, his own flesh and blood, regardless of any misunderstandings which might have existed in the past? He couldn't very well broadcast the information he had given her, the information nobody else had, namely, that he wanted to retire. Alexandra would give a pretty penny to know that. But why should she know it? Anchylus had his reasons for opposing Alexandra while at the same time leaving himself open to an offer from Hurd-Hudner: very good reasons, too. And what about her, Sharon? Why shouldn't she act on all this, try to see what she could do? The only possible objection was the promise she'd given Alexandra, and that was ridiculous. A promise wouldn't bind if it was forced on you, and Sharon could see now she'd been forced. Even that handshake across the breakfast table had been like a child's game: cross-my-heart-and-hope-to-die if I don't choose you first on my side.

This was one time Alexandra wouldn't get chosen first. The first choice, as always, had to be Brad: clearly it was her duty as a wife to get in touch with him as soon as possible and tell him what was in the wind.

8 THE OPERATOR REPORTED a fifteen-minute delay in obtaining a circuit. She said she would call back. Sharon begged her anxiously to call as soon as possible. It now seemed a matter of the greatest urgency to reach Brad immediately.

Waiting for the call, she lighted a cigarette and walked up and down in her hotel suite as if picketing the telephone for an unfair practice. If only Brad were at home! He should be: with the three-hour difference in time it would be almost seven in Washington. She knew his habits. Unless something unusual were afoot he would still be dressing for dinner. Or he might be sitting in a bathrobe, a towel wrapped around his pink, delicately padded torso, making his evening telephone calls, a preliminary cocktail frosting at his elbow.

Dear Brad! She could almost hear his nasal, rather drawling way of answering calls that came in on the private line after all the secretaries had left. "Iverson speaking."

She was, she realized, still anxious to make their marriage work—though she was by no means now the hopeless thrall to him she'd been when they first separated. It annoyed her, and hurt in some vague way as much as it annoyed, when people hinted that they'd heard, as of course they had, the news that was getting around. "He's such a wonderful guy," they said, pleading for him with the facile sponsorship adjunctive to lost causes.

"But of course!" she would answer, stoutly loyal, flashing the smile true and steadfast as if to tell them the cause wasn't lost after all.

The hell Brad was a wonderful guy. He was a horrible guy, career driven, self-important, clever in petty ways, mean in big ones, a climber, a sycophant (when it could serve him), a tyrant (when chance presented) and in addition to all this probably a faithless husband as well. She couldn't imagine him living the life of an anchorite in the relaxed sexual atmosphere of Washington. All he'd had in the way of marital life (and all she'd had) in the last eighteen months had been three hurried visits on his part to San Francisco, two for business and one at Christmas, and a few brief periods when she'd joined him in Washington to help him with some parties. It had been scant comfort to discover she was still an asset to his dinner table when her importance was so negligible in his bed.

The ring of the telephone startled her. She took a long, firm breath before lifting the receiver.

"I've reached Mr. Iverson's residence, Mrs. Iverson," the operator said. "He's not there now but they have a number where he can be reached. Do you wish me to try him at the other number?"

"Yes, yes, I do," Sharon said. "Please keep on trying, Operator." She squashed out her cigarette and resumed pacing.

What was the use of lying? She was more than fond of Brad. Much more, even though their last illusions about each other had slipped long ago (like clods loosened by their kicking feet) over the precipice which might soon engulf their whole relationship. She knew exactly what he was, but he was hers, she was committed; she had to have him back, no matter what. And what better way to do this than the way Anchylus, with his tricky, smart approach at lunch, had dangled in front of her eyes?

Anchylus was in a tough position. She didn't blame him for trying what he could. He'd said a number of things that made sense: that about her willingness to go along with Alexandra.

Why, she'd been idiotic! She'd been like a child. Naturally, Alexandra had a purpose to accomplish, and a selfish purpose: she always did. Meanwhile she, Sharon, got nothing out of the deal at all except maybe a few extra dollars, which she didn't need.

"San Francisco calling the Massachusetts Marine Operator. Person to person for Mr. Bradley Iverson on the yacht *Sabrina* . . ."

Sharon grimaced. It was exactly like Brad to be off on a yacht somewhere while she'd pictured him slaving away in Washington. Her latter concept had at least the support of documentation, since she had at hand a telegram, received from him the day before, expressing his regret at being unable, due to press of work, to fly to San Francisco for her mother's funeral. Not that the discrepancy of being reached, now, through the Massachusetts Marine Operator would bother him in the slightest degree. He'd have an explanation, if he bothered with one at all: his labors had been so intense that, to facilitate them, and at the same time to ensure the privacy that they demanded, he'd had recourse to a floating conference room.

Bleep bleep. The operator had finally reached someone on the yacht. Sharon heard her saying, off the mouthpiece, "Yes, we are paid." Then came a silence full of static not unlike a ship's creak at her moorings—though of course it must be due to something else.

The operator came on again. "They're trying to locate Mr. Iverson," she said.

"All right," Sharon said. "I'm holding on."

She found it was a little hard to breathe. Quite suddenly she realized that of all the many calls she'd made to Brad, and he to her, these last months, this was the most important. Possibly it was the most important that either of them had ever made to the other. With this call she was bringing him a gift, rare and unduplicable. Not the gift of herself. That had been brought a long time ago and was no longer of much trading value. She was bringing a newspaper, a gift he might want because it was business and he might see a way to make use of it. A gift which, if offering it, would make her for a moment, at least, the old Sharon, the one who had helped, whom he had relied on and of whom he had sometimes said, clowning, of course, but meaning it, in a way, "I owe everything to my wife."

Never again would she be able to offer him so beguiling, so restorative a present. If he accepted, that might mean the beginning of a new order, or at least the revival of one still dear to her, whatever it was to him. And if he rejected it, then that rejection too would have a meaning—perhaps a most decisive one.

"Iverson speaking."

"Are you Mr. Bradley Iverson?" the operator cut in, at which Sharon burst out with a sudden loss of patience, so disturbing it was to her to hear his voice and, with it, face the reality of this moment of truth, "Yes, all right, operator, I'll talk now. . . . Brad, how are you, dear?"

"Why, fine, fine," Brad said matter-of-factly. "How are you, kiddo? Feeling any better?"

It took her a second to co-ordinate this query with her own upset condition when she'd called to tell him about her mother's death. "Why, yes, dear," she said, "a little better. The funeral isn't Wednesday, as they'd planned. It's been put off till Saturday."

"I see," Brad said. "Well, as I said in my wire, Shar, I'm heartbroken at not getting out. But—you know. Some big stuff is breaking, and . . . upshot of it was a few of us flew over to Herb Linnet's yacht here, to work on the over-all picture. If there was any possible chance of my making it I'd—"

"That's all right, Brad. I'm sorry, but I understood, of course."

"I knew you would," he said heartily; "I've sent a most appropriate wreath in both our names, a very large one."

"Thank you, dear. That was most thoughtful of you," Sharon said.

The sound of what might have been a feminine voice, somewhere in Brad's vicinity, made Sharon wonder whether some native girls had canoed out to the *Sabrina* as it passed Marblehead. Or did the over-all picture involve bringing women from Washington? She experienced a hot surge of jealousy—a stupid emotion in view of the present situation. What must be corrected, with as little delay as possible, was Brad's apparent conclusion that she'd called him to urge his attendance at the services.

276

"I know you can't be here, much as you want to," she said. "I'm calling about something else. I had lunch with Father today. He's very much upset."

"Well, naturally, Shar," Brad said in a soothing tone. "After more than thirty years of marriage you can't expect a man to—"

"I don't *mean* about Mother," Sharon said firmly; "he's upset about that too, of course. But there's also another situation. One that involves *The Day*."

"Oh?" Brad said politely. He didn't sound as interested as she'd hoped he'd be when she mentioned *The Day*.

"I meant to write you about it," she said, "but I haven't had time. It's a situation about the stock. It seems he didn't hold as much as we all thought and there may be some battle for control. The meeting's on Friday, you know."

"What meeting?" Brad asked.

"The stockholders' meeting," Sharon said. "I don't want to go into the whole thing. I'm not even sure that I understand it. But the point is, as I said, I had lunch with him today and he asked me was there still any chance—now, this is the important part, Brad—was there still any chance Hurd-Hudner was interested? You know what I mean?"

"I'm sorry, kiddo," Brad said. "I wish I did. I wish you'd be a little more specific about this, Shar; I just don't know what the heck you're talking about, and there's a racket going on here. Why don't you just write me a letter about it?"

"I'm being as specific as I can, Brad," Sharon said, "and I haven't got time to write. This can be quite important. I wish you'd try to understand. Anchy wants to know if Hurd-Hudner wants to buy *The Day*. They did once, you know. I had lunch with him and that was what he asked. He wanted to know if you could find out."

Sharon could tell, by the different feeling of Brad's silence, that he was definitely paying attention now.

"Hmmm," he said.

"What, dear?" Sharon said.

"I didn't say anything," Brad said; "I'm trying to get the picture. You sort of caught me with my pants down."

Sharon wondered as to the proportions in which, in this familiar figure of speech, reality supplanted metaphor.

"Well, dear?" she said.

"Well, yes," he said, "I guess I can find out. But—what's the next angle? If they should be interested, what does he want to do?"

"He hasn't said right out," Sharon said. "You know how he is—he makes you think he's telling you everything while he's telling you nothing. I went back to the office after lunch and he showed me a lot of figures, mostly about voting in the stock and who he thinks might win. But there doesn't seem much doubt that if my stock and Pamela's and his is all voted the same way he could make it easy—that was the word he used—for another company to buy him out."

"Do you mean he'd sell out?" Brad asked.

"I think so," Sharon said; "perhaps not completely. He said there would be conditions, and he showed me a lot of figures that I didn't understand. But the main thing was, if he is going to get kicked out, he wants a real newspaper outfit in there. And he has no objection to a chain."

"Did he mention H-H specifically?"

"Yes, he did."

"That's sure a switch. Hurd-Hudner used to be a four-letter word to him."

"Two four-letter words, hyphenated," Sharon said, "but he's changed; there's no doubt of that at all. So, as I say, I thought I'd pass the idea along. You're free," she added, with some chilling of tone, "to do whatever you like about it."

"Well, kiddo," Brad said, "don't get jumpy now. This could be interesting. I just don't know. I could speak to Harold Hudner. He's supposed to be up here tonight or tomorrow. He's got a Snipe in the regatta."

"A what?"

"A Snipe. It's a kind of boat."

Once more a distracting noise—this time a laugh, unmistakably female—sifted through the instrument at Brad's end.

"What was that," Sharon asked, "one of the snipe giving its mating call?"

"I don't know what you mean, Shar," Brad said.

"Well, never mind; I suppose you have all sorts of things to do."

"Nothing but work, kiddo," Brad said. "We're really pounding. Wish you were here, though. You'd enjoy the races. Those little babies really go."

"What babies?"

"The boats, the boats," Brad said.

"I'm sure," Sharon said. "When will you know about Harold? Do you want to call me back, or don't you think it's worth a call?"

"Now take it easy, Shar," Brad said; "you know it's worth a call. I'll get back to you as soon as I can. Maybe around this time tomorrow night. Okay?"

"Okay," Sharon said. "Don't forget. And have a good time, dear."

"Look, Shar," Brad said, "I wish you wouldn't talk that way. I'm in the middle of some darned important meetings. *And* phoning out two thousand words per diem on the old ship-to-shore. If you think that's a vacation, you're mistaken."

"I'm sorry," Sharon said. "I didn't mean it to sound suspicious." Sharon felt genuinely repentant. Always, after the slightest temper flare-up on her part, she backed down—from force of habit, or as if she could still keep from losing him. As if he were not, already, virtually lost.

"It's been nice talking to you, Brad," she finished.

"It's been swell," Brad said, "and I'll get back to you as soon as I have some word. 'Bye, now."

"Goodbye, Brad," Sharon said.

She heard the ship-to-shore bleep out as he closed the connection. Then she hung up. She pushed both hands against her temples, the fingers gripping her head under the piled, short, crisply curled black hair—hair like her mother's but not dyed as Jessica's had been, hair that still, at thirty, had no trace of gray in it. She didn't know when she had felt so angry and, at the same time, so hopeless. She had been excited about her news, convinced, in spite of all misgivings, that Brad would be excited too—and he had talked to her as if she'd been a child! He could have pretended a little interest, even if he didn't feel it: at least she'd taken the trouble to call him, she'd been telling him by implication that she'd missed him, that she'd been thinking of him, whereas he had been having a ball on somebody's yacht!

And with women aboard.

She raised her head. Her eyes flashed. "Just let him deny it," she said aloud. She got up and walked to the window, then came back and stood beside the bed. Tears shoved out of her eyes and ran down her cheeks. With a sob she threw herself across the bed, laying her face against the rough spread. It was time she stopped being such a pushover. She had tried, she had waited, she had hoped. All her life she'd wanted only one thing—a person to love and admire and look up to and serve. First it had been Alexandra. That feeling had never quite worn off, as proved by Alexandra's capacity even now to make her see *her* side of things; but with marriage Alexandra's influence had lessened, Brad's had wonderfully taken its place.

Sharon couldn't explain to herself why, even in childhood, her parents had never had the status in her eyes which first a sister, then a husband had so successfully filled. It had seemed as if their love had been spread too thin, at least after the coming of Pamela, to inspire the proper response in her. Perhaps they had been too much concerned with other things—her father with business, her mother with her entertainments, church activities, the responsibility of running a big household. Not that love had been absent. It had been there, parentally, only it hadn't shown itself in just the right way. The time had never come for it, or had come and passed by in the rush of the years. Then at the last, in the terrible finality of Jessica's illness and its termination, in the unstoppable time machine of her final moments on earth, that love had flickered up again.

That last morning Sharon had gotten up early and gone to the hospital at once. She'd been intending to go later; she knew they didn't like visitors at St. Ann's before the regular visiting hours but she'd felt compulsively that she must be there, that Jessica needed her. Like Anchylus, she'd bypassed the admitting office with its rigmarole about passes; she'd gone straight to her mother's floor and seen, as she came out of the elevator, a wheel-stretcher. She'd had no way of knowing positively that Jessica was on the stretcher but she had run toward it, reached it just as it arrived at the smaller, special elevator, the one at the far end of the floor that was used only for surgical patients. The patient on the stretcher had been Jessica, sure enough. They'd given her a shot of something, but she had remained conscious, lying there quietly with her eyes turned toward the running, tip-tapping feet.

Sharon had taken her mother by the hand. She'd felt Jessica's hand squeeze hers and she'd ridden up in the elevator with her, squeezed in beside the stretcher. During the course of the ride, short as it was, Jessica had fallen asleep. Sharon had tried to go into surgery with her: she'd been quite angry when the people in charge wouldn't let her.

Dr. French had sent a nurse downstairs to find a place for her to wait. From the window she had seen Letty Meeker arrive and she had seen her father drive into the court in his blue car and enter through a side door with Matt Brody. Sharon hadn't wanted to speak to any of them. She knew they were coming because Jessica would never wake up again, but at least she herself would always have the memory of that elevator ride when Jessica had held onto her hand.

She had waited in the room until Dr. French and another doctor had come down and told her what had happened. Not that they'd had to tell her. She'd known it was going to from the moment she felt Jessica's grip slack off. Until that moment the love which had never come through in just the right way before had been there, strong and hopeful, as if there had been a whole lifetime for it to expand in, instead of a few seconds, but after that it had been run over by the machine that was running over Jessica. No love, even one which had never given up, could survive when the machine was through with somebody.

Dr. French had offered to drive her home but she had told him that would not be necessary. The admitting office had called a cab for her and she had ridden back to the hotel.

9 SHE COULDN'T EXPLAIN why she had changed from resentful thoughts about Brad to a sorrowful reverie about her mother. Perhaps the sorrow itself, the need to escape it, had been why she'd built such high hopes around the telephone call. The pressure of the sorrow had been present also during her lunch with Anchylus. It was what had made her take him to task for putting off the funeral, even though she understood his reasons for doing it. She had really been angry about this, angrier than she had allowed herself to seem, and in upbraiding him for this had been expressing her reaction to another source of annoyance as well, her indignation that he, who was to blame (as she saw it) for everything that had gone wrong with the family, should officiate over the sorrow as he had officiated so long and so undeservedly over all other family matters. She resented him as a mourner just as she had resented him as a father, but she couldn't, she knew, cast him off in the same way.

The sorrow was in all of them these days, yet it was making them behave in curious ways. Instead of softening them, as sorrow was supposed to do, it was building up tensions; instead of bringing them together it was making them fly at one another's throats. It was embarrassing, this squalling beside an open grave, yet there it was—a fact you had to face.

She pitied them all. They were in it now and there wasn't any way of backing out. She even pitied Anchylus, just as she had pitied him when she'd told him to stay out of Indian Pipe and seen his fingers flopping on the desk like unhooked fish. That time, though, she'd gone ahead and done what she had to do and she would now too: she would look out for herself. If his suggestion about Hurd-Hudner was going to help him, that was all right too, but she hadn't acted on it for his sake; she'd acted on it for her own.

The only person whom she didn't pity was Brad. He had, as usual, refused to take her seriously. He'd been too boxed up in his own affairs to care about hers. He'd sounded completely indifferent.

All right. Fine. Let him enjoy himself on the good ship *Sabrina*; he wouldn't be indifferent long. She, for her part, was all through being half-rejected, neither single nor quite married, on her way to being a cast-off but still wearing the nominal privileges of a wife. It was ridiculous, and about time it ended, about time she got over the idea she was in love with him. She had plenty of grounds for divorce; he'd left her alone for weeks on end. Wasn't desertion considered grounds in any state? And she, Mrs. Meatball, turning down chances to go out, living alone, digging up harmless vegetable types to escort her to cocktail parties now and then, and even this with fear Brad would hear about it and be angry that she'd been out with another man while he—God!

"Just let him tell me," she thought, "that those women paddled out from Narragansett to trade coconuts."

She jumped off the bed. If it came down to men, she had the phone numbers of dozens of them, attractive ones too: she kept them in the red morocco book Jessica had given her one Christmas, alphabetically listed. Telephone numbers of single men came in handy if you wanted to give a party, the kind of party she and Brad had given so often on Floribunda Avenue. Never mind thinking about Floribunda Avenue now. This was no time for regrets. She went to the desk, pulling out the drawers, searching energetically for the book and finding it at last in plain sight, tucked into a corner of the blotter. She wondered, touching its gilt-edged pages, whom she would call and what excuse she could use—that she needed advice, that she besought consolation? It didn't matter. Possibly a drink would provide some notions. Dropping the book, she reached for the telephone to call room service, only to find as she lifted the receiver that the line was buzzing with an incoming call.

"Mrs. Bradley Iverson, please. Long distance calling."

"This is Mrs. Iverson," she said.

"All right, Operator," Brad's voice said. Then, "Kiddo? Listen, I got hold of Harold."

This statement didn't demand a reply. Sharon was content it didn't; her voice, she was afraid, wasn't under control—it never was when she was taken by surprise.

"Sharon?"

"Yes, darling."

"Did you hear me?"

"Of course, dear."

"What's the matter?"

282

"Well, I suppose I'm a little surprised, that's all. You said he wasn't coming until tomorrow."

Brad's snorting, satisfied chuckle interrupted her. "That's right," he said, "but I called the yacht club, just playing a long shot. He was just walking in the door."

"Why, how wonderful."

"I don't know if it was wonderful," Brad said incisively, "but he was there." He was evidently in excellent humor. "Look, Shar, he's interested. But definitely."

"You told him that—"

"Naturally I told him. And when I say he's interested, that's an understatement. He's hotter than a two-dollar pistol. There are some angles to this thing, kiddo, that even I didn't know about, and they go right along with the thinking you expressed. I'll tell you about them when I see you."

"When . . . you . . . see me?" Sharon said uncertainly.

Of the two of them she was the calmer now. Brad sounded genuinely keyed up.

"—which might," he said impressively, "be sooner than you think. Incidentally, they know all about your mother's sad demise. Harold asked me to express his deepest sympathy. He's sending flowers. But on the other hand this is a matter of business. We may have to act pretty fast."

"Of course."

"Now, in the first place, is there any chance of having this stockholders' meeting postponed? I mean, if we wanted to?"

"Anchy has been asked that and he has decided not to."

"Well, in that case what Harold wants to do is this. He wants to call your father direct. That is, if you don't have any objection. Then if the deal shapes up the way you indicated, either Harold himself or our top legal man, Pilbrick, will fly out for further conferences. And I'll come along."

"Why, Brad!"

"Pleased?"

"You know I am."

"Same here, kiddo," Brad said. "I've been missing you. And I want to tell you, you've been right on the ball in this matter. I'm proud of the way you've handled it. Harold mentioned the same thing."

"It's sweet of you to say so, dear. And tell Harold thanks."

"I will. And I mean it—from the heart." Brad's voice had the choked quality he always injected into it when he mentioned his heart.

"We've been a little lucky with the job we've been kicking around here," he said; "it's shaping up to where I may be able to pull loose. At least for a few days." He had evidently recalled his telegram saying how his work had made impossible his attendance at the funeral. Sharon, however, had not been about to remind him of it.

"Oh, Brad," she said.

"All right, now," he said, "let's hope it all works out. If we're coming out we'll leave sometime tomorrow, probably in the A.M. I'll wire you the arrival time and flight number. Of course, you don't have to meet me if you don't want to."

The last statement was a joke. Sharon tried to laugh at it but failed to bring off the effect she wanted. Happiness rather than pain was an emotion which often deeply upset her.

"Darling," she said feelingly, "I can hardly wait."

10 IN THE NIGHT AIR smelling of carburetors and fog Sharon watched the plane settle on the runway. Its grace was stolen instantly by contact with the earth: that was the law of its existence; it could be alive and beautiful only in an alien element. There were people like that, people who could hardly function at the level of ordinary life. They needed hate, height, speed, danger, the packed power of violent emotions and exciting deeds to make them whole. She wished, at moments like this, that she were one of them (as Alexandra was), but it was an absurd wish: earth-bound forever, she was the hoper, the patient waiter—one of those who made gains slowly, counted them over desperately and then tried, often in vain, to hold onto them.

Two men in coveralls—tiny figures, measured against the great, captive ship—had wheeled up and attached a gangway, a door in the plane's belly opened, and people began to emerge. Brad was the second passenger off; he saw her right away and waved to her with a rolled magazine. Inside the fence they kissed self-consciously, Brad setting his briefcase at her feet and reaching around her with the hand that held the magazine. He turned to introduce a sharp-looking, pucker-faced man who had followed him out of the landing area.

"Dear, I want to present Myron Pilbrick, head of our legal department—my wife Sharon."

"How do you do, Mr. Pilbrick," Sharon said. "Did you have a pleasant trip? You both look very much relaxed."

This was true of Brad, who had a wonderful tan; less so of Pilbrick. With his semi-starched collar and well-pressed brown suit he would have passed more easily for a sales manager than a lawyer.

"Marvelous, thank you," he said.

"It was a fantastic trip, kiddo," Brad said; "they gave us cocktails over Kansas City."

"How thrilling," Sharon said. "Airlines must be changing."

"Just growing up, perhaps," Pilbrick said. "Do you fly much, Mrs. Iverson?"

"Not too much," Sharon said. "I don't often have the opportunity."

She was afraid she had sounded sarcastic and looked nervously at Brad—she'd made up her mind to let no act or speech on her part spoil the reunion. But Brad didn't seem to have heard her.

"See you tomorrow, Myron," he said. They all shook hands again. The person from H-H who had shown up to meet Pilbrick had been hovering in the background, and Pilbrick and he now went off together. Brad took her arm and they strolled through the airport to claim his luggage. When they settled into the upholstery of the hired limousine, he surprised her by leaning over and kissing her again.

"It's good to be home," he said.

This speech dumfounded her as much as the kiss. It was un-Bradlike but it gave her a warm feeling, and she moved over against him in the wide back seat and slipped her hand into his.

"Oh, sweetheart," she said, "I'm so excited. I can hardly believe you're really here."

She was glad she'd engaged the Tanner car. It was so much more appropriate than a cab and so much easier than driving the small coupe she kept in the Mark garage. This was the way Brad liked things to be—first cabin, to use his own expression.

"There was no time to fool around," he said. "Myron and I made a beeline for that plane. And, incidentally, thanks again for the call."

"Darling," Sharon said, "I'm your wife. You don't have to thank me."

"Well," Brad said, "you were certainly beamed in."

"If I was," Sharon said, "there's a fairly good reason for it. I happen to love you."

The declaration didn't have quite the ring she'd meant. Possibly such an avowal between people who had been apart so much was premature—still, she felt electrically happy and alert. She felt as if he would understand anything she said. But Brad's mind was shooting off in another direction.

"You'll never believe the background on this thing," he said.

She waited for him to elaborate on this. When he didn't she inquired, "Did Harold call Father? You said he might."

Brad nodded. "Our team—that is, Myron and myself and Hy Nysam, the H-H bureau head. This is a big deal, Shar. It's major. That's why I say, if I told you all the ramifications you'd never believe them."

"Tell me," Sharon said.

Brad grinned. "All in due time," he said; "let me get used to being with my gal again. Back in my old home town."

The car was cresting the hill over Visitation Valley. Below them the city spread its intricate pattern of light, and dead ahead a new moon poked a slender foot through a scud of cloud.

Brad gazed at these sights appreciatively until Sharon gave his hand a wifely squeeze, to bring him back to her.

"What ramifications, dear?" she asked.

"You remember my saying on the phone there were some things I hadn't known myself? That's what dumfounded me, when I found out. H-H has been buying Day Pub for six months."

"They've been buying our stock and they *didn't tell* you?"

"That's right."

"I just can't imagine such a thing."

"That's how big companies operate, kiddo," Brad said laconically.

"But if they were interested I should have thought—"

"You might," Brad said, "and a lot of people might. But that isn't how they operate at H-H. I'm not on the policy-making level, I don't claim to be, but Harold made it all clear. He was coming to me later, as a friend—once he knew what the shape-up was going to be. I don't have to tell you they've wanted a West Coast outlet for a long time."

"You'd mentioned it a few times, but—"

"There weren't any buts, kiddo," Brad said; "it was top secret. Time, Inc. was after *The Day*. And the Ridder Chain too, though they're less sure of that. All our buying had to be undercover and it had to be handled just right—different brokers used, and so on. Harold knew you had some stock, all right. He probably even knows how much. But when a major company gets into a deal like this they don't depend on intrapersonal relationships. We'd picked up a lot of stock and nobody knew a thing about it!"

"That's simply incredible."

"Also pretty smart. We'd have been ready to move in a month or so, regardless of any developments at your end."

"But what did Anchy *say* to Harold Hudner?"

"Just confirmed what you'd told me. Your dad's wedged into a corner and he's ready to make a deal. He said there'd be some things to iron out. We don't know what they are yet."

It was not simple to Sharon. She was by no means convinced that she could sort out all this and catalogue it for future procedure: she'd have to go over it in her mind later. Leviathan negotiations had been set in motion and her own part in them, first conceived by her to be so vital, was in danger of being forgotten.

This thought filled her with terror. "Oh, I hope—" she burst out, then paused.

"You hope what?"

"I hope everything turns out all right."

She had twisted sideways in the seat, her face close to Brad's. Her lips were parted, her dark eyes intense and sparkly. The hope she had kept herself from uttering and the only one which had sustained her through dry areas of loneliness and rocky plateaus of self-contempt had nothing to do with the acquirement of Day Pub by the Hurd-Hudner Corporation or any other combination of interests. It had to do with the recognition of her as a woman by the man to whom, however worthless he might be, she was irrevocably bound.

"Oh, Brad," she said, "I hope it so much."

He stared at her. With her head thrown back that way, brightened and darkened by the lights of passing cars, she looked young, eager, strong and pretty, and she stirred responses in him all the sharper for having been, in recent months, so thoroughly forgotten. It was as if the years had peeled away and revealed once more, magically preserved, the dark, gentle, willful girl whom he had married fifteen years earlier—married, yes, in spite of grave misgivings because . . . well, because he'd known in his heart that he would never find another human being who could love him so much!

"It's got to be all right, kiddo," he said, "got to be!"

His arms went around her. His mouth found hers, his nerves expanding in the glow of imagined pleasures still to come.

11 IF THERE was one sound Sharon enjoyed hearing it was the sound of Brad Iverson singing in the shower. Not that he could sing a note. He was flat in the upper register and sharp in the lower: in between he couldn't carry a tune. These technical flaws were, to her ears, virtues; because of them Brad sounded helpless and appealing. If he could have sung like Crosby or Sinatra it would have been a bore.

Lying on the bed, she listened with her eyes half closed, floating in a rosy haze. The singing wouldn't last very long. When Brad turned the water off he would turn his voice off with it as if both were controlled by the same tap. He would come out of the bathroom drying himself, leaving wet footprints on the rug. No matter what sort of a mood he had been in before, he would be in a better one. You never knew what he would do. He might crawl into bed and go to sleep like a log. Or he might suggest that they get dressed and go out somewhere. You never knew, but whatever he did it would be just the right thing.

"It's good to be home."

He'd said that to her days ago, it seemed, though actually less than two hours. She felt as if she, not he, had been away; even her suite at the Mark had never been more to her than a place in which to keep her clothes. It was a home now because it had stopped being her suite and become theirs—or would become so as soon as his bags were unpacked. Brad was the sort of man who never unpacked for himself. He was capable of living out of a suitcase for weeks, burrowing through layers of clothes and toilet articles to search for what he needed at the moment—an untidy habit and an uncompanionable one. He wouldn't be solidly a part of her life again until the luggage had been got out of the way, his suits hanging in the closet, with his shoes placed two by two below them, his ties on the rack and his underclothes in the chiffonier drawers.

Sharon slipped out of bed. If she worked fast—and she was good at this sort of thing—she could have him all moved in before he got out of the bathroom and she found out what the new mood was to be. She raised the lid of Brad's wardrobe suitcase and took an appraising look at what was in it. It was full, of course—Brad never packed with an inch to spare—and its contents at first glance seemed to be nothing but shirts: button-down shirts of linen, striped shirts of cotton and wool, sport shirts with long sleeves and with short sleeves, dress shirts, heavy silk shirts from Sulka's in rich solid colors. She filled two drawers with the shirts and another with ties and socks; Brad might not be the most brilliant journalist in the United States, she reflected, but he was certainly one of the best dressed. He took care of himself in that department and at least, when he packed, he put the shoes on the bottom. Sharon lifted them out. She was about to take the empty case off the rack provided for it and lift on another one when her hand, making a sweep at some tissue paper, came in contact with a bobbypin. She held it up to the light—a standard wire bobbypin of a dark shade, the sort that is manufactured for brunettes. She was standing beside the empty wardrobe case holding the bobbypin and thinking about it when Brad came out of the bathroom. His mood was buoyant, not sleepy—that much was clear at once—and his body was only slightly moist except for his legs and feet, which were dripping wet. He stood in front of the mirror polishing himself and speaking to her over his shoulder.

"You know, kiddo, I've got an idea."

"What, dear?" Sharon asked.

"Why don't we go out somewhere and have a snack? They gave us dinner pretty early on the plane and, well, I could stand eating something. How about you?"

"Why, I think I'd like that," Sharon said. She spoke a little slowly. This was the time. Either she walked up to him and held her hand out, showing him the bobbypin, or she didn't. Actually, of course, there was nothing fundamentally wrong with finding a bobbypin in the bottom of a man's suitcase, especially one that was her own color. The suitcase wasn't new and she and Brad had shared its use on a number of occasions. Not for a long time, it was true, but a bobbypin could stay in the bottom of a suitcase practically indefinitely. It was a very small object.

There would have been nothing wrong at all about its being where it had been except for one factor which, to be fair, you couldn't avoid taking into consideration. She didn't use bobbypins.

"We might even find a place where we could dance around," Brad said. "We could sort of celebrate. How would that be?"

"I think it would be dandy," Sharon said.

"Then," Brad said, "don't get all dressed up. We'll just find some little offbeat place down in Chinatown or somewhere. The way we used to do."

The phrase *the way we used to do* was a poetic license associated with his mood rather than with any body of fact. There hadn't been more than four or five occasions in their entire married life when spontaneous dinner-dancing had been the order of the day. However, the suggestion was not one which could be lightly rejected. Nor was Sharon going to turn the evening into a shambles because a bobbypin had somehow found its way into a suitcase—a bobbypin which could be dropped into a toilet or a wastebasket in the twinkling of an eye and forgotten forever.

"Darling," Sharon said, "that's a marvelous idea. Just give me ten minutes and I'll be ready."

VIII

The Gathering Storm

"Who wouldn't rather be polite than rough
If only things in general weren't so tough!"
—BERTOLT BRECHT

1 NEWS TRAVELS FAST in the compressed, teeming universe of a modern city—particularly the kind of news that is not immediately printed. News, for instance, of the coming struggle for *The Day* had achieved considerable penetration: it had been discussed and dissected and weighed in recent hours in some widely separated areas—Cypress Gardens, where Pamela and Cliff Harper, with the children in bed and supper eaten and the dishes rinsed and stacked, were enjoying their first leisure moment of the day; in Bardelli's Restaurant, where Matt Brody and Pete Zorach, having notified their respective wives that they would not be home till late, were engaged in a campaign conference, the motif of which was "How will we keep Hurd-Hudner from knocking off the old man?" Also in the Pacific Union Club, where George Dudley had been collared on his way to cards by young Winterhalter and borne back to the bar for some rather morose chitchat regarding a conference scheduled for early next morning; in Mill Valley, where Dan Winkler and his daughter were starting for an early movie, as in Burlingame, Atherton and Menlo Park, to mention some outlying sections,

not forgetting the immediate hearths of Pacific Heights, Nob and Russian and Telegraph Hills, and the peripheral respectability of St. Francis Woods, Marin County and Piedmont, where, although no principals resided, the subject was one of general interest and, like other such subjects, it had been relayed from Montgomery Street by people whose jobs took them down there and who got to hear things and so, naturally, enjoyed repeating them.

Outside those in Anchylus' confidence, or closely connected with his company on its upper operation levels, no one had details. The word was that *The Day* might change hands. That was the gist of it. A chain might buy in. Some said Time, Inc., others said Scripps-Howard or Norman Chandler. Chances were Anchylus was going to be bounced on his butt. That might be hard to take, for a man of his age—in his late sixties and already a legend, the legend itself making him seem older. Then his clothes, and that face! A landmark in his way.

It wasn't as if *The Day* weren't a good newspaper. What was the sense of letting some Eastern smart alecks step in and haul it away? That was what people said. Eastern money was getting in everywhere: give them a foothold and they brought in all their friends. You wouldn't sell them Golden Gate Park. You wouldn't sell them a bridge or a church or the Ferry Building. Why should you sell them *The San Francisco Day?* Too bad. You used to fight your sister for the comics Sunday morning, till you tore them in half sometimes and your mother took them away. You used to try to read the sporting page over your dad's shoulder at the breakfast table. Later on you had a *Day* delivery route. You found out what a newspaper meant to the people. Sometimes in the early morning, when big stories were breaking, the subscribers came out to meet you: they stood in the doors and leaned over their front gates as you rode up the street on your bicycle, flipping the folded papers right and left.

One man with even more interest than most as to what was pending with *The Day* was Ling Tung Chow, once a police go-between, now head of the Asia and Pacific Trading Corporation. He had been mulling over this matter for several hours, sitting in an office less than half a block from the cabaret in which Sharon and Brad Iverson, after some debate, had chosen to eat and dance. The office was in a building owned by himself and bearing little resemblance to stereotyped notions of how office buildings ought to look, having a roof designed in imitation of a Buddhist temple and a doorway with a wrought-iron dragon flattened in front of the plate glass. Like Anchylus, Ling Tung Chow was something of a holdover from earlier times, but he was older than Anchylus; he had adjusted to his status. A regular life had kept him healthy. He never touched liquor or tobacco, was careful in his diet, and smoked three pipes of opium a day—never more. In an area of josshouses, souvenir shops, tearooms, tan games and grocery stores where one could buy octopi, dried bats, fresh sharks, canned bird's-nest soup and hundred-year-old eggs, Ling Tung Chow conducted an exporting business which grossed several million dollars a year, a large part of which was profit.

Ling Tung Chow was a patriot. He loved China—a land which he had never seen. He had been born on Grant Avenue, San Francisco. Before progressing to the tong job which had brought him to Anchylus' attention, he had been collection agent for an herb doctor and one of the three bodyguards (the other two were white) of Fung Jing Toy, better known as Little Pete, who ran Chinatown for ten years, not without certain personal risks. To supplement the bodyguards Fung Jing Toy wore a coat of chain mail under his clothing and a thin steel helmet under his hat. One day, however, as he sat in a barbershop, and Ling Tung Chow stood on the pavement outside, a customer got out of an adjacent barber chair, stuck a gun under the mail shirt of Fung Jing Toy, and pulled the trigger several times. Thus Fung Jing Toy lost his insides and Ling Tung Chow lost face. He had long regained it by the time he served Anchylus as a purveyor of harness-slashers.

Ling Tung Chow's mother, a prostitute, had been beaten to death by one of her white customers. Ling Tung Chow had helped her down the Clay Street hill, looking for a doctor. He had been five years old then. Even then, Ling Tung Chow was concerned about his own people—the voiceless ones, jammed precariously between a new land which did not want them and a homeland to which they could never return. He made money fast. Soon he had good contacts in the white man's world where guns and ammunition could be bought. He sat in the conferences when Sun Yat-sen, in San Francisco, planned the revolution which overthrew the Manchu Dynasty. Ling Tung Chow shipped Sun Yat-sen many articles the latter wanted—for a price. A later customer was Chiang Kai-shek: Ling Tung Chow had on his office wall a framed letter from the Generalissimo thanking him for services in the cause of China.

When the Issimo, like Sun Yat-sen, had ceased to be a customer, Ling Tung Chow had found others. It was possible, he found, to ship a locomotive from San Francisco to Hong Kong with a red star prow ornament cast in steel at the factory and painted red, according to the customer's specifications.

Such services Ling Tung Chow performed for the sake of China. His patriotism had made him rich: he had one of the best collections in the world of Chinese jade, carved emeralds, period chessmen, Manchu daggers and teak miniatures. He went regularly to theater first nights, had a box for the opera, and took frequent trips to Europe as well as those (made necessary by his business) in the opposite direction. He was the director of the bank which financed his operations and of the insurance company which underwrote them.

It was the voiceless poor—the transplanted, the homeless, the lost, womanless, remodeled and bedeviled Chinese of San Francisco whom Ling Tung Chow loved with a sick, disgusted kind of love, hating their helplessness, their petty shrewdness, the peasant inadaptability that made them all—except the chrome-plated, garish third generation—reverently observe, in spite of difficulties, the customs of a homeland which had renounced them.

What he wanted for them was not prosperity: that was an American, alien thing, of no value inwardly. Ling Tung Chow had it himself and it was of no value to him except in superficial respects. What he wanted for them was a reasonable participation in the affairs of the hemisphere in which they'd held so long this small, evil-smelling bridgehead. He, Ling Tung Chow, wanted this for them without any sacrifice of what he had acquired for himself, but he did not see that any sacrifice should be involved. He remembered walking down Clay Street that time holding his mother's hand, looking horribly at the blood that wetted places where she stepped. If he ever did anything for the Voiceless Ones it would be as an act of reverence for his mother.

After the departure of the visitors who had told him about *The Day*, Ling Tung Chow sat for some time doodling on a pad. Then he picked up a telephone. Though connected with a public operator of the Pacific Telephone and Telegraph Company he did not give a number but asked for a friend by his name. "Hung Toy," he said. The operator, who to carry on her job had committed to memory the names of the 2,100 subscribers in the Chinatown Exchange, connected him at once. Ling Tung made a request and in a few minutes his friend entered without knocking. Ling Tung Chow passed on what had been told to him, together with his own conclusions regarding it.

Hung Toy listened phlegmatically. He was a solid, bull-necked Cantonese of sixty whose large bald head was creased by a ruddy knife scar. Hung Toy had been marked for death by his uncle, a War Lord, because of his Occidental sympathies. Leaving China hurriedly, he had entered the United States without papers, crossing the border at Tia Juana, Mexico, under a truckload of fertilizer. The initial jobs held by Hung Toy in San Francisco had retained a touch of the aroma which had characterized his entry. However, like Ling Tung Chow himself, he had progressed. He moved from Grant Street to Montgomery Street—a step achieved by few San Francisco Chinese.

Hung Toy had come to Ling Tung Chow's attention early in this process and had been useful to him in a number of negotiations; it was Ling Tung Chow who had secured for his friend a position with a brokerage house. Hung Toy had become adept at his new employment; he now handled all of Ling Tung Chow's stock exchange transactions and had even arrived at the point of giving him advice. Today, however, Ling Tung Chow paid no attention to anything the broker said, and Hung Toy in return showed his annoyance by speaking in English—a tongue used among the Chinese at his social level and of his generation only when they were doing business.

"You say Mr. Wilkins came himself?"

"With his partner, Mr. Shimenko."

Hung Toy weighed the importance of this. It wasn't often that two Caucasians of such stature called on Ling Tung Chow.

"I have been advocating for some time that you sell this stock," Hung Toy said. "This would seem to be an excellent opportunity."

"They didn't seek to purchase it, Hung Toy. They wanted me to exercise the voting rights in their favor."

"Maybe. But they will purchase, nevertheless," Hung Toy said.

"Why do you say so?"

"There has been some talk in the street. Since the mother's death the daughters have rebelled against the father. There is a profit to be made here. I would sell if I were you."

"I had thought of it," Ling Tung Chow said, "but I have a duty to my conscience."

"Perhaps then you should buy this newspaper yourself, Honored One," Hung Toy said.

Ling Tung Chow sat chewing expressionlessly. He could see that Hung Toy, with his mundane brain, accustomed to deal only with material things, had not grasped the problem.

"I do not anticipate turning *The Day* into a Chinese-language paper," he said sternly. "The main use of these is in washhouses where

297

the shirts of the white customers are wrapped in them. I want the Voice to be there, even when it is silent. I want the Voiceless Ones to be heard."

"You feel then that Mr. Wilkins and Shimenko would silence the Voiceless?"

"I don't know. But I don't think they would know how to run an honest newspaper."

Hung Toy grunted. Finally yielding to temptation, he helped himself to some beetles.

"Ling Tung Chow," he said, "there are now about thirty thousand Chinese in San Francisco. The circulation of *The Day* is two hundred and twenty thousand. I have never known when Mr. Saxe spoke for the thirty against the two hundred and twenty."

"He may not speak so," Ling Tung Chow said, "but he feels for them. He knows they are there."

"How do you know the others would not?"

"They are not honest. It is something I feel."

"And you feel that Mr. Saxe is a pillar of honesty?"

"You forget, Hung Toy," Ling Tung Chow said with dignity, "I knew this man in my youth."

"Nevertheless," Hung Toy said, "he is no longer young; he is not as great as he once was. Or as powerful. People can get unbiased news in many ways now. They listen to the radio. They see newsreels."

Ling Tung Chow shucked off the stiff black shells and popped the beetlemeats, sweet as caviar, into his mouth.

"First," he said, chewing, "there is no unbiased news. Let's start with that. Second, all newspapers seem much alike. Why is that?"

"It is because of the way they are edited, Honorable One," Hung Toy said.

"Explain it to me," Ling Tung Chow said. "I am not sure that I know about this."

"The news is sent to many papers at the same time," Hung Toy said. "It is written by some people in New York, who telegraph it. That is what is called 'the wire service.'"

"Good!" Ling Tung Chow said. "And what else? This doesn't account for everything."

"No," Hung Toy said, "there are also the handouts."

Ling Tung Chow had heard this phrase before, but he looked slightly puzzled. "Tell me," he said.

"The handouts, Honorable One," Hung Toy said, "are stories on a great variety of subjects. They concern activities of one kind or another, mostly to do with making money, and are written in advance by men called press agents. They are sent through the mail by tons or thrust through the editors' transoms. Then they are picked up and sent to the printer. It is quite a simple process."

"You would say that this process involved courage and talent? I am merely asking for information."

"You mock me," Hung Toy said.

"I beg your pardon," Ling Tung Chow said; "perhaps I was not following you."

"That is of no consequence," Hung Toy said. "I have told you all I know. It is not much."

"It is interesting, though," Ling Tung Chow said. "I am glad to know all this. I have never been in a newspaper office. Possibly someday I shall go. I am just a humble reader and I read the news each day. A plane crash. Ten English die. Well, there are more where they came from. A thousand Arabs die; more where they came from. A plague, a famine—or your uncle. Fifty thousand Chinese die. They are my countrymen, but—am I heartless?—there are more, many more, where they came from. But if a cat is hurt by a car at Stockton and Clay that has meaning for me. And Mr. Saxe will print it. Do you admit that?"

"He will print it with a picture of the cat on the front page," Hung Toy conceded quickly, "and of a child, if one is the cat's owner."

"Even a Chinese child," Ling Tung Chow said. "Do you admit that also?"

Hung Toy shrugged. "Chinese children are very photogenic, Honorable One," he said. "That is one reason."

"The picture," Ling Tung Chow said, "would not be there for that reason. It would be there because this happening with the cat is a San Francisco happening—cat and child and readers all being San Franciscans together. The Voiceless together with those who do nothing but talk. You have told me what you know of newspapers, and I thank you. Now I shall tell you what I know of Mr. Saxe. As I say, I knew him in my youth. So listen."

Hung Toy bowed. "I shall esteem it a privilege," he said.

"He is a lonely man," Ling Tung Chow said; "he has many enemies and few friends. Having few friends, he doesn't go to a club to eat with the men wearing clothes exactly copied from each other. Men with the hearts of coolies and the fortunes of kings, whose fathers built the city with the help of the Chinese. Hence he doesn't print what some friend tells him to print about another friend. Or fail to print what should be printed because those in power wish it left in darkness." Ling Tung Chow reached for the beetles. "Mr. Saxe," he said, "doesn't drink ice and whisky with a probate judge each afternoon at five so he is not afraid to print it when the probate judge is stealing from trust funds. If he supports a police commissioner, he will also print it when the cops of the commissioner scavenge their meals from the refrigerators of prostitutes. He cannot be bought. It does not matter to me if he is disliked by his rich daughters. I feel comfortable with him. What use to me is a great profit on this stock? I shall do without the profit, which the Department of the Treasury would steal from me anyway, and keep faith with Mr. Saxe."

"Then you wish me to call Wilkins and Shimenko, Honorable One, and advise them of your decision?"

"You might as well," Ling Tung Chow said, "but you don't have to go to the stockholders' meeting. This time I think I'll go myself. I'm curious to see what will happen there."

2
Stay as sweet as you are
For as you are
You're divine, dear.
Stay as sweet as you are
And as you are
Tell me that you're mine, dear . . .

Alexandra hummed the tune, disliking it but powerless to turn off her attention. She wished they weren't always reviving old tunes on the juke boxes. The record shimmered on a stretch of years whose surface was dull now, worn down by the dancing feet of girls who hadn't stayed as sweet as they were and hadn't been any too sweet to begin with.

"Baroness," said Coley Fonce, brand inspector of Sonoma County, "without you I can't go on."

"Please, Coley," she said.

"I'm telling you the truth," he said. "I can't eat, can't sleep. Guess I never knew it, but I fell harder than turd from a tall ox."

"Tie a can on it, Coley," Alexandra said.

"That's how I feel about you, Baroness," he said; "you're my ideal. Jest call it that. You know what folks are sayin' about us? They're saying we ought to git spliced."

"Did you come all the way up here to tell me that?"

Coley's cherub face had a lost, leatherstocking look to it, but he rallied bravely. When he spoke it seemed to his listener that he deliberately exaggerated his native manner of speech, with a view to dramatizing its contents. He was playing the lovelorn cowhand of a comedy skit.

"What I'm saying is from the heart," he said, "since you and me split I come up with empty saddles. I swear I don't know where to head in."

"Just head back where you came from," Alexandra said.

"Now, take it easy," Coley said; "is that a way to talk to yore ole buddy?"

"If you keep on this way, Coley," Alexandra said, "I'm going to throw up. I'm warning you."

Coley blinked at her under his forelock. Then he put his head back and snickered with lusty enjoyment that left her wondering whether the "Baroness" bit and the rest of it were genuine or whether he'd concocted it as some foul kind of joke.

"You got spunk, Zan," he said when he had recovered some control. "You can still break in half an' swaller yore head. Yes sirree bob."

In his jubilation he went off into another bucking spree of mirth, finishing with an attempt to put his arm around her. This she parried with her elbow—automatically but not maliciously

"Coley," she said with sudden suspicion, "what started you on this marriage business? You used to have more sense."

"I guess I know how I feel, honey," Coley said plaintively.

"Of course," Alexandra said, "but you used to have more sense. What started you on this? It wasn't something you read, was it?"

Coley gave his forelock a twist. She could tell by the way his eyes dodged that her guess had been a good one.

"Well, now. I won't say that. But—hell, folks have been talking."

"*And* someone put a piece in the paper saying you were going to be my 'next'? There was such a piece, you know."

"That so?" Coley said with smoky innocence.

"Yes. And you know very well, I think. Well, let me tell you about that piece. It was put in by a spiteful old woman who has always hated me and given me trouble. I read it the day you stayed at the ranch. The one time, remember? That was the day I told you to get out. And I told you we were through."

Coley gazed miserably into his drink. "I could have blown my brains out that day, Baroness," the brand inspector said.

"Why didn't you?"

"Don't fuss me," Coley said. "I read that piece you bring to mind. I did, for sure. Not then, but later."

"Aha!"

"I figgered it was right sweet. It sort of started my brain working. If that's what folks are saying, why couldn't it come true?"

"I knew it." Alexandra said evilly. "I knew that was where it came from! Coley, if I could tell you how I feel about—"

"Now look here," Coley said. "What's so bad about that idea? We sort of cottoned to each other. And we had some laughs, didn't we?"

"The laughs are over, Coley," Alexandra said. "This is the last of them, even if it's the biggest. For your information, we are not going to get hitched. We're not even going out together any more. Go put another quarter in the juke and get me one more tiny drink. And then I have to go."

In the past week she'd forgotten Coley so completely he might never have existed. She'd been at the ranch seldom, then only for a few days at a time—the last of these visits interrupted by George Dudley's call about her mother. Since then there'd been much to keep her in the city; for convenience she'd taken a room at the Francisca Club—a neat, hygienic little lair, with men strictly ruled out. Actually he'd been so well behaved she'd felt almost happy when she saw Coley's pickup parked around the corner from the club. It was an ambush, she'd guessed at once, though not a very effective one: she'd had to knock on the window to wake up the ambusher, who'd gone to sleep looped over his wheel. The nearest bar had seemed the logical place to go—and here they sat, she in her mink coat, he in his Stetson, jeans and fancy boots, like fugitives from some improbable movie.

She shouldn't have rapped on the window. This was her punishment now, listening to the dreadful bilge he'd put together out of his self-pity and the inspiration he'd derived from Letty Meeker's item. She'd received many proposals in her time, and there had been few, even the most abject, which hadn't had in them something flattering, some cost to the applicant for which, if it had been in her power, she would have reimbursed him. Yet this proposal turned her stomach. Coley was just mixed up. A country Romeo of some repute, he might never have had a woman jilt him—or he might be really fond of her.

"I couldn't git my mind on working," he said when the juke had been refinanced and the new drinks were on the table. "Had to

302

borrow gas money to come see you. It's a lonesome trail, when you travel without your partner."

"Everyone's lonesome sometimes, Coley," Alexandra said.

Her tone was too sympathetic. Yet she hadn't meant to "fuss him." Loneliness was a fact she'd faced up to for several years now— ever since she'd seen Nick Drobny walking away from her, tall and straight, between the man in the felt hat and the man in the derby.

Coley Fonce swallowed his drink at a gulp. He gripped her knee under the table and pushed his face up close, his small eyes misted with emotion and the effects of alcohol.

"I say it again, Baroness," he pleaded, "what about you and me standin' up in front of a preacher?"

"You don't want that, Coley."

"I shore do."

"No, you don't. I hurt your pride, that's all. You'll get over it."

"Not in a million years. I want to put that ring on your finger worse'n a little red wagon."

"The answer is no. And you ought to stop going to those mesquite movies. Your dialogue is terrible."

"You used to like them movies," Coley said plaintively.

"Well, I haven't got time for them now. I don't want you calling me. And I don't want you coming here to the city and looking for me. I'm very busy."

"We can't even party like we used to, when you come up to the ranch?"

"I don't know. I'll have to see."

She stripped this statement also of not quite all but almost all hope because Coley had to have some glimmer left: otherwise he might become obstreperous.

"Now look," she said quickly, anxious that this time there should be no misunderstanding, "I'm going to give you money to get home on. Gas money and eating money—that's all. No more where that came from, so don't sit here and drink it up. Now I'm going to get up and go. Don't follow me. And, since you seem to have found out where I'm living, don't you ever dare come to the Francisca Club and make a scene, because if you do I'll call the police. Is that perfectly clear?"

She laid ten dollars on the table and walked out of the bar. Not more than half a block away the fine, dignified façade of the club loomed up, its protective doors always open to her—a half a block, but how many thousand miles away from the dingy bar and the man and the insane conversation. Hurry, I must hurry, she thought, and she did, almost running toward the protection of what she needed most, the walls dividing class from class, asserting she was one kind of person—thank God—and he quite another. She was through with men, all kinds of them. She'd proved this triumphantly not only now but for days, turning down the prep-schoolish but ardent passes of Tim Wilkins (turning them down adroitly, whimsically even, since it wouldn't do to make an enemy of him). She was through until a stable as well as an intelligent and attractive man came along—someone like Nick, if that mold hadn't been broken forever and its last products wiped off the earth by the firing squad and the torture chamber. Marriage to a person like Coley Fonce wasn't, thank God, even a remote possibility.

3 THE MAILBOX at the club was stuffed with telephone messages, some taken while she was at the beauty parlor, others during the time wasted with Coley: Tim seemed to have called every half hour, with Leon Shimenko putting in two calls and Mr. Wilkins, Sr., at the bank, one call. Something of interest must be happening; she hoped not a situation which had been impaired, an advantage lost because she hadn't been within reach of a telephone. The slight fog resulting from the drinks she had taken had already been dispelled by the brisk walk; her head was clear, and after one short jolt, drunk neat from the bathroom glass, to give her confidence, she threw her purse and fur coat on the bed, kicked off her shoes (one stupidly flying into the wastepaper basket) and settled in a chair to talk to Tim.

"Holy Pete, Zan, where have you been?"

"Having my hair done," she said coolly. "Why?"

Her heart was pounding. Something had happened; she could tell from Tim's voice: he was positively squeaking with excitement. Oh, she should have kept in touch; it was criminal not to. This was the only thing that made real sense—the fight to assert her rights as a human being, to wipe out Letty Meeker and, if necessary, Anchylus, so that her own life, the wonderful life she dreamed of, and of which she'd had a taste with Nick could actually begin at last.

"Well, all hell's been breaking loose here. We bought three hundred shares this morning at six and a half. That's for the W-S account. We're bidding seven and an eighth now; none offered. We'll go to eight if we have to."

"But why do you have to buy more shares? I thought we had enough."

This, when they parted the evening before, had been his last word to her—that the Wilkins-Shimenko-Saxe account, with more than 27 per cent of *The Day's* stock on hand, held undisputed control.

"Well, we haven't," Tim said; "we got troubles. Did you talk to Sharon last night?"

"No," Alexandra said, more puzzled than ever. "Should I have?"

"Could be," Tim said. "Anyway, I've got a hunch she's left us. Brad Iverson flew out here with a Hurd-Hudner attorney. My secretary has a boy-friend in the H-H office here, so we got the straight poop on this. They had a meeting with your dad this morning and he offered them his stock if they'd give him two seats on the Board and a contract for five years as editor-publisher. They turned him down."

"I can't seem to get this through my head, Tim," Alexandra said. "You mean Sharon's voting with Father now, and she never mentioned it to you either?"

"I don't mean anything of the kind," Tim said; "she's voting with her husband. That's who she's voting with. She probably tipped him off to the whole action. That's the only way I can explain it. In plain language, she's sold us out. And it almost worked. The only reason it didn't, quite—or may not—is Anchylus' conditions. He made the bargain too tough so they told him to go to hell. They must think they have the deal sewed up without him."

"I just never heard of such a thing," Alexandra said, her eyes wild and her breath coming in jerks. "I just can't conceive of it."

"Well, it's happened," Tim said. "The question is, how far do you want to go?"

"What do you mean, Tim?"

"I mean we've got twenty-four hours till the meeting. We might just be able to grab off enough stock in that time to pull the rug from under H-H and your old man too. But it will take a hundred thousand bucks, maybe more. That's how Leon and I figure it. How soon can you get down here to the office?"

"Why, right away, I suppose."

"Then step on it. And look, Zan, can you stop at the bank first and talk to Tim Senior?"

"What for?"

"For dough, for dough," Tim said, "the dough we're going to need. I just mentioned the figure. Leon and I can't manage more than twenty-five thousand at the most."

"Well, if you think I can put it up you're simply out of your mind," Alexandra said with indignation. Some of the temper was a carry-over from her talk with Coley Fonce: everyone seemed to be after her money today. Then all these developments—Hurd-Hudner bidding for *The Day* and Sharon going over to their side. She felt as if the world had suddenly gone mad.

Only a shocked, empty silence greeted her statement at Tim's end of the line. Alexandra went on almost plaintively, "I've put up every cent I have already, and you know it."

This was true. The only ready cash available to her was the remains of the divorce settlement from Schuy Cutting, somewhat reduced now but still a formidable sum, and all of it, since the initiation of the deal to take over *The Day*, placed in a margin account with Wilkins & Shimenko.

"You'd better get down here, Alexandra," Tim said coldly. "Just get down as fast as possible. Then we can figure out which way to go."

"I intend to get down," Alexandra snapped, "but I'm telling you how I stand, so this won't come as a shock. I have absolutely no more money."

"Please," Tim said, "let's not go into this on the telephone."

"We've been going into it," Alexandra said, "so we may as well finish. Was that what you meant when you asked me how far I wanted to go, you meant how much more I'd put up? Because if you think for a minute that I—"

"I think this, Zan, that we'd better have a talk," Tim said. "Don't bother with the bank; just come straight here."

A flash of fear, a premonition of bad luck or evil of some kind—induced in part by puzzlement at all this news which had been shoved at her so fast—gripped Alexandra, turning her hands cold, draining the strength out of her so that she almost dropped the telephone.

"I'm wondering whether I should," she said. "I'm wondering what good it will do."

"That I can't tell you," Tim said. Now that he had run into opposition on her part he sounded much more manly. He hardly squeaked at all. "But I can tell you this," he finished, "if we can't get a hundred thousand on the line before the market opens in the morning, we'll be euchred out of this deal."

4 SHADOWS ANGLED into the downtown streets from the high buildings. Buses were lined up for the daily marathon to Oakland and Marin. Cops took their places to direct rush-hour traffic at the downtown intersections; bartenders chilled rows of cocktail glasses, loaded highball glasses with ice; and the sky softened from yellow to gold, the pure, tender light falling softly on the city and the first shreds of the afternoon fog edging through the Gate. Under the bridge, a little Japanese freighter, low in the water, bucked its bow into the muscles of the incoming tide.

A bank policeman with a bunch of keys chained to his pistol belt let Alexandra out of the side door of the Pacific Midland Bank; she thanked him, without looking at him, with a radiant, mechanical smile.

Within herself she wasn't smiling. She had just mortgaged her ranch for seventy-five thousand dollars, the maximum the bank would extend, this sum having been immediately credited by means of a cashier's check, messenger-delivered, to her trading account with Wilkins & Shimenko.

Well, the step had been taken. There was no use worrying about it. She knew all about the dangers. Naturally, if the Wilkins-Shimenko group should win there would be compensating factors, gains rather than losses. If, on the other hand, they should not get control . . .

Alexandra knew all about that. T. W. Wilkins, Sr., himself had explained it to her, insofar as it needed any explaining. He had started with a calculated, humorous clearing of his throat. Ahem. Very bankerish. You didn't have to feel that it was humorous unless you wanted to. He might, he said, be speaking against his son's interests, ahem.

Young Tim had told him what was in the wind.

T. W. Wilkins, Sr., stroked the full, white, soft mustache which, in the manner of the late A. P. Gianinni, bannered his upper lip.

An ambitious fellow, young Tim. Always believed in going his own way. Nothing wrong with that, but this scheme now . . . possibly a little unfortunate, a little grim. Mr. Wilkins, Sr., personally speaking, had never entertained any feeling but friendship and respect for Anchylus Saxe.

These family quarrels, always painful. Best to stay out of them, no matter who else turned them to advantage. Profits to be made. That sort of thing went on. But one shouldn't be blind to the risks involved.

She had thanked him and signed the mortgage application and the first trust deed where he, or somebody, had already made an X in red crayon, indicating the place for her signature.

There was no taxi in sight. Alexandra walked rapidly toward Market, wishing she'd had her previous cab wait. The one emotion that had dominated her through the session with T.W. and, earlier, with young Tim and Leon Shimenko had been impatience—an eagerness to have the papers signed, the last stage of the battle financed so that she'd be free to have it out with Sharon, face to face and toe to toe.

"Mark Hopkins," she said as a cruising Yellow pulled up for her. She jumped in and slammed the door. She hoped they'd all be there, Brad Iverson and the Hurd-Hudner people. It would please her if they all heard what she had to say.

Not that she cared about Hurd-Hudner. Sharon was the one she wanted to get at.

The cab charged up Nob Hill. Alexandra opened her purse. So as to have the fare ready, she took out a dollar. She was about to close the purse when her eye fell on the small flask which she carried for emergencies. The liquor in the flask was medicinal because it was gin and Alexandra hated gin: she would never touch it for pleasure; it was only good when she was having a period or felt depressed for some reason, such as now. She had really had a pretty trying day, with worse perhaps ahead, and it was comforting to gulp the fiery, bad-tasting stuff from the little rhinestone-studded flask—one of the few presents Nick Drobny had ever given her. She swallowed painfully; then with moist lips and a sudden pain in her heart because she missed Nicky, damn it.

"To you, darling," she said aloud, "wherever you are."

The cab was stopping. She poked the dollar into the driver's hand and dashed into the hotel. It would be polite to call on the telephone, of course, now that Brad was in town, but calling would waste valuable minutes. If you couldn't go up to your sister's suite in a hotel without asking permission, where could you go? She turned her back on the elevator operator to get the benefit of one last heartening gulp from the flask. Did she have a mint? Yes, there was one, fortunately, loose from some used-up pack and grimy now from sliding around with her change in the bottom of the purse, but a mint was a mint and if Brad just happened to be there she'd prefer not to greet him with a blast of juniper on her breath; he was such a fuddy-duddy. She couldn't help smiling, hurrying down the hall—why did they have such long corridors in hotels?—as she wondered what would ever have happened if she'd run away with Brad instead of Schuy Cutting the night of her debut; she could have, easily enough. He had been absolutely mad about her. Sharon, certainly, had never been better than second best. Even now if she, Alexandra, crooked her little finger she could probably bring him scampering back.

The corridor was really endless. She hurried around the last corner so fast that she almost lost her balance, and a well-dressed man and woman, heading toward the elevators, drew back to get out of her way, the woman looking at her with distaste, the man, it seemed to her, with admiration. Alexandra suddenly perceived, not without surprise, that the man was Brad, the woman Sharon.

"Alexandra," Sharon cried, "what in the world—"

Alexandra chose to ignore her. That seemed the best course at the moment. She would speak in her own good time. On the other hand, she had no objection to speaking to Brad, fuddy-duddy though he might be.

"Hello, Brad," she said.

"How are you, Alexandra?" Brad said.

She didn't miss, as she drew herself up coldly and proudly, the meaningful look which passed between Brad and Sharon. That sort of look was enough to infuriate anybody. Alexandra had been about to show a reasonable amount of courtesy, if not cordiality, but the look put even courtesy out of the question. She decided to refuse the hand Brad was extending.

"You can shove that up your backside, my dear fellow," she said, articulating with great care. "Saying hello to you doesn't mean I want to shake hands. I don't. And I won't."

She'd spoken a little louder than she had intended. Not that it mattered. The sooner they got down to brass tacks the better off for all concerned.

"And for you," she went on quickly in the same tone, wheeling to face Sharon, who'd been edging around behind her, "let me tell you, I know what you've been up to. Well, you can't get away with it."

"Alexandra," Sharon said severely, "this is no place to make a scene."

"Oh, isn't it?" Alexandra said. "What sort of place would you like—a law court? You broke a promise to me. We shook hands on

309

it. I happen to know what you've done since. Brought in that man—" here she pointed venomously at Brad— "that man and his boss and all the rest of those Hurd-Hudner stinkers. You won't get away with it. People can sue over things like this, sister or no sister."

She could see that she had scored. Sharon looked frightened. At the same time her face curled hatefully. She positively sneered, opening her mouth to make some answer. Alexandra longed to wipe that sneer off her face. She moved forward, driven by emotions so powerful that she felt nothing could stop her. Brad, however, stepped forward. He slipped his arm through Alexandra's. She pulled back, trying to free herself.

"Take your hands off," she said breathlessly. "I will not be mauled by you, Brad Iverson."

"I think we'd better go back to the suite," Brad said.

Sharon's maid was removing glasses and bottles from the living room. Evidently a number of people had been drinking here—no doubt some conference connected with *The Day* and Sharon's effort to steal it for Hurd-Hudner.

"We were just going out, Alexandra," Brad said rather formally. "Otherwise I'd offer you a drink."

"Don't bother," Alexandra said. "I've had one."

"That's fairly evident, dear," Sharon said. "Would you like to lie down?"

"Just be careful, Sharon," Alexandra said. "You can be rude once too often. You—plotting and scheming. Honestly, I'd like to . . . But it doesn't matter. You're beneath . . . Oh, God!"

"Beneath what?" Sharon demanded with a very cold face.

"Contempt! Yes, beneath contempt. It was all my idea, you know . . . and you promised, and then . . . but you'll find out. . . ."

"*What* was your idea? Voting *The Day* stock?" Sharon burst out. "Tell her, Brad. He can tell you, how much it was *your* idea. Tell her, please," she said furiously to her husband.

Brad nodded. Whatever their past or current difficulties, it was clear that he and Sharon stood together on this matter of *The Day.*

"Alexandra," he began slowly and haltingly, "for your information, the Hurd-Hudner Corporation has wanted a San Francisco unit for a long time. We've been buying *Day* stock. Confidentially, the corporation now has quite a large accumulation of it, so if you—"

"You see, you see?" Sharon cried. "*Your* idea. I love that! All you knew was you wanted to get Letty Meeker fired. That was the extent of *your* idea. And I promised you nothing. Nothing!"

Alexandra gasped. "You didn't promise that you'd vote your stock with mine?" she said hoarsely. "You didn't agree it was time to get Anchy out?"

"All I said was I'd think it over. That I thought perhaps we might do something if—"

"Liar!" Alexandra said in a low voice. "Oh, you liar."

"Brad," Sharon said, "I will not be insulted. Please ask my sister to leave."

"Great. Throw me out," Alexandra said, her eyes flashing. "Just what I might have expected from a person who would back out of a deal. Sharon, I hate to say this, yes, I do, because we used to be so close. I could have loved you even now, if you—" Alexandra stopped. Her mouth shaped several words which made no sound. "But no, but no," she finished, "you had to lie and cheat. You couldn't even telephone to say what you were doing, and all that time I thought— All right! Who cares? You'll never get *The Day*. Never! Because— Don't say a word. Don't you dare open your mouth, when all that comes out of it is lies. I've put up every cent I have to buy stock, and tomorrow I . . . take control . . . Hurd-Hudner! Baa—"

This long speech she brought out with tremendous effort, finishing in a menacing whisper. She felt at that moment that she'd gladly sell her soul for a drink; with some idea of going out to the pantry, she rose, facing Sharon, who had remained on her feet, looking at her with a posed, unbearable expression of superiority.

"That will be very interesting," Sharon said. "Congratulations."

"It happens to be true."

"I'm sure of it."

"Call the bank. Call Wilkins and Shimenko. They'll tell you if I'm lying. You're the one that lies, not me."

"Of course," Sharon said, "not you. Why didn't anybody realize you were a business genius? Even counting all the men you've slept with called for higher mathematics."

"Girls, girls," Brad said unhappily.

Neither his wife nor his sister-in-law was paying the least attention.

"Yes, you're right, I loved a few men," Alexandra yelled, "a few wonderful, adorable men who found me a little bit attractive. Don't you wish you had? Then you might not be married to that miserable ugh—" her liberal gesture took in the entire section of the room where Brad was standing—"that *thing* I turned down when I was—"

A blow, then a scream, amputated the sentence. Brad groaned as the two women, locked in each other's arms, fell across the cocktail table, upsetting a standing lamp next to it.

"Please, Sharon . . . for God's sake . . ."

"I'll . . . kill . . . her," Sharon gasped. Speech was difficult. Her head was twisted to one side by a hand pushing up at her chin from below. Alexandra, though the stronger of the two, seemed to have been partly knocked out by her fall. She struggled to rise, sinking her teeth in Brad's forearm as he made an effort, timid and ineffectual, to break up the fight.

"—kill . . . her . . ."

"You—"

"Listen to me, Sharon . . ."

"Ooow . . . aiiii . . ."

Brad, bleeding, scrambled out of harm's way. He picked up the telephone. Should he call downstairs? Help might be on hand in a few seconds, but—the scandal! There might be no way to keep this quiet. He hesitated, suddenly pleased to see Sharon holding her own again.

From the suite's service quarters the French maid appeared. She stood in the doorway, her hands pressed to her mouth, as the sisters broke their clinch, and then, with insane faces, flew at each other again. To the maid the scene was not credible in any respect: since it failed to conform to any pattern of behavior she had been taught to expect from people of the *haut monde*, it appeared to her in the light of some fantastic joke, in the worst possible taste, and it was on this conception that she based a quiet but frantic plea, addressed to her mistress.

"*Madame*," the maid begged, "*pas de plaisanterie, madame . . . pas de plaisanterie . . .*"

5   Dr. Hugo French, who had stayed in his office somewhat later than usual, took the call himself, both the receptionist and his nurse having already left.

"Dr. French speaking."

"This is Pamela Harper, Doctor."

"Yes, Pamela."

"I'm here at the house, Dr. French. Do you think you could possibly call and see my father? I'm a little worried about him."

"Yes, of course," Dr. French said. "I'm just leaving. I'll stop on my way home."

"Oh, thank you so much."

"Not at all. How does he seem?"

His tone was casual, but he asked the question because he wondered whether, as sometimes happened, the caller (out of ignorance or the convention of not giving way to alarm) was failing to indicate an emergency situation. The "little worry" to which Pamela confessed might thus be the justification of the large one which, two nights earlier, had led him to stop on his own initiative to examine Anchylus.

"Just tired. But so very tired."

"That's to be expected, under the circumstances."

"I know. But it's not just . . . because of Mother Saxe. There has been a dreadful strain. And he hasn't slept. He's had meetings every night and I don't think he's slept more than two or three hours, for several nights. I'll be awfully grateful if you can make him rest."

"That we can do," Dr. French said cheerfully. "I'll be with you in a few minutes."

"Thank you again," Pamela said. "Goodbye."

"Goodbye, Pamela," Dr. French said.

If fatigue was all that was wrong, the old devil was lucky; he'd been driving himself beyond all reasonable limits of safety. Not that he wasn't tough, but at his age you didn't clout yourself around the way Anchylus had been doing. Also there was another person's death involved: a person close to him. Sometimes that was all the tough ones needed. They kept going like machines until that happened, and then, *blam*, they were gone.

Dr. French took off his office tunic. He brushed his hair and washed his hands with surgical soap. He performed these actions mechanically yet, in spite of the rhythm established by long habit, he was hurrying just a little more than usual.

Pamela put down the telephone quietly. She had used the one in the hall because Anchylus was in the library and she thought that if he knew what she was calling Hugo French about he might object: better to face him with the deed accomplished. During the week, leaving Cliff to put the children in bed, she'd driven into town several evenings and dined with her father. Tonight they'd been having highballs when he'd suddenly confessed to feeling tired and gone to lie down on the couch; when she saw his eyes close and his head nod she'd tiptoed out of the room to make the call. It wasn't the first time he'd dozed off in this way, but as a rule he'd roused himself and, after wolfing some food, gone on working till past midnight. Now, however, for the first time his immense vitality showed signs of deserting him: his color was ashy gray, there were brown smears under his eyes and his hands had shaken a little as he poured out the drinks.

Tonight, she'd thought, he must sleep or he'll collapse. Everything's been done that can be done; his success or failure in the stockholders' meeting may turn on his having one last burst of strength—the strength that a good sleep might give him.

Re-entering the library, she drew in her breath sharply. Anchylus had set his glass down on the floor—had set it down carefully, since not a drop had been spilled—and next to the glass, trailing down from the low, broad sofa, was his right hand, the mashed fingers curved into a fist, as if, even resting, he must be ready to deal with his enemies. None of these things were in themselves alarming, but what was alarming, and so much so that her heart contracted painfully, was his pipe—one of the heavy briers which he handled with such deftness and which he had never, as far as she could remember, let fall in this manner.

The pipe was still lighted. Pamela picked it up and laid it on the desk. She slipped to her knees beside the sofa, studying her father's face. There was a light flush in his cheeks, his mouth had fallen open and he was snoring—not the stertorous snore of illness but an easy, reasonable kind of sound.

Pamela got up. She felt relieved. She wouldn't wake him. Hugo French could do that if he wanted to. She was even sorry she'd telephoned: it seemed ridiculous to wake a man up to see a doctor who'd been called to make him sleep.

IX

Room 100

"*Blow, winds, and crack your cheeks! rage! blow!
You cataracts and hurricanoes, spout . . .*"
—SHAKESPEARE, *King Lear*

1 ROOM 100 in the Day Building was known also as the Directors'
Room. Its walls were oak, stained and waxed, darkened by time
and hand-rubbing to a rich, leathery brown. Upon them, in
heavy gilt frames, were fierce-looking portraits of Jacob and Fabian
Rupke and a somewhat more modern one of Anchylus Saxe. Arranged along with these were framed copies of certain celebrated
Day issues, the Battleship *Maine* issue, the McKinley Assassination,
the Fire and Earthquake issue (the latter printed on the presses of the
Oakland *Tribune*), Woodrow Wilson's Declaration of War on Germany, etc. Also photographs of company outings, and a snapshot
of the first motor circulation truck, complete with crew.

The windows of Room 100 were high and narrow, protected by
thick drapes; the carpet's brindle wave rolled up to cover a small dais
where the conference table ordinarily rested. The table was there no
longer. Early that morning four men from the maintenance department had moved it down to the middle of the room and set it
against the wall to serve as a buffet. This had been done at Dan

317

Winkler's orders. Dan felt that the stockholders who turned out for the meeting deserved some sort of welcome from Management, even if they had come to vote against it; he'd had the cook who prepared the meals for the executive dining room come down early to provide some large urns of coffee and many plates of sweet pastries and little sandwiches.

Dan had told Matt Brody that he expected an unusually large turnout. The guess proved to be right. In past years the record number of stockholders attending an annual meeting had been thirty-seven out of a possible five hundred: today by Matt's count ninety-one were on hand by ten minutes to ten—a really extraordinary showing. The parking lot was soon full and all available parking places on the nearby streets occupied; cars jammed into the alley reserved for circulation trucks, and a number of chauffeur-driven vehicles were parked in the loading zones on Hazard Street. Usually at such an hour a morning newspaper is just getting its eyes open: even in the business departments nobody has much to say and work gets started slowly, with as many planned interruptions as possible.

Today all this was different. The knowledge that the paper was fighting for its life had penetrated all departments with the result that even the most essential daily acts seemed suddenly pointless. All sorts of rumors circulated—none of them accurate, all of them hotly discussed. The inky, exhausted air locked in the building overnight, that air which usually rushed out when the first doors were opened, lingered everywhere, banked over the silent presses, poured like glass into the dungeonlike engraving room where two old men, their hands covered with blue scars, talked angrily, not knowing why they quarreled. Hope was at a premium. A copyboy claimed he'd seen Mr. Marvin, the assistant cashier, sorting a pile of pink slips three feet high. . . . Wouldn't a paper give some notice as it died, wouldn't it cough, way down in its guts, or something? Wouldn't it maybe throw itself once more powerfully out of the seas and go booming to the surface with one last tremendous flip like a strong old sperm whale before it bellyflopped back into whatever salt, secret and blood-spumed oblivion its killers had prepared for it? That would seem right, seem how it ought to be. But you couldn't tell.

Things were bad. Things were tough all over.

Seventy-five folding wooden chairs, in banks of six, had been placed in Room 100, facing the dais—seventy-five being all the seats that available space would hold, allowing for the buffet and the chairs of the incumbent Board. It was the custom at these meetings for the directors to sit in a half-circle on the dais, "defying the stockholders," as Matt Brody had once put it, with Anchylus' monolithic throne chair in the center.

No member of the Board had as yet appeared. The proxyholders milled around and chatted, drank the coffee and nibbled the refreshments. Some also read a circular which had been handed to them as they entered the building by two pretty girls wearing placards reading, in large letters, it's TIME FOR A CHANGE!

The placards, like the circulars, had been prepared at the expense of Wilkins & Shimenko, who had also hired the girls. Tim Wilkins thought that having girls as distributors would be an endearing touch. It would make more palatable the attack on Management contained in the circular. The attack was a little rough, and Tim had had his doubts about it, but Leon Shimenko, who had helped a public-relations man to prepare it, felt that it was necessary.

This was to be a day of truth. Always in the past, when the report recording what had happened at the annual meetings was sent out, it was found to contain phrases like "your fellow shareowners then decided . . ." or "the stockholders thereupon voted to . . ."— euphemistic expressions implying that the holders of certificates actually had something to say about the company, whereas the truth was they'd never had anything to say and wouldn't have known how to go about it if they had.

Today, no matter how you looked at it, the situation was different. The stockholders had suddenly become important, their wishes no longer fantasies, their favors earnestly and even desperately sought.

The stockholders knew this. As they stood in the hall smoking and talking and moved in and out to the buffet, they had the air of persons dedicated to great affairs. Some walked alone, others clanned into knots of three and four and twirled into corners for hurried, intense little powwows. They were mostly men, with here and there a shareholding wife or girl friend who had come along to see the show.

Like the stockholders of all middle-sized companies, *The Day's* nominal owners fell into several separate categories. On the bottom were the pensioners—the longtime *Day* employees who had received their stock, paid for in part by Management, as recipients under the company's retirement plan: these were with Anchylus to a man.

Above them—a larger group numerically, as also in point of certificates held per individual—were the investors who had bought the stock as a long-term investment or (lured by its recent gyrations) for a quick profit. The members of this group differed widely in personality and occupation, and their attitude on the issues before the meeting was completely unpredictable. Finally, at the apex of the power pyramid, were the big fellows—brokers holding stock "bene-ficiarily," with authority to vote it for their clients, and private in-vestors with holdings of ten thousand shares or more. To this divi-sion belonged Ling Tung Chow, present in person today, fatter and paler and somehow less functional out in public (where he rarely went) than he seemed in his office. Also Gregson Reed, Oakleigh Donovan's partner, who in spite of (or possibly because of) Oak-leigh's presence on the Board had several fair-sized blocks of shares to vote—the same being true of Sven Ritter of the Crocker Bank and Tom McAvity, trustee for a famous Comstock Lode estate. These more solid personalities, disdaining the hivelike activity around them, were among the first to be seated, waiting patiently for pro-ceedings to begin.

The Hurd-Hudner group had already taken their places. They had chosen the front row, on the left of the center aisle. Pilbrick, in the same brown suit he had worn on arrival, sat with an attaché case on the floor beside him. He leaned over to touch this from time to time as if its waxy English pigskin contained some weapon he might need at short notice. Sharon was next to him, with Brad on her right. She wore black, as necessitated by her state of mourning, and looked handsome and composed. (It had been understood that her name would be put before the meeting as one of the names on the Hurd-Hudner slate.) Farther along in the row were two unim-pressive, balding men high in the Hurd-Hudner hierarchy, on hand to fill out the five-man slate of candidates—Hy Nysam, head of H-H's West Coast department, and Harry Claiborne, a wire-service executive who had flown up from Los Angeles.

At 10:04 Dan Winkler, Matt Brody, Oakleigh Donovan and George Dudley walked down the aisle. Since it was now clear there wouldn't be enough seats for all the stockholders, the bolder jammed in rapidly to find places, a less numerous segment settling back to stand along the wall by the door.

Earlier in the morning Alexandra had telephoned Miss Wilke, asking that an office on the executive floor should be set aside for the Wilkins-Shimenko group to work in. This request Miss Wilke re-fused on her own authority. The idea of having the office had popped into Alexandra's mind at the last moment. She hadn't ex-pected to get it, but the refusal annoyed her, nonetheless, and she persuaded Leon and Timmy that whatever could be gained by talk-ing to stockholders just before the meeting would be too little and too late. She wore her mink coat to give her confidence, and she needed confidence today because her face had been scratched in the free-for-all with Sharon and the make-up she'd put on to hide this, bunching in the scratch, made her look as if she was scarred. She felt like a gangster's moll, scar and all, walking in with four men—Tim and Leon and the lawyer, Garber, and one of Garber's partners. Reaching the front row, she turned and looked at Sharon—a look which she tried to make ironic but by means of which she hoped to find out whether Sharon had been marked up too. It was disgusting to discover that Sharon was outwardly unharmed.

Alexandra turned her back on her sister. She sat down on the right side of the aisle, in the place reserved for her between Tim and Shimenko. She lighted a cigarette and blew the smoke toward the dais.

2 ANCHYLUS' CHAIR was still vacant. It bulked there on the dais like some ogre-land throne a child might invent. The steel rails that served it for footrest gleamed dully, its ore-slab seat squatted on the heavy legs which moored it to the floor, its arms of polished and varnished wood spread like a mechanism for execution. A man who would dream up a chair like that for business purposes would have to be somewhat out of his mind. So, at least, a number of stockholders thought that morning—stockholders who had nothing to do for the next few minutes but stare at it. A crazy kind of chair, all right, yet there was a crazy Shakespearean appropriateness in it, as if the chair had been constructed out of the same foggy myth that had shaped the man and from the same violent, haphazard materials, volcanic and enduring, so that even in his absence (since for his own whimsical reasons he had evidently decided not to be on time, or maybe not to come at all) the chair, the chair alone, could represent him, yawning there in all its immovable and senseless grandeur as if to say, "Why doesn't one of you come up here and sit in me?" Nobody could, of course. The chair was like the sword Excalibur which had been given to King Arthur by the Lady of the Lake and which only the king could ever use.

It was 10:12. Insulting though the fact might be to all present, it was conceivable that an old man who happened to be president of a company as well as chairman of its board might get to a stockholders' meeting fifteen minutes late. Nothing to do but wait. While they waited, many of the stockholders smoothed out the Wilkins-Shimenko circular they'd been holding crumpled in their hands or stuck in their pockets and read it again, to see if they had missed anything.

We address this letter to you publicly, Mr. Anchylus Saxe, because you refused to talk to us in private. We—the undersigned candidates for places on the Board of our company—hoped by a personal interview to iron out dissatisfactions. We wanted to ask you why *The San Francisco Day*, once a great newspaper, has slipped far behind in this parade. We wanted to ask you why the dividend rate represented less than 3 per cent on invested capital, why circulation has been dropping while overhead remained the same, why certain abuses in management should continue to be tolerated.

We wanted to ask why, for thirty years, you have run a company that is owned by five hundred stockholders as if this company were a roadside fruitstand with you, and only you, behind the counter, peddling its merchandise.

You weren't very nice to us, Mr. Saxe. You refused to meet with us. Then, in an advertisement, you called us some names. You said we were renegades. You called us "fly-by-night people," meaning, as near as we can gather, that we wore pointed hats and rode broomsticks. In fact, to anyone not better informed—as we hope most of our stockholders are by now—it would have seemed that we were an undesirable group indeed, a dismal enclave composed in equal parts of witches and hoodlums.

Such were your suspicions. May we express a suspicion of our own, Mr. Saxe? We suspect that anyone who dares to pry into the company which you consider yours (and which we know to be ours!) assumes for you the shape of a witch or the smell of a hoodlum. We suspect that you want to go on running *The Day* as long as you live with the same intolerant, superior attitude you have previously demonstrated.

How superior are you, Mr. Saxe? Have you really always stood, as you said in your advertisement, "personally and publicly for the best interests of this newspaper and San Francisco"?

Let's look at the record. What does it show?

(A) It shows that early in your career as a company executive you used blackmail as an approach to selling advertising space. (There are several businessmen still living who can testify to that: we would gladly supply their names now if we didn't know that you would use this information to injure and defame the persons in question by slurs and derogation.)

322

(B) It shows that police had to intervene on an occasion when you used violence to keep a competitor's papers off the streets.

(C) It shows a suit brought against you in another state (and never brought to trial) charging you with being the father of an illegitimate child.

Why go on? We hold that to stand on tradition as a reason for remaining in office a man's record should be cleaner than that. We hold that yours, far from being in "the best interests of this newspaper and of San Francisco," is an embarrassment to this company and a slur on the name of our fair city. We hold that it's time for a change.

WHO HAS BEEN FLYING BY NIGHT, MR. SAXE? COULD IT BE YOU?

Here followed a breakdown of circulation and advertising figures, rating *The Day* against its competitors, *The Examiner* and *The Chronicle*, to the detriment of *The Day*. Whether or not the figures were accurate nobody knew. It is doubtful, indeed, whether anybody read them. The personal attack was what promised the fireworks, and it was this that attracted the attention of opposition and pro-Management forces alike.

3   IT WAS 10:18. For a number of minutes there had been restless stirrings among the princes on the dais and the laity on the hard chairs, a rustling and whispering and glancing at watches. Dan Winkler scribbled a note and passed it down to Matt Brody. "Can you find out where he is?" Matt looked across at Dan and nodded. He was just starting to get up when his eye fell on Miss Wilke, who had just entered the room and was coming down the center aisle toward the directorial semicircle. Reaching Matt, whose seat was at one end of the horseshoe, Miss Wilke said in a low voice, "He's on his way, but he wants you to begin."

"Is he all right?" Matt asked worriedly.

It had occurred to him, as it had to everyone close to Anchylus, that the old man hadn't been looking well the last few days; his failure to appear seemed ominous.

"I think so," Miss Wilke said. "I didn't talk to him, though. Pamela telephoned. She was at the house. She said he overslept."

Matt thanked her. The explanation didn't seem too likely, but it would, he supposed, have to do. He crossed to Dan Winkler, at the opposite side of the dais, and passed the information along to him.

". . . wants us to start."

"Can we, without him here?"

"I don't know. How about that, George?" he asked, addressing George Dudley, who had come over to join them. "Can a meeting be opened if the Chairman isn't present?"

"Yes, yes," Dudley said, "that is, I'm quite sure of it."

"Well, are you sure or not?" Winkler asked practically. "Because if you're not—"

"I'm *quite* sure," Dudley said in his precise way, "that it's stated in the charter, in the absence of the Chairman the Secretary will preside. That is, if a quorum is present."

"A quorum of directors or stockholders?"

"A quorum of the Board," Dudley said. "In my opinion you can go ahead."

"I'll call to order, then," Dan Winkler said.

Matt and Dudley resumed their seats while Winkler crossed toward Anchylus' chair. For a minute it looked as if he were going to sit down in it, but at the last minute he changed his mind and merely stood beside it, picking up the gavel and rapping sharply and unnecessarily loudly.

"The meeting will come to order."

Pilbrick was on his feet, beating Garber to this position by a tenth of a second. "Mr. Secretary—"

"Mr. Pilbrick, I shall recognize questions from the floor at the proper time."

"I rise to a point of order," Pilbrick said. "Have we authority to open this meeting without the Chairman? Further, I should like to add, where is he?"

"I have just been advised," Winkler said, "that we have such authority. I shall ignore your second question as irrelevant. The meeting will proceed."

Garber was now also standing—a thickset, senatorial man with long, houndlike grooves in his cheeks. "Are we to understand, then, that the Chairman doesn't plan to attend?"

"On the contrary," Winkler said, "he's now on his way. I shall answer no more questions; kindly take your seat, sir."

Garber looked over at Pilbrick to see if there was going to be further objection from that quarter. When none came, he slowly sat down, letting his deepening cheek grooves register his protest. The President, the Old Party, was the one they were after. Without him

324

to attack and, possibly, tear to bits, the meeting had no point—or so at least the cheek grooves seemed to say.

Winkler addressed the room. "Our purpose here today is to elect five members to the Board of The San Francisco Day Publishing Company . . ."

While Swift & Fallbrook, a bookkeeping firm, was being elected to count the proxies, and while the presentation of documents, proof of a quorum present, and other necessary but dull rituals were being enacted in Room 100, the butler, Reuben, was kneeling in front of Anchylus Saxe in the chief bedroom of the California Street house, easing his master's thick legs into a pair of striped worsted britches. Pamela stood by with a cup of coffee but didn't offer it—her father had already drunk three large cups and seemed to be coming around. He had never, to anyone's recollection, overslept before: that he had done so on a day which might well be the most crucial day of his life was due to a combination of circumstances, principally his exhaustion and Dr. French's pills.

He hadn't left a morning call. He never did. For years the signal that he was awake and ready for the day had been well established —the thump of his feet hitting the floor at seven o'clock and the four heavy steps that took him into the bathroom where his cold bath waited, run warm the evening before and allowed to chill during the night. Pamela had hoped that for once he wouldn't wake up at his usual time. He'd slept peacefully on the library sofa after dinner; after a couple of hours he'd awakened and made some phone calls, then gone up to bed. Reuben had brought him some hot milk laced with bourbon and Anchylus had used this draught to wash down the two seconals that French had left. Sleep, the doctor had said, was his principal need: he shouldn't, if it could possibly be avoided, be disturbed. Pamela had passed this instruction on to Reuben. She'd gone home to attend to her own family, coming back a little after nine, expecting to find him dressed and ready for the meeting. Instead, he was still sound asleep.

"He won't be more than a half an hour late," Pamela had told Miss Wilke on the telephone, "but there's no way to get him there before that. Do you suppose you could go up there and make some excuse for him?"

"I don't know," Miss Wilke said; "he doesn't like excuses."

"Just tell them something," Pamela said, "anything at all."

Miss Wilke snorted. "I'll tell them he overslept," she said; "that ought to fix them!"

"Tell them that, then. It's the truth."

"He's not sick, is he?" Miss Wilke asked sharply.

"No, he isn't, Miss Wilke," Pamela said. "I was afraid last night that he was going to be, but he looks fine. He's had a good rest."

"Fine," Miss Wilke said. "Tell him to come a-shootin'."

"He will," Pamela said. "I think he's ready."

"He'd better be. They're all up there waiting for him," Miss Wilke said. She swore, compactly and interestingly—something Pamela had never heard her do before. "—— hyenas," she said. "I won't go up there for a while. Let them sit and stew. It will do them good"

"Good idea, Miss Wilke," Pamela said.

As a piece of campaign strategy, arriving late might not be bad. It would be fine, Pamela thought, to have him walk in like a lion, his head cleared by the good long sleep and the seconal dredged out of him by the coffee. Calm and crafty. That was the way. Not angry—and he got angry so easily when he was tired. To get angry after the fight was raging might not be too bad, but to arrive that way would be a handicap. It would be an advantage to the hyenas. Once he was dressed in the striped pants and the tailcoat with silk-faced square lapels which he always wore to annual meetings he was calm enough, fully in possession of himself, and during the short drive to the Day Building he studied some notes Donovan and Dudley had prepared relating to questions that might be asked. He hadn't had any breakfast yet, but he often went without breakfast: at least he hadn't taken anything to drink, as Pamela had been half afraid he would. On the whole everything had turned out as well as could be hoped, up to the time he entered the building to go upstairs, at which time the good luck which had attended the morning suddenly came to an end.

Anchylus got angry.

It was all the fault of the girls with the circulars. They'd discarded their placards and the tinsel coats they'd worn while handing out the printed forms upstairs: their job was done, all the people who had been supposed to receive circulars now being inside Room 100 with the doors shut. The girls were leaving by the Hazard Street door when one of them saw Anchylus coming in; she ran back to him and stuffed a circular in his hand, smiling at him brilliantly—both girls had been instructed to be sunny and feminine, whenever possible.

Anchylus smiled back and thanked her. He didn't look at the circular as he rode up in the elevator but he still had it in his hand as he marched down the center aisle, and after he was seated on the dais he started to read it.

At this point the proceedings were limping along, under half a head of steam. Dan Winkler had finished the minutes of the last meeting, something nobody wanted to hear. So that the meeting could listen to somebody besides himself (Dan made a tired little joke out of this, which fell as flat as he should have known it would) he'd called on Oakleigh Donovan to read the Treasurer's Report. Oakleigh's delivery lacked platform fascination, as did the contents of the report, but he was plodding through it manfully when a hearty curse behind him made him stop. The curse had issued from Anchylus, who sat hunched in his throne, gripping the circular in both hands and staring at it with an expression of demonic fury.

"Something, Anchylus?" Oakleigh said, partially turning.

"No, no," Anchylus said, "pardon me. Go on, go on . . ."

". . . whereas accounts receivable show a slight drop, due to current conditions," Oakleigh droned on. "It must be borne in mind that the company's liquid position . . ."

Anchylus' hands were sweating. He wiped them with his handkerchief, dropping the circular to the floor, then picked it up again, checking to make sure it actually said what at first glance it had seemed to say.

It never occurred to him that the terminology employed in the circular represented only the feeblest paraphrase of thunders he had hurled, at other times, against his enemies. What occurred to him was that he suddenly wanted to kill somebody, it didn't matter whom: "the rascals," as the *Day*'s editorial stereotypes defined all dissenting parties, "the foul perpetrators of this outrage." Nor was his rage to kill a theoretical matter. Kill and stomp, knock down, strike with a blunt instrument, exterminate. Any jury in the old days would have condoned any or all of these courses: horsewhipping would have been a mild, an almost sissified, alternative. He could have killed just for that remark about the illegitimate child, for that struck at the heart of him and at the distant nerve center of all that had hurt him through the years and all that had gone wrong with his hopes and his love and his pride.

4 THERE HAD BEEN a ripple of clapping as Anchylus took his place. Pilbrick turned sharply around, scanning the faces behind him to identify what spies or shillabers, in defiance of Hurd-Hudner's interests, had been encouraged to make this demonstration. The Wilkins-Shimenko platoon on the opposite side of the aisle seemed less concerned. Leon Shimenko looked covertly at Garber, who was noncommittal, then at Tim Wilkins, who whispered, "They're kidding, aren't they?"

Alexandra didn't appear to have heard. She was staring at her father with a rapt face, locked in the grip of some private reverie.

Now the meeting had some architecture. There was a man in the big chair where before only a phantom had sat. Those who had come to destroy him were free to examine the condemned. Those who had come to uphold him could view their leader.

Sharon put her hands against her face. She pressed her fingertips against her eyes in the manner of one suffering from eyestrain. Sometimes that did good. If you caused total darkness to make a tent in your brain, if only for a minute, things were different when you saw them again. People were different too. Yet, when she removed her fingers Anchylus was still hunched in his chair in that queer way, reading. The men ranged on each side of him might as well not have been there, he seemed so alone. He seemed also old, forlorn and sort of crazy—something she had never thought of in connection with him, craziness. Yet, that getup, the swallowtail and so forth: it was all wrong. Could that be the explanation of the jam he was in and that they all, in a sense, were in, that he wasn't tracking mentally, that perhaps he'd never really tracked, in spite of his great talents? Why, he looked like some old actor who'd outlived his reputation and got himself up in fancy dress to read one of his old parts—to read for a producer who would surely turn him down. She felt . . . but no, it was quite impossible to feel sorry for a man who had brought about his own downfall as Anchylus had.

Sharon looked away, trying to recapture the mood of anger she'd felt at the previous meeting when Anchylus had told what he wanted from Hurd-Hudner: surely any sane man would have known such demands were impossible. No chain would put out a huge sum to buy a newspaper, then let the former publisher go on editing and running it. If he'd been trying to trick them when he agreed to the negotiations, he had certainly failed: he had been his usual highhanded self, and there was no use slipping, out of weakness, into pity for him or feel guilt for what she had helped to bring about.

Well, if he hadn't learned then not to hurt people he would find out today. Out of the corner of her eye she saw him crush the circular and flip it away, a draft at once taking the crumpled sheet, drawing it down into the aisle. . . .

Alexandra touched the circular with her foot. She didn't want it rustling around, disturbing her. She had been dreaming of a scene which she had imagined many times before—one of supreme importance, for which the present situation was merely a dull though necessary introduction. In the scene of her imagination she walked quickly down a corridor in the Day Building. She came to a door behind which someone was typing; she entered without knocking, the typing stopped, the old woman in front of the machine looked up in desolate terror. Alexandra smiled at her.

"I believe you know, Letty, that I've bought *The San Francisco Day*," she said. "You're fired."

In all the times she had made up this scene it never came out the same. She had tried once more now only because, with the actuality so near, the way it came out in her mind might be nearer to the truth. Nearer, but not wholly the truth, because that would be a surprise, like all great moments; it might be less wonderful or more wonderful, you couldn't tell, but it would be different. Nothing in the scene, no essential quality, had blurred with repeated imaginings but had become only more distinct, more stylized. All that had been lost was the motive for reflection on this subject: that, in course of time, had disintegrated until it was no longer clear to her why she hated Letty or why firing her would set straight an old and perplexing score. The motive didn't matter any more. Kicking the crumpled circular aside, she wondered suddenly whether Letty were in the room right now. It was rather an exciting idea. All long-time employees had stock the company retirement plan helped to pay for: certainly she would have wanted to vote hers for Anchylus, her god. Alexandra twisted around. It was as if some instinct had advised her where to look—for there was Letty, sure enough, her little, blotchy, dead-white face quite unmistakable even though only a part of it was visible, behind some man's face. Alexandra wondered whether she was taking notes. It would be ironic if she were. Letty always wrote obituaries of society people, and these notes, if there were any, would be her own obituary, figuratively speaking. This, she thought happily, was Letty's last appearance as an employee of *The Day*.

329

Pamela's breath caught in her throat. Something was wrong on the dais—Anchylus' strained attitude and then his action with the circular were danger signals. Not having read the circular herself, she didn't know what had disturbed him; she misinterpreted his behavior as a sign, possibly, that he wasn't feeling well. Any collapse or weakness on his part now could be ruinous to his chances; he needed all his power, all his control. If physical illness wasn't what had upset him, what could it be? She made a movement as if to push past the people around her—late-comers who, like her, had been unable to find seats and were standing four deep against the wall on the far end of the room.

"Please . . ." she said, "excuse me, but I must . . ."

Those nearest her looked around in surprise. She didn't clearly realize what her intention was, except that she felt she should be nearer to Anchylus. As she edged forward, through the small gap which her movement had opened for her, someone took hold of her arm and she found herself next to Hugo French.

"He's all right," the doctor whispered.

"Why did he drop that paper?" she said. "I couldn't see well, but I thought . . ."

By way of answer Dr. French gave her his own copy of the circular. She unfolded it, not quite understanding, and read the first few lines, then broke off. She couldn't concentrate. It was good that Dr. French was here, though; she hadn't known that he was a stockholder. Perhaps he wasn't: perhaps his being here had quite a different meaning, a professional one. . . .

George Dudley, who had been reading something on the platform, broke off. Anchylus thumped the gavel.

"I declare this meeting open for nominations. . . ."

A man she didn't know, sitting next to Sharon in the front row, got up and read off five names in a high, fuzzy voice. Among the names were Brad's and Sharon's. Tim Wilkins got up and stood there while the man finished. Anchylus nodded to him.

"Do you have a nomination to place before the shareowners?"

"I do, sir," Tim said. "In behalf of the Stockholders' Protective Committee, I should like to nominate as members of the Board of this company my partner, Mr. Leon Shimenko, of San Francisco, and the Baroness Alexandra Drobny, of Sonoma."

Leon rose. He nominated Tim Wilkins and someone else. The man who had spoken first, from the Hurd-Hudner group, was on his feet again.

"Mr. Pilbrick . . ."

"I should like to ask a question."

"I'll take questions later," Anchylus said.

Leon's voice interrupted. "Mr. Saxe, is it true that your personal automobile is being operated at company expense? We would also like to have some facts about—"

"I said I'd take questions later."

Pilbrick had his hand up, shaking it like a schoolboy who needed to go to the john. "Point of order," Pilbrick said, "will the chairman recognize a point of order?"

"Later, sir," Anchylus said.

"I represent, sir," Pilbrick shouted, "that the Chair is out of order. By the terms of the agenda questions should be taken after nominations."

"The Chair," Anchylus said, "is not out of order but you are out of order, Mr. Pilbrick. I should like to remind you that in addition to being Chairman of the Board of this company I am also its President. It is proper for the President to address the meeting before questions or anything else, if he wants to, and I want to. It so happens I have a few things to say."

5   SOMEONE IN THE BACK of the room laughed. Someone else shushed him. Two or three stockholders applauded, and again a nervous spurt of handclapping, spotty and possibly derisive but still rather favorable to Anchylus, made itself heard. Anchylus, who had ignored it the first time it happened, rose to it now as if it were a coliseum ovation. He left the big chair and walked to the edge of the dais and stood looking down at all present with a pleased, confident smile.

"Ladies and gentlemen," he said, "my esteemed shareholders! It's gratifying to see so many of you here today, at our regular annual meeting. I feel honored and I may say that I was doubly honored and most pleased, listening to the nominations that have just been made, to note that two of my daughters are standing for the Board. I'm glad that they're taking an interest in our business. It took quite a while for them to get around to it, but that's the way we'd like *The San Francisco Day* to be—just one big happy family."

He paused, but if he'd expected a laugh on this he was disappointed. The room was too tense as yet to break its mood. A few chuckles were heard, about equally divided on the left and right sides of the aisle—the narrow open strip which had by mutual consent been taken as a dividing line for the contesting parties.

"Most of us have been together in this room a number of times before. Not all of us, of course. Some of you are new here—" he looked down first at the Hurd-Hudner delegation, then at the Wilkins-Shimenko bunch—"and to those I say, welcome! We're glad to have you! I was puzzled, I'll admit, to find that some of our very newest stockholders weren't quite confident about our enterprise. They seemed to feel they needed protection, coming into it—apparently a protection against me, since they got themselves up into a buying group and called it a Protective Association. I hope before they leave they'll feel a little safer. I hope they'll decide we're fairly civilized, here at *The San Francisco Day*, no matter how old-fashioned we may be."

With this statement, Anchylus folded his arms. He lowered his bushy head with such beautifully sardonic modesty that for the first time he drew a real laugh.

"You tell 'em, boss," someone said from the rear. Anchylus raised a finger to discourage such interpolations. He went on quickly, "Oh, yes, we've been called old-fashioned. And we don't deny it, it's quite true! We've always been that way. We like to make a dollar, but we also like to stand for something in the city— tradition or principle or whatever you might choose to call it. From some aspects no doubt that's been a mistake; business isn't supposed to be conducted that way nowadays. When I took an advertisement in our own pages to set forth my views on this old-fashionedness of ours, I had to pay the penalty. I was personally attacked in an unpleasant way—" for the first time his voice took on a serious emotion—"in a dastardly and cowardly way, in my opinion, by the same stockholders' group that needs so much protection, the group which with no previous experience in the newspaper business says I'm running *The Day* all wrong and wants a chance to run it better."

Anchylus was really building now, his voice vibrating with the fury which he had been trying—successfully, so far—to keep out of his words.

"—that is," he said, "that is, if they feel like running it at all . . . if they don't think on wiser reflection that there might be more in it for them just to pull the paper to pieces and sell off the scraps for junk. When I walked into this building today, a building which I planned and helped to design and borrowed the money to pay for, I was handed a contemptible document purporting to come from some of the stockholders. I don't believe it represents what you would like to say to me. In my opinion those of you who thought enough of *The Day* to buy a share in it would have thought too much of me to write those words. Such words could only have been conceived by the raiders who want to cut me up. Calumniators! Plotters and connivers, thugs and hoodlums, trying to use investment techniques to effect a burglary—the larceny of my life-work. Well, let them try. I don't think they can succeed. Their methods are too obvious to fool a child. Why, you know they had to go back to my start in life to find something they could sneer at. Then, they said I was too tough. I got the cops out. I printed the truth about people. Do you know something? That's all true too. If you weren't tough, if you didn't print the truth, you didn't get far with a newspaper. Not in San Francisco."

He got a real hand now. It was spontaneous, explosive. Even those who had come to the meeting with proxies already committed to one opposition side or the other paid him a tribute. He was selling his life hard, as everyone had known he would.

Anchylus waited with backturned head and slabby jaw upraised till the noise was over. Then he went on in a pinched, bitter way that reflected real hurt.

"No, my friends, I didn't mind that. What I minded was what you'd have minded too, if it had happened to you. They mentioned a suit. Oh, yes, there was one—way back somewhere. I know when. You don't forget those things. No indeed. You don't forget them— and you don't try to defend yourself thirty years later, when there's no need to. But—but, gentlemen, what kind of ghouls would pry into the dust to rake up something like that, bring it to light to hurt, not me, I can't be hurt by it, but a lovely and innocent and helpless woman? They talked about blackmail. What are such slurring innuendoes but the foulest, slimiest kind of blackmail? And here's what I want to ask you: Do you imagine for a minute that the kind of grave-robbing night crawler who would make a negotiation weapon out of an old tired scandal, which moreover never really was a scandal, do you think reptiles like that could run a newspaper you'd want to read and have your children read? That's a rhetorical question, my friends. I'm not going to answer it. I'll let you compare the journalistic content and intention of that circular —I'm sure you've all read it—with the newspaper we're now discussing. That circular, my friends, may be—and I pray God it will be—the only San Francisco publication these would-be editors ever have a chance to edit!"

"Whoopee!" yelled the interrupter background voice over the

howls and clapping of the anti-Wilkins-Shimenko and pro-Management factions. "You called their bluff, Anchylus. Give 'em hell!"

Pamela looked at the circular in her hand. So that was it. The wheel had certainly come full circle when her own birth was an issue in the conflicts of businessmen. She wasn't particularly shocked or upset. She'd lived with herself too long for that, and whatever suffering had had to be done for the conditions of her birth had been done by herself and others, long ago. She folded the circular, however, and put it away for future reference. It would be interesting to read it over.

Anchylus looked at Dan Winkler and Matt, understanding what he wanted, crossed to the speaker's table and hammered with the gavel until order was restored.

Anchylus then continued. "I'm pretty near through talking. I'd be all through if only *one* union of burglars wanted *The Day*. All of a sudden, for a paper that's been called decrepit and washed up, it would seem to be a very valuable property. Now not one but two separate, distinct jackal packs are fighting over it, telling you it's worthless and at the same time telling you how much they want it for themselves.

"We've already dealt with the first bunch. I don't think I need to say any more about *them*. As for the second bunch, let's call them by name—the Hurd-Hudner Corporation, newspaper publishers. They're professionals, I'm the last man in the world to deny that. They publish a lot of newspapers and some of those newspapers make money.

"Well, now, what about that? Maybe chain newspapers are a good thing. Suppose you're traveling. You get to a new town. There's the chain market, the chain drugstore, the chain hotel and the chain theater. So before you're off the train the porter hands you a chain newspaper and you feel right at home. It's hard to tell you've ever *left* home, if you don't get to read the sign on the station [scattered laughter]. Hard to tell, that is, unless you come from a city that's never been chained—even *The Examiner*, in San Francisco, isn't a chain paper in a way of speaking, because it's the original, the daddy of them all.

"No, my worthy friends—my kind investors—I won't criticize Hurd-Hudner. I just want you to make a comparison. I want you to look over some Hurd-Hudner papers, without leaving your seats, and if you think they're better than *The Day* just mark your proxies for Hurd-Hudner. And remember, no matter what proxies you've signed before, it's only the *last one* that counts. Thank you . . ."

334

He sat down so fast, nobody had a chance to clap. The attention of his listeners was now focused on four newsboys who, grouped in the door, came in at a signal from Matt Brody and marched down the aisle with their arms full of papers. The boys were nice looking and trimly dressed. They were *Day* contest winners. Two of them wore the canvas caps and lettered canvas apron which *The Day* supplied its carriers, the other two were labeled "Hurd-Hudner." This was a stunt Matt had come up with at one of the night conferences and which Anchylus had okayed—possibly not a very good stunt but at least an unusual one. One of the teams handed out Hurd-Hudner publications from bailiwicks east of the mountains—Racine, Kansas City, Minneapolis and Cleveland—thin, small-circulation sheets with uniform mastheads and make-up and a dreary, mortal sameness about them. The other team handed out *The Day*.

6 THE LITTLE SHOW enlivened the proceedings. It also changed their nature. Though perhaps so far it could be said they had needed little enlivening, the entrance of the newscarriers, the fuss of passing out the papers, handing them along the rows, and so on, lifted tension from a verbal level to action. Garber rose with a sarcastic question as to whether ". . . we should adjourn for a reading period . . ." and Pilbrick wanted the minutes to record that the Chairman was turning the session into a farce.

Anchylus gravely ordered this comment to be entered, with the qualification that it was Mr. Pilbrick's personal opinion. He knew he had made his own point—the contrast between *The Day*'s traditionally home-slanted, multipage make-up and the raffish handful of alien newspapers. Even the invocation of other, smaller cities —faceless little places, lost out there in the wastes, behind the protective Sierras—gave San Franciscans a sense of happy superiority.

Should their own great, fascinating city have its doings documented in the hopelessly commercial fashion of these nameless clusters of tepees? That was the question he wanted to dramatize. The feeling in the room was favorable to him, the stir and rustle of unfolding the papers was pleasant—a chance to relax, a chance to gab with the man next to you (no matter how he might be going to vote his stock).

It was a friendly feeling, a San Francisco feeling. Proof the home-town product wasn't so bad after all.

Anchylus followed up his advantage quickly. While Pilbrick was still on his feet, trying to frame a further objection, he shouted, "Stockholders! There is one last thing I want to say. I've been told in the last week—and by two separate groups of contestants—that I was out. Yes, sir, out in the cold. That's what they said. They'd bought the stock, they said. Also, they'd canvassed, they'd circularized. They had the proxies, yes, yes, yes. You good shareowners and *Day* readers were sick and tired of me, they said. That's how it was and I had better make my mind up to it. By God, I had. Well, I don't mind telling you I felt pretty bad. I felt sick. I felt scared. That figures, doesn't it, my friends? I guess if a man works thirty or forty years and thinks he's getting someplace and then someone tells him he's an old fraud and they're wise to him at last and he better go curl up and die, he gets the bejeesus scared out of him and if he isn't pretty smart he just gives up and does what they tell him. So I pretty near did. All that kept me from it was hearing it from *two sides*. I couldn't get it through my head how they could *both* be right." (Laughter; subdued hisses.)

Anchylus signaled Matt to bang the gavel.

"So before we vote—"

Mr. Pilbrick was up again. "Mr. Chairman—"

"I said *before we vote* I want to know if I've got any friends left here—"

Garber was up too. "Point of order, point of order . . ."

Anchylus ignored both of them. "Just to satisfy my curiosity, tell me—are you with me or agin' me? What about you, Ling Tung Chow? Do you want to throw me out?"

He couldn't have said why he picked out Ling Tung Chow. He hadn't exchanged ten words with the rich old Chinese in thirty years, and there had been nothing in their relationship since the harness-cutting episode that could have made him sure of Ling Tung Chow's support. Instinct, perhaps, was all that made him feel that Ling Tung Chow, who had never attended a meeting before, wouldn't have come today except as a friend.

If a Chinese wanted dirty work done he didn't handle it himself. He sent a hatchetman. Preferably an Irishman.

Ling Tung Chow bowed. "I am for you, Mr. Saxe," he said.

"Thank you, Ling Tung Chow," Anchylus said. He looked over the oblong of faces below him.

"This is an outrageous violation of—"

"Get an injunction, Mr. Garber," Anchylus said. "Anyone else who thinks this is an outrageous violation of something is free to leave the room. What about you, Mr. Reed—are you sick and tired of the way we're running *The Day?*"

With his partner Oakleigh Donovan on the dais in front of him, it was safe to conclude that Reed favored the status quo. But there was sure to be a certain number of stockholders who wouldn't be aware of the connection.

"My shares will be voted for Management, sir."

"Thank you, sir," Anchylus said. His eye fell on an acquaintance, Howard Ashmore of Ashmore Stores, who seemed to be looking at him in a friendly way. The Ashmore Brothers—four of them, all wealthy—had been among *The Day's* earliest investors, and the wives of two, James and Lawton, had worked with Jessica in the Grace Cathedral Altar Society.

"How about you, Howard?"

"I'm afraid I can't answer that, Anchylus."

"All right, all right," Anchylus said quickly. He saw he'd made a mistake, but before he could slough it over by calling on another name, Howard Ashmore went on. "I wish to indicate no persuasion for or against Management or for or against any group seeking representation on the Board. But I do wish to indicate opposition to vocal commitment. I support the objection made by the gentleman in the front row that such procedure is out of order. I think we ought to go ahead and vote our proxies in the regular way without all this flim-flam."

"We share your view, sir," Pilbrick yelled above the other voices. Half a dozen stockholders were asking recognition now, some apparently backing Anchylus, others against him. Barber's voice was not to be denied. He took over from Pilbrick as if the two of them were working for the same side instead of against each other.

". . . scandalous disregard of all . . . recourse to legal action if and when—"

"The Chair," Pilbrick interfered, "the Chair is already out of order, by the terms of the agenda, in refusing to take questions. May I now be recognized to ask some?"

7   MATT BRODY, from the far end of the dais, saw the look of satisfaction in Sharon's face. Her eyes caught his for a moment, then scurried away: he thought he had never seen so much spite in a human face. God, he thought, they'll go after him now for fair. But there was no use thinking about that. Anchylus had been

337

superb and his strategy a good one: if he'd been able to stampede the meeting into a public show of loyalty he might have won control without further discussion. It was unparliamentary, all right: there was even a chance that a court might have declared the meeting invalid but not much chance that any court could have reversed a vote, once it had been taken. Now the questions were coming thick and fast, Garber starting with the previously unanswered one —his lead-off inquiry about Anchylus' car.

The answer was forceful, though not quite convincing.

"My automobile, sir, has been used in part for myself, in part in the interests of the corporation. And in view of this—"

Garber was demanding recognition. "The stockholders' committee would like to have information on . . ."

Some of the questions were merely annoying, easily parried, others dangerously pointed toward managerial negligence, incompetence, self-indulgence.

Anchylus tried tact, anger, mockery—and, when backed into untenable positions, pleaded bad memory, responsibility delegated to others, lack of facts on hand. He might have convinced some stockholders that they had to buy his gasoline and pick up his entertainment checks, but he was less convincing when the contesting and at times, as it seemed, collaborating lawyers picked up speed. He was asked the ratio of editorial costs to advertising, about a paper mill The Day had owned and sold too cheap, about the failure of the "economy program." No one fact or single line of questioning was conclusively damaging, but all taken together added up to what the opposition wanted—a picture of a proprietary company that had gone soft and slack, of Management funneled into the hands of a man who listened to nobody, of old-fashioned methods that had never been changed.

Both opposition teams bore down hungrily on the surplus cash which had accumulated in the treasury. Anchylus couldn't explain the cash. He'd wanted it there, that was all. He felt safe with it there. He remembered depressions. Why was it bad to have something for a rainy day? He lost his temper, swore at Garber.

"Why do you keep on saying it's the stockholders' money?" he said. "It's The Day's money. We needed it. That's why we kept it. If we'd paid it to the stockholders, we'd have been broke."

"Then you preferred, sir, to keep the stockholders broke?" Garber said unpleasantly.

Anchylus spluttered some reply that no one heard. He was getting

338

tired. At lunchtime Pamela and Dr. French closed in on him; the three went down to his office together.

Brad Iverson crossed the aisle and shook hands with Tim Wilkins. "You're looking fine, Tim," he said; "how do you stay so young?"

"Like Ben Hur," Tim said, "at the galley oar, at the galley oar."

"I know what you mean," Brad said. "It was a tough morning."

"That it was," Tim said. "Nice to have seen you, Brad."

He started to turn away, when Brad touched his arm. "We're all going to Jack's for a bite," he said. "Would you and Mr. Shimenko care to join us?"

Tim hesitated. "Let me speak to him," he said.

Matt Brody, who had heard the interchange, watched anxiously as Tim and Shimenko conferred. Both men turned to Alexandra, and Matt concluded they were asking her opinion. She was dusting her scarred cheek with a powder puff and she looked over at Sharon and shook her head emphatically. Tim called to the Hurd-Hudner group, "I'm afraid not, Brad—thanks just the same. It seems that we're due somewhere else."

Matt breathed a little easier. A coalition of the attacking forces would have meant the end of Anchylus, whose main hope (if he still had any left) lay in their continued division. No one so far had brought forward a strong program as a substitution for the policies that had been criticized—outside of immediate split-up of the Treasury surplus into dividends, the only point, apparently, on which both raiding teams were in agreement.

Alexandra and her cohorts lunched in the St. Francis. Matt sent a legman there and another to Jack's, each having instructions to eavesdrop and to telephone at once if there was a move by the two rival groups to join up over coffee. No such move was reported, and Matt, having gulped a sandwich and a cup of coffee at his desk, was about to start for the court-martial (as he now thought of it) in Room 100 when his intercom buzzed and he flipped the key to hear Anchylus asking if he would come up.

"Where?"

"To my office, for Christ's sake," the old man snorted. "Where else?"

Matt found him at the desk, gazing walleyed into a series of smoke rings. He took his pipe out of his mouth.

"I'm not going back there again," he said as Matt sat down; "no point in it. Let George and Dan carry on. They don't need me."

Matt stared. He felt sick. Then he nodded. "Whatever you say."

"I've had about all I'm going to take."

The sick feeling remained in Matt's stomach. This refusal to go back made sense but—what a way to surrender!

Maybe this was how defeat came to the old—a last great show of strength, then sudden collapse. True enough, the issue by now was doubtless decided. Anchylus had little to gain by subjecting himself to further pounding. But to sneak off the field, as it were, by night, yielding a consent victory, stripped even of the glory of handing over one's sword: it was a morbid, an ignominious end. An unsuitable end for Anchylus.

"Don't you think I should go up and tell them?"

"Plenty of time for that," Anchylus said. "Did you ever get a run-down on that atom-bomb fella, the one that wanted to be strapped on?"

It seemed to Matt that the strain of his recent ordeal was making Anchylus' mind wander.

"Why, yes," Matt said, "as a matter of fact, I did. Wheatcroft found out his name. He's quit Oppenheimer, bought himself a row-crop farm back in New Jersey."

"Row-crop farm! Say, that's great. Perfect." Life and interest streamed back into Anchylus' face, so empty a moment before. "What kind of row crops?"

Matt tried to remember. Any fact pertaining to a story in the or-dinary routine of his working day would have been ordinarily on the tip of his tongue, but the type of row crops now being raised by a man who, to absolve his secret guilt, had expressed a wish to be blown apart by atomic fission appeared irrelevant when considered in relation to the man before him, who, as far as you could tell, had been stripped not only of his business and his pride but of his senses as well.

"Celery. Seems to me Wheatcroft said it was celery."

"It *seems* to you," Anchylus roared. "God, man, don't you *know*?"

"It *was* celery, sir."

"Better and better. Miles of celery, this little fella standing on the edge of it. Maybe with a hoe. Did Wheatcroft sign him for an ex-clusive?"

"He can if you—"

"Christ, Matt, where are your brains? We'll do a Sunday feature on him—insert of Hiroshima and so forth. Oppenheimer too. And an artist's dream-up of the bomb falling, this celery farmer strapped onto it. Hell of a story. I'm surprised at you. Hell, this is the atomic-age man in person. We might even run a life story in his own words."

"I'll get right on it," Matt said. He used the meek and beaten tone of a cub reporter who had goofed his first assignment. He looked at his watch. Half past two—the time set for resumption of the meeting. The stockholders would be back in their seats upstairs.

"Sir—"

Anchylus was relighting his pipe. "About this morning—" he spoke with great effort, reluctantly forcing himself away from the row cropper—"about this morning, I felt kind of stupid. On one point, that is. That stinking coffee machine! I think we'd better rip it out. It's no damn good."

"Rip it out?"

"Mind you, I'm not saying they were fair about it—those . . . lawyers. I hate the whole breed. They were trying to make the economy program around here sound like a whore's nightmare, and they didn't get anywhere with it, except when they talked about the pissolator or whatever you call it—"

"Dripovendor."

"Well, as I say, I felt ashamed. Maybe it was an economy but it wasn't in *The Day* tradition."

"I never thought of that angle," Matt said. It was necessary in all this to hold on firmly to some peg of sanity, if you could find one.

"You heard me defend it. But I couldn't put my heart in it. That was the only place I thought they scored. Can you imagine *Day* personnel, first-class newspaper people, having to walk past a monster like that Crapodropper on their way out to buy a decent cup of coffee? I don't want that happening around here any more, so get rid of it. In the future they can go to Sam's for coffee, like they always have, without feeling they're being disloyal to me."

In the future. The words exploded with a delayed meaning. So that was it—the future, the glories ahead: Saxe-paid, loyal, expert *Day* employees filing out for coffee before, or between, the brilliant stories they would write. The golden future, with the atom-bomb worker's life story running day to day and the Sunday feature section splattered with his fragmenting guilt. Anchylus had already mentally bypassed the meeting upstairs and its terrifying consequences for himself. He had decided not to return to his ordeal, not because of an inability to face defeat but because of a preformed conclusion of victory.

He was assuming he had won!

"I'll have it taken out tomorrow," Matt said jubilantly, "perhaps today. I'll phone the people that put it in, tell them to come and get it."

341

"Fine, fine," Anchylus said. "Now about the editorial meeting. I thought—"

"Mr. Saxe," Matt interrupted, "may I make a suggestion?"

"Why, certainly, boy!" Anchylus seemed surprised by his intensity. "Go right ahead. What's on your mind?"

"I'd like to discuss the editorial meeting later, sir, if it's all the same to you. I'd like you to do something for me—as a personal favor."

"Anything you want, Matt. You know that."

"I'd like you to go back upstairs."

"But there's no need. I just said that, and you ag—"

"I beg now to disagree."

"Why, man, Dan's in the Chair," Anchylus said aggrievedly, "and Pamela's there. She has all the proxies. They'll move to vote now, any minute."

"I realize that. I'd like you to be there when they do."

Anchylus started to make a dissenting reply, then broke off. "You really think some purpose would be gained by—"

"I do, sir."

Anchylus stuck out his lower lip. He sat like a pouting child, rubbing his cheek distractedly. "I felt they were *with* me, almost to a man. They weren't taken in by all that lawyer garbage."

"I don't imagine most of them were, sir, but—"

"I felt it was all decided," Anchylus said. But as he looked at Matt the latter saw a faraway doubt flicker in the little bearish eyes.

"There's a strong favorable undercurrent, I think. But I'd still like to see you present when the voting starts."

"God damn it to hell," Anchylus said, "I don't want to go back. The minute I'm there again, those lawyers—"

"I know, sir. But, if you're there, it will make a fine impression. Tie everything together."

Anchylus was still sulking. "You insist then?"

"I don't insist," Matt said; "I put it on the basis of a personal favor."

"By God, Matt," Anchylus said, "sometimes I lose my patience with you. Are you implying that if I don't go back—"

"I'm not implying anything, Anchylus," Matt said, allowing himself for once the use of his employer's Christian name; "I'm just telling you I think it would be a good idea for you to get back up there. Right away."

Anchylus glared at him. Then he pushed back his chair. "All right, then. For God's sake, let's go."

342

X

30 and Out

"Here is the man with three staves, and here is
the Wheel and here is the one-eyed merchant,
and this card, which is blank, is something he car-
ries on his back, which I am forbidden to see."

—T. S. Eliot

1 JOHN FALLBROOK, of Swift & Fallbrook, public accountants, had
eyes like small change and a mouth like a dollar sign. He greeted
Miss Wilke with the same half smile, the same courtly flex of his
body that he had practiced for her benefit for twenty years. It was
his habit to be polite to secretaries just as it was his habit to bring
over in person, instead of mailing, the reports he prepared for his
client corporations. After the smile and the bow he would raise his
briefcase to desk level, open it, and produce an envelope. He would
lay the envelope in front of Miss Wilke with the words, "Will you
kindly call this to Mr. Saxe's attention?"

"I shall, Mr. Fallbrook," Miss Wilke would answer, focusing on the
envelope so that she wouldn't have to smile in return. She didn't
like Mr. Fallbrook; she couldn't have said why. He was like a suit and
a briefcase walking around by themselves.

"Thank you, Miss Wilke," Mr. Fallbrook would say. He would
smile again, close the briefcase, bow once more, and leave, to return,
she knew, exactly three months later. He was like Time itself, measured, abstract and merciless. He gave her the creeps.

345

Today the envelope was the same size and kind that Swift & Fallbrook used for the quarterly statements, but its contents were so much more significant that Miss Wilke couldn't bear to look at it at all—that is, unless she immediately opened it, which was not permitted. Her face was frozen and she knew that, as always happened when she was in the grip of strong emotions, she was getting goose pimples. He knows, she thought, he knows this very minute. He and his clerks have counted the proxies and he knows how the vote came out and all he does is put an envelope in front of me and stand there with that dollar-sign smirk on his face as if it didn't matter.

Possibly Mr. Fallbrook read her thoughts (a not inconceivable feat, under the circumstances). Either that or he noticed the goose pimples and construed their meaning. At all events the smirk faded out. For the first time in the history of their relationship he didn't close the briefcase but stood waiting as if he expected her to say something.

"Mr. Fallbrook," she said, "would it be presumptuous of me to ask . . ." She hadn't planned the question. It had come out of her mouth, as it were, by itself. Since she was incapable of finishing it she answered it. ". . . but I suppose . . . you're not allowed to tell what . . ."

Amenity deserted Mr. Fallbrook's manner. He turned from Miss Wilke in a shocked way, as if she had asked him to take off his trousers.

"Our reports, Miss Wilke, are always made in writing."

"Oh, I understand that," she said hastily. "I only thought . . . I suppose you know how we all feel here, wondering about—"

"I do understand, I do indeed," Mr. Fallbrook said. He spoke coldly but, having spoken, he hesitated; he laid his briefcase on the desk and twiddled with its clasps.

"If Mr. Saxe is in his office," he said, "I could take the report in to him. I could take it in personally, and then no doubt—"

"He's not in, Mr. Fallbrook."

"He's at the—"

"Yes."

"Oh, I see. I had hoped to catch him before he—"

"He didn't come in this morning at all. He went directly to the cathedral."

Mr. Fallbrook nodded several times, then glanced at his watch. He was tall and thin and his neck was the tallest, thinnest part of him; when he nodded, his small round head bobbed around on it like an apple on a blowing branch. He seemed to accept as comprehensible,

346

even though irregular and perhaps not completely praiseworthy, the fact that a Swift & Fallbrook client might omit going to his office on the day of his wife's funeral.

"God, how I dislike these proxy counts," he said. "We were up all night. Please extend my greetings to Mr. Saxe."

Gradually, the dollar-sign smile growing dimmer, as if he were dissolving, he eased out of the room. Angela Wilke sat at her desk looking at the envelope. "I'm going to open it," she said aloud. "I'm going to. Yes, I am." But in her heart she knew she wouldn't open it, though all the fiends of hell enjoined to urge her. The habit of conformity was too strong; the law of obedience to the established order of things held her in its grip. Oh, God, she thought, if only he'd come in. If only somebody would tell me what to do. . . .

2 Clouds banked the sky. Moved by the wind, their edges shifted, opening and closing so that light came through in jolting shafts.

The earth responded to this play above it. When the light shone, it expanded, everything became clear, drawn in detail and lighted with a hard, sad luster—the slope with the gravestones, the Doric outlines of tombs, the open grave and the people standing near it in constrained, sorrowful attitudes.

Then as suddenly as it had come the light would be shut off. The landscape shrank. An intolerable weight fell on the heart and the very dead themselves seemed to burrow deeper into the ground.

Jessica's coffin rested on four strips of tape. These strips were adjusted so as to hold the coffin well above the grave into which it would shortly be lowered. A large mat of flowers covered most of the coffin lid. At the foot of the grave were piled other flowers, wired in sprays and wreaths, brought out from the cathedral, where they had been on display.

Fifteen hundred people had been present at the services. These had been held an hour earlier and conducted by the Episcopal Bishop of California, the Rt. Reverend Karl Morgan Block. Three police officers had been on duty outside and a portion of California Street had been closed to ordinary traffic, just as it had been for the coming-out party. Here, however, a different kind of protocol existed; only relatives and a selected few of the oldest of the old friends were permitted to be present. The friends stood on the east side of the grave, the relatives on the west, the Bishop at that end of the coffin

347

which contained the head of the deceased. He held a psalter in his hand, reading the prayers of commitment.

"Unto Almighty God we commend the soul of our sister departed . . ."

Anchylus raised his head. He stared around him. A sweet, salty wind blew into his face, stirring his shaggy hair. He gulped it into his lungs. It tasted good after the stuffy air of the church.

This was strange. He stood here among his daughters, Sharon with her husband, Alexandra so close he could have put out his hand and touched her! Yesterday they had been enemies. Now, in defiance of the enmity, which was itself a kind of bond, they had acknowledged a deeper, older bond—the law of family. The mysterious force welding them into this unity had been Jessica's great gift to them, a force issuing from her spirit. Even in this final hour, out of her dust, this force compelled them to take leave of her in a loving, united and respectful guise.

"And we commit this body to the ground; earth to earth . . ."

An act, now, was taking place: a small act, but one that could shatter forever Anchylus' faith in the livingness of Jessica—or, rather, his dual concept of her, as alive and dead at the same time, the concept that had made him shout her name in the hospital Repository and later chat with her, with no feeling that he was doing anything unusual, in Appleton Brothers' slumber room.

Bishop Block had reached down. He had dipped his fingers into the earth piled beside the grave. He had taken a pinch of earth into his fingers. He now brought his hand forward and slightly raised it, obviously with the intention of sprinkling or throwing that pinch of earth onto the coffin.

An ache struck through Anchylus. A great pain like the stroke of a knife sliced into his nerves. Oh, no. By no means. Throwing earth. You did that only to a dead person. To a person never more to be seen or spoken to or held by you, lost and foregone. You did that only to one beyond recall, as the saying was.

Anchylus growled. He was conscious of nothing except the terrible hurt which until now, by a tremendous effort, had been kept at a distance. He had warded off this pain all these days from the time in the hospital hallway when he had spoken to Dr. French and Dr. Immelman. Now it was getting into him. He trembled with the shock of it. Pamela, standing beside him, pulled his sleeve. But she saw at once that he was not ill. This was something else.

Anchylus took a step forward. The Bishop, still raising his hand in that solemn, awful, ritualistic manner, stared at him, but Anchylus took no notice. His own hand shot out and he caught the Bishop's wrist. He held him like an enraged bear. It was important for him to stand there forever, if possible, keeping the Bishop from throwing dirt on Jessica.

Bishop Block was a large man but not a powerful one. His arm, with Anchylus' huge grip on his wrist, felt cut off from his body. He had no ability to move it. At the same time, from some source he could only feel was the Grace of God, he found strength. He refused to let Anchylus push his arm down. He still stood with the arm extended, the pinch of dirt clasped in his fingers. Like Daniel confronted with the lion, he sent a gaze like a lightning bolt from his eyes into Anchylus' eyes.

". . . ashes to ashes," he whispered, "dust to dust. Release my hand, sir."

Anchylus opened his mouth, then closed it. His jaw muscles swelled. He glared at the Bishop, returning his angry look in kind. No sound came from him.

While those around the grave, not knowing what was going on, looked on dumfounded, the two men stood locked in a wordless struggle. Anchylus breathed in great gasps. The Bishop hardly seemed to breathe at all. At this moment the sun went behind a cloud, and the cemetery with all the gravestones, the tombs, and the faces of the mourners, the Bishop and the chauffeurs watching from the wall by the street shrank to half size.

The strength went out of Anchylus. He loosened his grip on the Bishop's wrist and stood back with a bemused, puzzled look on his face.

The Bishop sprinkled the earth on the coffin. Then with his forefinger, in the sprinkle of earth, he made the sign of the cross. His deep Episcopal voice, which had dwindled to a thread during the contest with Anchylus, came back, full force.

". . . in sure and certain hope of Resurrection unto eternal life, through our Lord Jesus Christ."

3   THE PEOPLE turned from the grave. They came slowly down the white gravel cemetery path, and the chauffeurs who had been watching from the wall got back into the big cars with the funeral stickers on the windshields and started the motors. The quiet, secret movement of gasoline into the carburetors, the flow of oil and the flex of pistons and the deep pulse of the spark were a means of

bringing reassurance after the spell of the burial. Even the engines, inanimate as they were, had life when compared to the dead.

Once the motors were started the drivers got out again and came around to open the doors and assist their passengers into the back seats.

Pamela Harper walked beside her father, leading her daughter Margot by the hand. There had been a question as to the advisability of bringing Margot, and Cliff and Pamela had talked it over at some length. Margot was a great one for asking questions. She had a bright, active mind and she would let no aspect of the funeral go unexplained. It would be all very well to talk about heaven and about God putting Grandmother Saxe to sleep, to talk soberly and authoritatively, as if they, the adults, understood these matters. Margot would want to know why. She would pin you down. She might brood about it, Cliff thought.

"She really hasn't got a brooding nature," Pamela said; "she's not a bit like me in that respect. She's more like you—spunky."

"You've got spunk, too, plenty of it," Cliff put in quickly, but though a faint gleam of pleasure rose in his wife's eyes, she let the compliment go by. She was more worried, she said, about how Georgie would behave, especially in the cathedral.

Actually, there hadn't been a squawk out of Georgie until the Bishop started reading at the grave. Then he started howling, and Cliff had to take him back to the car. Thus Cliff missed the contest between Anchylus and the Bishop and had to be filled in on it later. He waited impatiently in the car for Pamela to say goodbye to her father and come back to him. It seemed as if she had been gone a long time. He leaned over to open the door for her. Margot jumped in the back and Pamela moved Georgie away from Cliff and held him and Cliff made a U turn in the broad avenue and headed back toward Cypress Gardens.

Pamela sat quietly, patting the baby now and then when a traffic noise or a dip in the paving made him stir. She felt at peace. No intense sorrow had moved her at the graveside. She had done her sorrowing when she first heard of Jessica's death, and it had seemed to her that in a way she'd had a share of blame for the death as for every change and misfortune that had fallen on the Saxe family. The feeling had been unreasonable, she knew, but when she took stock of what had happened to the family she wondered whether there was not some truth in it.

Had her own adoption been the mistake from which bad luck had come? That was what had made a division. It had given fate a crack to enlarge until a wall fell, exposing them all to the winds. If there was blame to be laid it might be hers, if only in some ancient, superstitious sense, and she had faced up to this possible blame the day George Dudley had told her about Jessica. That was why she had taken down the book and read about Jonah. She had asked herself whether she too hadn't been a kind of Jonah. Once the worst of her grief had passed, however, the superstitious blame-taking had passed also.

Today she'd had another idea. It had come to her when she saw Anchylus grab the Bishop's hand to keep him from throwing earth on the casket. This strange act had puzzled everyone who saw it, but it hadn't puzzled her. She knew Anchylus had still been trying to keep his wife out of the final clutch of death. He had been fighting, no matter how illogically, to retain what he loved, just as he had been fighting to keep *The Day*. He had lost Jessica, but if he kept *The Day* it would be proof somehow that the division in the family hadn't destroyed him.

"Cliff," she said, "after we get the children home, I want to go back to the city."

She had spoken in a low tone, so as not to wake Georgie, and for a moment she wasn't sure whether he'd heard.

Cliff kept on driving without looking at her, guiding the station wagon with great skill through the press of traffic.

"What do you want to go back for?"

"I thought perhaps I ought to be with him today. Just this one more day."

"You've been with him pretty much, Pam," Cliff said.

"I know," she said. "I just thought—perhaps I ought to go back one more time. Don't you think so?"

Cliff drove awhile in silence.

"If it's bad news, baby," he said gently, "there's not a darn thing you can do. Except hold his hand. And he doesn't need that."

"He'd need something," Pamela said, "he wouldn't have much left of anything."

"He'll make out."

"Do you really think so?"

"He's quite a man," Cliff said. "Win, lose or draw, he gave them a hell of a fight."

"I won't go if you don't want me to."

"I just figured you'd done pretty much," Cliff said. "We've sort of missed you around the château. How long has it been now, a week?"

"Six days," Pamela said.

"You go ahead if you want to," Cliff said.

"No, Cliff, I don't want to, honestly," Pamela said, "and I know he'll be all right. Only I can't stand not knowing what's happened. They must be through counting by now. It stands to reason."

"We'll find out," Cliff said; "we'll call up the paper as soon as we get home. If the news is out, somebody over there will have it. But for Pete's sake don't fold up if it's bad. He won't, so why should you?"

"You should know by this time that I won't," Pamela said severely, "but I hope it's good news. Oh, I hope so much it is."

From the moment Anchylus got back in the car, Matt Brody knew something important had happened to him. He knows she's dead now, he thought, watching Dino tuck the chinchilla robe across the massive, squarish body. He's finally said goodbye.

This was the moment he had been afraid of, for Anchylus. The old man had built up a barrier against it in his mind. He'd had to do that, so as to have strength to fight his enemies. Now he'd given in. He'd let the hurt into him.

It's a good thing that he stayed away from it till now, Matt thought. That's where he was smart. If the funeral had been before the stockholders' meeting instead of after, he'd never have had a chance. They'd have walked all over him.

During the past week Matt had been able to carry out his complicated function of employee, confidant and bodyguard, as loyalty demanded, but the frontier of grief was one that loyalty could not cross. The grave was for the relatives. Matt had stayed down in the street. When he saw Bishop Block go up the path in his robes and the group at Jessica's bier draw in to hear the committal prayers, he had turned to a purpose of his own.

"Dino," he said to the chauffeur, "I need a telephone."

The Italian looked startled. He was suffering the nervousness which afflicts all Latins in the presence of death; when Anchylus left the car he had taken off his hat, glanced once in the direction of the grave, and crossed himself. Then he had gotten back behind the wheel and slumped down, staring straight ahead of him.

"Here they don't have no phones, Mr. Brody."

"We'll go over to Daly City," Matt decided, "and take a right. I noticed a gas station along there somewhere."

He rode in front beside Dino, the better to watch for the station, and was pleased, when he found it, to note the telephone in a closed booth. Shutting the door of the booth, he called the office and asked for Miss Wilke.

"Oh, Matt," she said as soon as she heard his voice, "I'm so glad you called. I just don't know what to do."

She sounded pitifully rattled—a condition which, for Angela Wilke, had no parellel in Matt's memory.

"What's wrong?"

"Mr. Fallbrook was here. His firm has finished the count."

Matt kept a firm grip on his own nerves. Obviously, the news must be bad.

"Well?"

"He . . . he left an envelope."

"Angela, spill it. What's the word, how did they vote?"

"I haven't opened the envelope, Matt," Miss Wilke said with dignity. "Do you think I should? That's what's been bothering me."

"God Almighty, open it."

You never knew, he thought, when people would fall apart. And Miss Wilke, of all people.

"All right," Miss Wilke said, "if you'll take the responsibility. I don't want to have my head blown off."

"Open it, Angela," Matt said in a tight voice. "Just tell me what it says."

Miss Wilke sighed deeply—whether with relief or exasperation Matt couldn't tell. He could hear the crackle of the paper and the sound of the letter cutter as she ripped the envelope. A silence followed as she read what was inside.

"Out loud, Angela," Matt yelled into the telephone.

"You don't have to speak like that," Miss Wilke said. "I can hear you perfectly well. It's rather a long letter. 'Mr. Anchylus Saxe, President, The San Francisco Day Publishing Company, Day Building, San Francisco, California. Dear Sir—"

"Skip down to the part where it says who was elected. The names. Just the names."

"I'm coming to that. 'Mr. Anchylus Saxe, Incumbent Chairman . . .' Oh, Matt, that's good, that's wonderful, isn't it?"

"Keep on reading."

Joy took hold of Matt, but it was a conditioned kind of joy. It all depended on what came next. Anchylus could have been re-elected to the Board but still have lost his company.

" 'Mr. Bradley Iverson,' " Miss Wilke read. " 'Mr. Myron C. Pilbrick.' Oh, Matt—"

353

"Who were the fourth and fifth electives?"

" 'Mr. Daniel Winkler,' " Miss Wilke read. " 'Mr. George R. Dudley.' "

Matt's body jerked in the phone booth as if he had come into contact with a high-tension wire. He tried to say something but what came out was a joyous croak that sounded like bububu.

"Is it really all right?" Miss Wilke asked into the twitching silence of the wire.

"I'll say it is. We kept three places, didn't we?"

"I know. But Mr. Iverson and Mr. Pilbrick. He won't be too happy about having them on the Board, will he?"

"He'll learn to love it, Angela. He's kept *The Day.*"

"Well, it *is* wonderful news, I suppose, but I *had* been hoping—"

"Never mind that, Angela," Matt said with more than a trace of impatience. "It wasn't in the cards for us to get a five-man Board. At least Wilkins-Shimenko got smeared. Cumulative voting is what did it. They must have spread themselves too thin. Hurd-Hudner must have figured they couldn't elect five—but they could elect two. And they did."

"I don't understand that part of it. But if you're glad, I'm glad. Do you want me to tell anybody, or shall I keep it confidential?"

"This is about as confidential as the Gettysburg Address and a hell of a lot more timely. Send the letter down to Pete Zorach. He'll know what to do with it. And will you take a letter?"

"Gladly, dear," Miss Wilke said. Her confidence restored, she sounded more like her normal, efficient self.

"*To All Employees, The San Francisco Day:* I am happy to inform you that, as a result of the voting at the annual stockholders' meeting, a majority of the directors named by Management were elected to the Board. All efforts by opposed financial groups to take over this newspaper have been defeated. The policies which have governed *The Day* in the past will continue unchanged. No changes in personnel are contemplated at the present time. Thank you for your support. Signed, *Anchylus Saxe, Editor and Publisher.*"

"Wait a minute, Matt. I think he ought to see this."

"Be a pal, Angela, and get it out for me. See that it's posted on the Cityside and Circulation bulletin boards. Will you do that for me?"

"Are you going to check with him?"

"Not until after you've done it."

Miss Wilke heaved another of her sighs. "I really wish you wouldn't write things in his name. He doesn't always like it."

"He'll like it this time. Chin up, Angela. We won, you know."

354

"I know," Miss Wilke said. "I'm just trying to get the hang of it."

"One thing more."

"Yes, Matt?"

"Tell Pete to hold Letty's story on the funeral until I see it. I'll be in a little later. And I'll handle the news meeting myself; he won't have to bother with it."

"All right. And I'm terribly glad everything worked out all right."

"Goodbye, Angela."

"Goodbye, Matt. Take care of him."

"Everything is okay. Goodbye, now."

Miss Wilke closed the connection. She switched onto her second wire, picking up a call which had been flashing for some time.

"Angela, this is Letty Meeker."

"Yes, Letty."

"Is everything all right?"

"I don't know what you mean, Letty." Miss Wilke couldn't help adding, "I thought you would be at the services."

"That's where I am. I went out to a telephone. I just wanted to confirm that everything is all right. With *The Day*, I mean."

Miss Wilke hesitated. She had been told by Matt that the news from Swift & Fallbrook wasn't confidential. Yet to tell Letty about it stole point from the bulletins she had been about to write. It was like putting the news on a loud-speaker.

"Yes, I think I can confirm that," she said with some reluctance.

She could hear Letty's fat little chuckle at the other end.

"Of course you can, dear. Three to two, wasn't it, in our favor?"

"If you know that much, why do you want me to confirm it?" Miss Wilke asked. "And how do you know it, Letty? I just opened the envelope five minutes ago."

Letty's laugh puffed up again, soft and cottony as her flesh. "I'm supposed to know things, Angela. That's my business."

Letty paused to let the mystery of this sink in. She well knew the legend around town that news came to her through telepathy or osmosis—a legend which she always publicly repudiated.

". . . I did happen to talk to dear John Fallbrook on the telephone this morning. Such a sweet man! His wife has been quite ill, you know. Alicia Fallbrook. She was Alicia Carrol of Piedmont. She . . . had to be confined. At one time, that is."

"Very interesting," Miss Wilke said, disliking Letty but marveling at the woman. Had she, in some incredible manner, managed to milk the results of the proxy count out of Fallbrook on her own account, cajoling him, or threatening him with some perfidious scandal about his sick wife? With Letty you never knew. On the one hand, that could be precisely what she'd done, in which case the purpose of the present call would be simply to brag about it. On the other hand, she might not have even talked to John Fallbrook: her apparent knowledge of the directorships might have been no more than a shot in the dark.

"Anyway, Letty," she said, "you're right about the count. Only Mr. Iverson and Mr. Pilbrick were elected for Hurd-Hudner. So your job is safe—but this won't be a scoop for you. I'm about to get out an interoffice memo on the subject. So if you'll excuse me, I'll get on with it."

"By all means, dear Angela," Letty said, "and thank you very much."

Through the window in the drugstore in which she was telephoning Letty could see Anchylus' limousine parked at a Chevron station half a block south and Matt Brody just emerging from the public phone booth there. She hung up swiftly and dialed the number of a line which connected her with her own office without contact with the company switchboard. Dot Fraser, her girl Friday, answered and Letty dictated the gist of her conversation with Miss Wilke and the manner in which she wanted the information presented in her morning column. Miss Wilke had been correct in saying, albeit rather nastily, that these facts wouldn't constitute a scoop for her, but if she couldn't scoop the world at large she could at least be ahead of her own Cityside: she would have the facts in the column and the galley on Pete Zorach's desk while his own rewrite man was still working on the story.

4 MATT TOLD DINO to go back to the cemetery and step on it. While they drove, he jotted on his pocket memo pad the information he'd received from Miss Wilke. Showing it to Anchylus might be easier than telling him about it—would certainly be easier if he could anticipate the old man's mood after the committal, and he thought he could.

This is the time, all right, he thought; he may not even care. I doubt that he remembers he was in a meeting yesterday or what it was about. Anything that snaps him out of it would be good or at least better than what he's going through now.

356

After picking up Anchylus as he left the cemetery, Dino drove across the city in the direction of Nob Hill. As the blue car turned into California Street Matt handed his boss the memo slip:

> *Elected to the Board of Directors, San Francisco Day Publishing Company, at the Annual Meeting of Stockholders, held 25 November, 1949:*
> > Anchylus Saxe (incumbent, Chairman)
> > Daniel Z. Winkler
> > George R. Dudley
> > Bradley Iverson
> > Myron C. Pilbrick

"Congratulations, Mr. Saxe," he said.

"Eh?"

"You beat them."

Anchylus raised the slip of paper. For nearly a minute he had been holding it in his hand without being aware of it. He glanced at it, then looked out of the window.

"I lost my wife, Matt," he said.

"I know," Matt said.

"Gone," Anchylus said. "You know what the worst word in the English language is? It's that word. Gone . . . I don't intend this as a profound utterance; just a statement of fact."

"Of course."

"Simple word, and a simple idea. Easy to grasp. No doubt you've thought, these last days, I've been behaving in an erratic manner. Is that true?"

"No, sir. I thought you'd behaved admirably. Naturally in a time of strain—"

"Oh. Now you've laid your finger on it."

"I didn't mean to imply—"

"Strain. That was it. Now that speech I gave, the long harangue in the meeting. Did you think that was out of line?"

"I thought it was splendid."

"Thanks, thanks very much. But I have no illusions. It wasn't politic. Not tactful. I was angry, possibly unduly so. The bastards mentioning the girl in that circular. Can you imagine it? Not *exactly* mentioning her but alluding to the . . . er . . . circumstances of her birth. That girl's an angel, do you understand me?"

"She's a wonderful person."

"More than that, much more. There's love in her. That was what my late wife had—love. Rarest thing in the world. Lots of talk about it. How many people ever felt it? You can count them on your fingers. She's the only one of the three worth the powder to blow her to hell. My late wife—"

"If you'll notice," Matt said, indicating the memo, "the Wilkins-Shimenko group didn't get any places. I guess the stockholders shared your resentment of the circular."

Anchylus nodded. Matt was still not sure whether or not he had read what was on the slip.

"When the Bishop took that earth in hand I almost hit him. Never been religious myself although my late—although Jessica was, of course. Her thought pierced beyond religion, reached into the infinite. If there's a realm of love up there she understood it, for she found it here below. And here was that mealymouthed soul-saver slapping dirt on top of her, dust to dust. Imperishable beauty. Do you think that can be dust?"

"I'm a Catholic," Matt said, "I believe in immortality."

"Whatever he meant," Anchylus said, "it's lucky I controlled myself." He crumpled the memo, flipped it away from him with the same scornful motion he had used to discard the Wilkins-Shimenko paper on the dais of Room 100. "I suppose now they think they've got their foot in the door. Well, they may have another think coming."

Matt felt his depression lift. For the past few minutes he had been listening less to Anchylus' words than to the sorrow that had weltered through them, like a broken bell. He pitied the man profoundly but, just as he had preferred not to go to the graveside, he didn't want to be involved in his feelings. It was better, if possible, to let the claims of everyday life reassert themselves.

"I sent out an interoffice bulletin announcing the results of the meeting."

"Fine, fine," Anchylus said absently.

"I signed it with your name. I indicated there would not be any changes in personnel."

"Good idea. I suppose there'd been some restlessness?"

"A little worry, maybe. The announcement will take care of that."

Anchylus nodded. Then he smiled. "The other bunch, though, the Hurd-Hudner bunch. They've got their foot in the door."

"Not that it will do them any good," Matt said. He tried to say it heartily—and did: he knew he sounded more optimistic on this point than he felt.

"I know the way they figure," Anchylus said. "Know 'em like the corns on my feet. You heard what I said about chains?"

"Yes, indeed, sir."

"They figure that there'll be another year, and another meeting. Is that how you look at it?"

"About that way," Matt conceded.

"Well, they're right. But this time we'll be ready for them."

"No doubt of that at all."

"Let 'em buy the stock," Anchylus said, flushing. "Let 'em buy till they go broke. We'll see what happens. We'll just wait and see."

The car had pulled into the courtyard of the California Street house. Dino jumped down to open the limousine door and Reuben appeared at the top of the front steps. Matt remembered seeing Reuben in the cathedral, seated just behind the pews reserved for family and wearing the clothes he had on now. Butlers, he reflected, are the only professional class, except undertakers, whose ordinary dress allows them to appear at funerals without change of attire.

Anchylus pushed the lap robe off impatiently. "Come in," he said. "Reuben, I want a bottle of champagne in the library and a few sandwiches. I'm hungry." He led the way rapidly inside, shedding his silk hat and dark overcoat as he walked.

"If you don't mind, sir," Matt said, "I think I'd better get back to the office. I sent word to Pete I'd take the news meeting."

"Never mind the stinking news meeting," Anchylus said. "Have you got the drawings for that atom-bomb man layout?"

"They're made and set up," Matt said. "I'll have the proof sheets this afternoon. We closed for his life story yesterday."

"How much did we pay for it?"

"Five thousand. I hope that was all right."

"For Christ's sake, don't ask me what was all right. You think it was worth five thousand. I think you got gypped, but what's the difference? It ought to be a great story. Conscience of the post-atomic world summed up in one guy's death decision. What angle are you taking?"

"Just what you said."

"Okay, then. What are you worried about?"

Anchylus dropped into one of the big chairs. He sat there brooding with his under lip stuck out, rubbing his cheek.

"I've got to talk to Dan," he said, "put on a circulation drive. Premiums, treasure hunts. All that sort of stuff. Once we build enough new circulation these two tinhorns on the Board will have the props knocked from under them. They'll never get a majority, never. You say Wilkins-Shimenko were completely smeared?"

"One hundred per cent."

"Great. I had a hunch they would be. I guess we gave them a fight, eh?"

"We surely did."

Reuben entered with a tray of sandwiches. He left, to return with the wine in an ice bucket; he set up the bucket on its stand and stood beside it, turning the neck of the bottle and looking inquiringly at his master.

"You can open that, Reuben, if it's cold," Anchylus said.

"Thank you, sir," Reuben said. He spoke as if he had just been granted a tremendous favor. Matt and Anchylus watched with attention as the champagne foamed into the glasses.

"Get another glass, Reuben," Anchylus said.

"Sir?"

"I said, lay up a glass, man. For yourself. We're going to drink a toast."

"Yes, sir," Reuben said.

Anchylus turned to Matt. "I don't believe in all this prayer palaver, as I said. Maybe that's why old Block irritated me so. Not personal, you know. A decent old bird in his own way, but to me the way to say goodbye to one you love isn't by pelting them with clods— Fill up, Reuben. Gentlemen, I propose a toast to my wife, Jessica, pure and stainless woman. Laid to rest this day, to be remembered forever. . . ."

"To Jessica," Matt said. Like Reuben, he followed Anchylus' example, raising his glass to the girlish, riding-habited portrait of Jessica over the mantel.

"Thank you," Anchylus said. He set his glass down empty, then pulled out his handkerchief and dabbed at his eyes.

"Wait for me until I change my clothes," he said, addressing Matt. "We'll ride down to the office." Turning in his usual brusque style, he made for the door. Reuben finished his own glass hastily and followed at a dogtrot, carrying the sandwiches and what was left of the bottle.

5   The BAGS were packed: Brad's English portmanteau and light airplane wardrobe and her own Samsonite set with the fourteen-carat initials that he had given her for a wedding anniversary, seven years ago. She remembered how much she had liked the set—how profusely she had thanked him and how delightfully, in other ways and in all ways, they had celebrated the occasion. Yet the truth was, she wished he had chosen some other gift. There had been, even then, something slightly ominous in a present which could be used only for traveling. The traveling could be enjoyed together, but there was also the intimation that its ultimate purpose could be separation.

"Seven years," she'd said, standing barefoot on the biggest of the pieces and putting her arms around his neck. "Have we honestly been married that long? It doesn't seem possible to me. Does it to you?"

She didn't remember what Brad's reply had been. No doubt it had been something affectionate and charming. On that anniversary they had still been in love with each other and the future had seemed rosy indeed: they'd had the house on Floribunda Avenue about a year, and the only cloud on the horizon had been Brad's disclosure that he would prefer a marriage without children. Sharon thought that she had come to terms with her disappointment on that score. She'd told herself that Brad was right. At the seven-year milestone his career had been the paramount project for both of them, and she had flattered herself that its successful flowering depended in no small measure on herself.

Stooping to her dressing-table mirror, she put the last touches on her make-up; she really didn't look bad, not bad at all, though it might be another story by the time she got to Washington. Straightening up, she shut her make-up kit and picked up her coat. She hated letting bellboys carry mink; they always mussed it so. You had to be careful with a natural dark mink coat, especially one that had been substituted for a family of children.

Better count the luggage. Seven pieces for herself, five for Brad. They'd be hideously overweight for the plane—not that it mattered. For a long time there had been no need to worry about expenses of any kind, let alone such minor ones as airline surcharges; now with her full title to the *Day* stock and the income therefrom, plus whatever Brad made on the side from stock profits and a possible bonus for this proxy business, they were richer than ever.

"Money, my dear," her mother had sometimes said, "does not fall in the domain of a woman. You should leave all that sort of thing to men."

So much for the wisdom of a bygone generation. There had been charm in that attitude—but was it tenable today? Sharon couldn't recall a time when money hadn't been one of her concerns, or even her major concern: she had never felt rich in the sense that Alexandra and Jessica and her father had felt rich; perhaps getting married, young, to a man who had to make his own way in the world gave you a different feeling about money. But even as a little girl she had paid attention to it. She had known it was important.

"We're checking out. Will you please have the bill ready? And send up two bellmen. Yes, they'll need a truck."

She sat down to wait, not actually in a chair but on the arm of one, since it would only be a moment; bellmen were always quick at the Mark. There would be time. Brad, who'd had to straighten out some final affairs with Pilbrick, wanted her to be ready in the lobby, and she would be there, packing done, bill paid and bellmen tipped. It had been a long time since she'd gone anywhere with Brad; it was vital that she perform her share of the preparations efficiently.

In the week that had passed since her mother's funeral she had thought a great deal about this trip and how she would conduct herself if she were allowed to make it. She had thought about it with a concentration which had increased unbearably as the hours passed and the decision remained in doubt. Brad had been very busy. That had to be taken into account. His attention had been focused on other matters. Nevertheless, he must have known what was in her mind; she had waited, with patience learned in the time of a closer, easier relationship, for him to open the subject. Opening it herself might be a mistake, but the hours had passed and the uncertainty had become more than she could stand.

One day, with a lack of premeditation which she knew she might regret, she put her fate to the decision.

"Brad," she said, "there's something I'd like to know. When you go back to Washington, do you expect me to go with you or stay here?"

He looked at her in surprise. They'd had tea sent up to the suite, a hearty tea fortified with cake and toast to tide them through until a late dinner with friends. Brad was sitting next to a tape recorder into which he had been dictating his column. The dictation had continued, interrupted with bites and gulps, throughout the little meal—an interlude which Sharon had hoped might renew their feeling of companionship. Since the stockholders' meeting and the funeral he'd had little time for her; he'd returned to the strenuous, self-centered schedule which was his usual habit and which had been so sadly interrupted during his current visit. He continued to hold the mouthpiece of the recorder in his hand, and his surprise at her question was confirmed by the fact that he had not stopped squeezing the connection switch; the twin spools of tape kept on twirling emptily and silently on their spindles.

"I do wish," she said, her determination growing with her annoyance, "you'd turn that thing off. I honestly think we ought to get this settled."

Brad set the mouthpiece in its socket, and the spools of tape, immediately still, set up an atmosphere of withheld violence in their strained, listening immobility.

"Why, for Pete's sake, kiddo, I thought it was all decided. You don't *want* to stay, do you?"

"No," Sharon said, "I don't."

"Well," Brad said with great good nature, "that's what I figured."

"But if I go," Sharon said, "I don't want it to be the way it's been before. I want to have an understanding about it."

Brad reached for a tot of rum, which had been sent up with the tea. "We've had a pretty good time, haven't we? I mean, this trip. It's been a pretty damn good trip, if you ask me."

"I know we've had a good time, Brad," Sharon said; "we generally do, if we haven't seen each other for a while—"

"You're not mad, then, are you?" He said this with his most winning smile. Downing the rum, slightly admixed with tea, he reached across the table to take her hand. Sharon drew the hand away.

"I'm not mad, Brad," she said, "but I'm all through playing games. Sure, we've had a good time. Why not? You'd just come from a yachting holiday, you were in a happy frame of mind. Let's not ask what, in addition to yachts, contributed to that. Also, I know it's been a good trip. You ran for a touchdown for Hurd-Hudner. All that's been fine. I'm not even demanding that you thank me for it; I make no demands at all except—I'd like to know whether I'm a wife or not a wife—"

"You're mixing metaphors, kiddo," Brad said, less amiably. "Touchdowns—roles."

"Maybe because I'm rather mixed myself," Sharon said. "I've been mixed for a long time."

"All right," Brad said, "let's take it from the beginning—"

"Not the beginning," Sharon said; "the beginning was perfect. Let's just take the last five years. They've been lousy. I wonder if you know or care *how* lousy."

"Have I," Brad said in a hurt way, "have I been treating you like an ex-wife?"

"I didn't say 'ex-wife—' "

"Excuse me, you said 'not-a-wife.' That would make me 'not-a-husband.' Was I behaving like not-a-husband the first night I got here when—"

"Brad," Sharon said, "when you have time for me we have fun. My point is, how much fun have we had in the time I mentioned?"

"Quite a bit. We've had trips. We've had—"

"A few weekends in Pebble Beach," Sharon said, "and a couple of months every year in Washington, so I can entertain for you. People in Washington know you have a wife who appears on the scene sometimes. When she doesn't appear you're free to do whatever you like. A perfect arrangement. You're even protected against other women who happen to get designs on you."

"*Other women!* Have you seen my name in gossip columns, have you heard scandal about me?"

"Brad—"

"I think you can apologize for that remark, Shar, or we can break off this conversation—"

"Do you want me to apologize for this too?" Sharon said dangerously. She tossed a small object onto the tea tray. It fell with a metallic but unmusical tinkle among the heavy hotel china. "I found it in your suitcase."

Brad turned the bobbypin on the palm of his hand. "Don't you think this is pretty silly?"

"Yes," Sharon said, "I do. Let me go, Brad."

He had leaned over to put his hand on her shoulder. Probably he envisaged a scene which, like their former quarrels, could be broken up, dissolved in pleasant tears, eventually in kisses, by the first show of tenderness on his part. She freed herself by rising.

"Fighting about a bobbypin," he said. "Good God, how do I know how it—"

"Maybe a chambermaid dropped it in there," Sharon said, "a chambermaid with a black permanent. Maybe you lent the suitcase to a friend. Do you really think I care? I never imagined you'd been living like a monk. I wouldn't mind what you did, as long as I came first, but when I don't come anywhere, then I mind!"

"I guess I just don't follow you, Shar," Brad said. "You do come first. You're my wife."

There was a tone in his voice she had never detected in any of their past quarrels. He was angry and unaffectedly puzzled. He was also scared. The balance of power had shifted; it had shifted in the last twenty seconds. Not because of the bobbypin, though that had been a hinge. It had shifted because of an alteration in her own purpose. She had begun talking in the immediate hope that he would take her in his arms and beg her to take the plane with him. Now she didn't want that any more, if she had ever wanted it. Two years ago, last year—perhaps even last month. Not now. She was too tired. She wasn't sure when the tiredness had come over her. Perhaps walking those few feet beside the stretcher, with her mother holding her hand. Perhaps looking at the long, shining casket as it slid down on its ropes and crunched like a ship onto the gravelly, unfathomable bottom where it would lie forever. Jessica was dead, but at least, while she'd been alive, she'd had something.

I want something, Sharon thought. And now I'm free to get it.

"A wife has to give, Brad," she said. "I don't know if I can any more."

Brad was lunging restlessly around the room. He seemed to be trying to work himself into a rage, but the fact that he was frightened was suddenly and subtly evident.

"Fine thing," he said, "can't *give*. Who's given more? You find a bobbypin and you go off into a tantrum."

He sat down and lighted a cigarette. He rolled smoke around his mounting dread. He doesn't want to lose me, she thought, and at the thought of his pain a sort of joy took hold of her. Now it's my turn to hurt, she thought.

"You said we could take things from the beginning. Maybe we ought to."

"Go ahead," he said.

If I can say and do just the right things now, I'm free. I can live again.

"Let's go back," she said, "to Indian Pipe. That summer when Anchy went there, you remember? Telling him to stay out of the club was my idea. That might seem a very trivial thing to some people. A comedy. But to me it was huge—telling my own father to stay out of a country club. What I was really telling him was to stay out of my life. My whole world of childhood, and all that, crashed down then. I didn't hate him. I did it for you—because my big, crude father was barging into our precious precinct—the existence you had made me like. Oh, sure, I wanted the house on Floribunda Avenue. I wanted children. I thought I could *really* be a wife, but—"

"Kiddo," Brad said quickly, "we're not ninety years old. If you want to raise a few kids—"

"It's too late now, Brad. Alexandra said a queer thing to me once; she said she'd had a mental . . . operation. What do you call it. Sterilization. I used to feel bursting with woman powers, and all that, but now I feel like her. That's gone and it's never coming back."

"You're nothing like her. Nothing. You're *married*. She's— Well, Shar, what's the use of— She's loose, that's all. To put it bluntly. Even if she's your sister. She's promiscuous."

Sharon gave him a long, steady look. "Brad, I shouldn't be surprised if, in the future, I were a little bit promiscuous too. I think it might do me good."

"You don't know what you're saying."

"I'm afraid I do."

"Sharon, what in hell's got into you?"

"Loneliness," she said.

"You won't be lonely any more. I see a few things that I didn't see before. I think I can promise, Shar—"

"You promised me we'd go to Acapulco too. How many zillion years ago was that?"

"We'll go. That might be a swell notion."

"Stop it, Brad."

He stopped. He sat looking at her foolishly. His face was white and drawn.

"We were talking about Zan," she said, "weren't we? I loved her too. When I was growing up I think I loved her even better than I loved my parents. One reason I kept coming back here to San Francisco, rather than moping around Washington, was to be with her. Yet when I had to make a choice between her getting *The Day* or you getting it I never hesitated. You saw what that led to, right here in this room. A cat fight. An old-fashioned hair-pull—"

"*That* was a comedy, if you like—"

"It was also the end of being sisters. Don't look so frightened. You can keep the proxies. You can get a medal from Harold Hudner and go on being a director; that can be my goodbye present to you."

Brad rubbed his mouth. He worked his lips around as if he tasted all the past and it didn't taste good. "What are you getting at?"

"I want to go away, Brad."

366

"I just said that we could."

"I don't mean us. I mean me. I want to go someplace I've never been. Paris or Istanbul or Shangri-la. Someplace. I don't want a divorce, unless you insist on it."

"I insist . . . Now, listen, will you let us talk some sense?"

"I'm talking sense," Sharon said, "for the first time in thirteen years."

"You'll be sorry for this," Brad said, threateningly and weakly; "you've had an aberration, Sharon. A mental lapse! I just don't know what's got into you, but I'll tell you this, I'll make a prophecy that within two days you come to me and say—"

"Whatever I say, Brad, I'll say now, not later, because later I might mix my metaphors. I might turn out to be just a piece of copy you were editing. You'll miss me, I'm sure, in a sort of way, but not the sort of way that would ever make me come back to you. You'll get along and I'll get along, and remember, no matter how bad you feel for a while, you'll always be Brad Iverson. No one can ever take that away from you. Please, don't hit me. You never have, but you look as if you might, and I wouldn't want that to spoil the way I feel. I feel so wonderful."

"You dirty—"

"Your vocabulary is better than that, Brad. So don't carry on. I want to remember only the nicest things about you. I'll ride back in the plane with you, if you like, and I'll be very nice to you, up to a point. We've always been nice up to a point; the only trouble was we couldn't agree on just where the point lay. You honestly look foolish standing there with your hand up that way, and I don't like you to look foolish, so if you don't mind . . ."

"Ahhhh . . ."

"If you don't mind," Sharon said, "I'll go and dress for dinner."

She sat in the lobby. She had paid the bill. One of the bellmen, properly tipped, had gone about his business; the other stood with the truck, just to the right of the lobby door. Through the glass, from her comfortable chair, she could see cars coming and going and the tall Irish doorman helping people in and out of them. Soon Brad would drive up in the Tanner limousine. She would wave to him through the glass and motion to the bellman, and the bellman and the doorman would load in the luggage and she would get in with Brad and they would drive out to the airport. On the plane Brad would offer her the choice of seats and she would sit on the aisle because he liked to sit by the window and they would have cocktails together, from the thermos in Brad's briefcase, before dinner. The rest of the time she would not interrupt him while he was working, as he was sure to do, using the briefcase as a desk. It would really not be too bad a trip. Should any of the other passengers happen to observe them it would be apparent from her rings and from their manner toward each other that they were man and wife and that in these roles they complemented each other well. No one would be able to detect that, upon arrival in the East, they would take steps toward a legal separation.

6 ANCHYLUS put the California Street house up for sale. He had tried living in it for a year after Jessica's death but it was no good; there were too many memories to plague him and, besides, the place was just too big. When it was announced that the purchaser would pull it down to build an apartment house on the same site, Letty Meeker commented with a nostalgic article.

> *. . . and thus the city* [she wrote] *will lose one of its* PRICE-LESS *landmarks. Woe and alackaday! What* AIRY BELLES *alighted in the forecourt to ascend steps hewn of Carrara marble! What* FIDDLES *played till dawn! Many San Franciscans will recall the party which Mr. and Mrs. Anchylus Saxe gave in 1934 to present their two older daughters, Pamela and Alexandra, to Society. On this occasion a* CARLOAD *of wildflowers, piny boughs and rare mountain shrubs transformed the grand ballroom into a secluded etc., etc., and the glamorous Alexandra Saxe* ELOPED *to Nevada with young Schuyler Cutting, whom she divorced to marry etc., etc. Sharon Saxe later conferred her hand on Bradley Iverson, now well known as a* COLUMNIST, *at a brilliant wedding which numbered among its guests etc. Few hostesses today can rival the charm and* ELEGANCE *of the late Mrs. Saxe, affectionately known as "Jessie," whose* UNTIMELY *death last year saddened her many etc., etc. . . .*
>
> Mr. Saxe will make his home at the Fairmont Hotel.

When she had finished writing, Letty sat quietly at her desk. It was getting on to presstime, the hour she liked best. Down in the bowels of the building now the press crew would be standing, their faces washed with a mute, soft expectancy while the warning bell rang, then the starting bell, and with a throb that passed through your bones no matter how faint, muffled and lost it was down there, the presses rolled, the raw stock slid over the rollers and bloomed with a dark skid of words, the folder whacked, and one young pressman, delegated for the job, took the first papers off the conveyer, the miracle of each day's life in the city, smelling richly of ink and damp paper.

Letty's small office was dim, lighted by a glass overhead reflector of a tired, rosy shade like a ripe peach. The air was always stuffy there. It stank of mustiness, of the cheap, old-fashioned perfume Letty used (a perfume that had once been the latest thing but was now sold in dimestores), also of dust and of the millions of words and bitter old scandals piled in the granitized filing books on the rows of shelves above and on all sides of Letty. A brooch the color and consistency of coal glowed on Letty's shirtwaist; her fleshy, patchy old arms, bare to the elbow and secured with sleeve garters, whirled with purposeful motions as she pulled the copy out of her machine and rolled in an interoffice memo sheet, complete with carbon.

To: Anchylus Saxe

Subject: Termination of Employment
From: Letty Meeker

Dear Mr. Saxe, [she wrote] today I have composed what I believe to be my last story for *The San Francisco Day*. I feel that I have passed usefulness to you. To continue covering Society, as I have done to the best of my ability for the past thirty-seven years, would have little charm or interest to me now that your family is no longer a part of the scene and that you yourself have withdrawn from it—else why would you sell your house? I have seen many changes, as have you, but you have kept your strength whereas I am getting old. I have not the wish to perpetuate myself in an era which has gone by. I must face up to the fact that I belong to the same period as the house itself, and now that it has gone, or is about to go, I should fold my tent as gracefully as possible and steal away.

Mr. Saxe, I have many news contacts in the city—it is by means of them that I have been enabled to do my job. Thus I am not unaware of the support which you have given me and the lengths to which, ignoring all costs to yourself, you have gone in defending me against my enemies. In return, all I can say is that it has been an honor to work for you. I could have asked for no better way of life. Now that it has come to

369

an end I had better break off before I become maudlin, and terminate this communication—as I have so many others—with "30," and out.

Letty rang for a boy. She sent her resignation to Anchylus' office, marking it *Private and Personal* and sealing it with Scotch tape so that Miss Wilke might thus be induced not to open it—though she probably would anyway. This done, she went home to her apartment on Twin Peaks, to her parrot, Emperor Norton, and her cat, Miss Atherton.

Letty's apartment was a conventional and, indeed, inevitable sort of place for a person of Letty's character—conventional and inevitable in every way, that is, except the manner in which the walls were decorated. The walls were unusual. On them, in large frames and small, in squares and rectangles and cutout panoramas of no ascertainable shape were photographs, several hundred of them, all of the same person: news-service shots, personal candids, shots taken by The Day, by Wide World, by Havas, and by Time-Life, all of Alexandra—Alexandra Saxe, Alexandra Cutting, Alexandra Drobny, as the case might be, in ball gowns and riding habits, in cocktail dresses, suits and furs and tennis clothes, standing at a ship's rail, at a table in the Stork Club, in the Enclosure at Ascot, at Fouquet's, at Piping Rock, at the Lido, at Menlo Park, at Loch Lomond, at Cap d'Antibe, at lunch at the St. Francis. Alexandra with many escorts, by no means all of them the husband to whom she was assigned at the moment, but always beautiful. No photographer had yet taken a homely shot of Alexandra and probably none ever would—but if this feat had been brought off Letty would never have permitted its results in her collection. She wanted before her only the perfected image of the person whom she herself would have most loved to be like. There was no way to be like her, of course: no outlet of any kind for the hopeless admiration for Alexandra which Letty had conceived when the latter had been just a little girl, an outgrowth possibly of her infatuation with Anchylus himself. There was no way to be like her because Alexandra was young and reckless, passionate and alluring, whereas Letty was, and knew herself to be, old, fat, timid and spiteful.

But even if there was no way to be like her, there was, at least, a way to get recognition. There was a way to enter into the sad, fairy-tale life lived by Alexandra, to bring about a relationship as close as that which Alexandra had with her husbands or her lovers, or even closer. You had to watch. You had to gather lore and under-standing so that you could hurt. So that you could lash out and make yourself known and felt and thus, for a moment, be a part of that person. So that, with your sting in the lovely, living flesh, you could exist awhile in that world which otherwise you must watch through a telescope, or from a hole in the ground: that world from which you were forever debarred.

Letty never tried to explain any of this to herself. To her there was nothing about it that required explanation. But there was one element that Letty did find strange and about which she often won-dered in secret. She sometimes dreamed about Alexandra, and in her dreams they were always the greatest of friends. Letty would apologize for items she had printed and Alexandra would wave her apologies away. If they were at a lawn party Alexandra would run up with a large pink bowl of sherbet for her. They would walk arm in arm in the soft, green meadows, shot with sunlight, and she would brag to everyone of how much Alexandra loved her.

The morning after sending in her resignation Letty arrived at her office with a drayman to pack up her files. She found on her desk the following memo:

> To: Letty Meeker
>
> Subject: *Staying on the Job*
> From: Anchylus Saxe
> What is all this nonsense about quitting? I expect you to run your department as long as you are strong enough to sit at a typewriter. After that you can learn to dictate.
> P.S. If you and Alexandra have had it, start a peeve with someone else and give 'em hell. That's the kind of stuff that *sells newspapers!*

7 ANCHYLUS got a good price for the house. Even the wrecking privileges proved valuable. Almost a mile of copper pipe was taken out of it. A museum in Texas bid on the orchestrion and the mechanical birds, and a Hollywood set-designer bought the ball-room chandelier, the staircase (intact) and the library paneling.

Contrary to gossip at the time, there had been no financial pres-sure behind the sale. *The Day* recovered rapidly from its slump and the dividend rate rose accordingly. It was clear that Anchylus would keep his executive control and his majority on the Board as long as he wanted them, but it was equally clear that Hurd-Hudner, which regularly elected two representatives, was slowly increasing its stock holding and would take over at his death. To this eventuality he was apparently resigned. He made one move in the next five years, and only one, to bring in some additional San Francisco money: the election of a new Board member to the seat left vacant by Dan Winkler's death—Mr. Ling Tung Chow.

Pam and Cliff Harper's third child, a boy, was born the year that Ling Tung Chow obtained his directorship. Anchylus had set up trust funds for the other two children and he did the same for the new one; the trusts consisted of cash and securities but no *Day* stock. As George Dudley, who drew the trust instrument, pointed out to one of the younger men in the probate department, people had to learn not to give away what they were going to need themselves.

Anchylus would never need cash. Nor had moving into the Fairmont diminished to any perceptible degree that standard of living which he found best suited to him. Once a month—no oftener—he drove out to Cypress Gardens to dine with the Harpers. He smoked all the pipes and cigars he wanted and drank all he cared to, and if Hugo French, who had tried to ration these tastes for him, didn't like it, that was just too bad.

Possibly the one disquieting element in a life which, in other ways, he found most satisfactory, were the rumors about Alexandra which occasionally drifted in. She was still in Sonoma but she was not—if these rumors were to be believed—behaving too well there. He didn't know. She'd lost a good deal of money when the stock fell, as it had to, after being bid up in the proxy battle. Tim Wilkins, Sr., called him once in some distress about the mortgage Pacific Midland had written on her ranch. Anchylus personally had made good the principal and interest. He was annoyed when he heard later that she'd gone up to Las Vegas and run in debt again playing some gambling game. That might not be true, of course. He waited. If she was in trouble she could always come and see him; she must certainly have heard what he'd done about the mortgage—if she'd needed an excuse to come she could have come to thank him, that was something anyone could do, say thank you.

He didn't believe in family split-ups. But often, after a long life, and a good one, you wound up with something you didn't believe in.

Time rushed by. Like a locomotive it went, with a shuddering noise that rocked the earth and sent terror to the heart. Time slipped past also in silence, glazed and still and black, immense and secret, without a sound, without a murmur. It went. That was all. In its slide, its cataract, its iron, ineluctable roaring, were all kinds of lost dreams and darkness and soaring, wild beliefs. There was the light of homely early breakfasts, the dumbwaiter ropes rattling their come-and-get-it signals, and the silver salvers of eggs, the deep-lidded dish of cereal put out for the children, Jessica in her place at the end of the table, half hidden behind the Lazy Susan. He himself, head of the house, coming in late, very gruff, very loving and highhearted, to be served and catered to. Would you like bacon this morning, darling? The big, steamy cup of mottled brownish chocolate at his right, the butter plate with the crisscrossed, not quite round butter ball and the hard French roll. The servants with their rosy or sleekly white neutral faces and the curtains parted to let in the sun that sheered up the hill out of the harbor. Ho, for the wonderful feeling of the family breakfast, the little ones in their places, the wife attentive, rosy and fresh from sweet sleep beside you, there to give quiet orders for this or that, and loving clucks and nudges of correction or suggestion so that the children would have good manners, so that they would be ladies!

Had that been the trouble, that they'd been such ladies, after all? And still the whispering panels of time sliding back before you, for the feeling of privilege, of selection, of control—the stiff, heavy, starchy napkins, a new one magically presented if a child dropped one on the floor.

(No bibs ever; bibs were plebeian.)

You had made it. You'd had all this, the wonder and flattery and hominess of it, the three faces lifted to yours, because you loved them all equally, the blonde, the redhead and the dark.

It was easy to remember. But how to reconcile the child faces and the prim, softly folded, not-yet-woman bodies with the shapely hard-faced women sitting with their men and legal hirelings, making notes, their ringed, perfumed fingers holding little gold pencils, women who had turned out to be daughters still but also enemies? You remembered the other, the stretch of world at your feet and the homely morning light of lost innocence and the strength and wholeness of the house.

Time passed. Fire the old woman. Stay out of the country club. Ha! Where did they get their poop on proxies, learn to hold the shoulders under the expensive fur turned at an angle, so upper-class, so terrible, cruel, scornful, harsh and deriding? How had they learned so much about business that even their lawyers-lackeys had to look up in the books? What had happened to the innocence, the quiet slide of peaceful days, the gentle, soaring hopes? Where had it all gone?

He sat alone often now, by preference, an old man growing a crust on him. If you locked the window, the past crept under the door. The little print shops with their sour smell and the hanging bulbs, the thump of the fodder, the initials whittled into the country-paper desks by done-to-death reporters with no more sense than school kids, and the same untidy habits. There had been a mistake somewhere. Not Red Margaret. Every man had a Red Margaret or he had missed one of the best things in life. God be good to you my Pulse and now it is time to say Goodbye . . . but a child, a child of your own. What about that? Refuse her? There were mysterious edicts written in clouds and darkness—the rulings that forced men to dress and think alike, that forced them to take refuge in tall buildings, in trees and in holes in the ground, upholstered in red, warm and easeful as death itself, the tall drink in the thin iced glass ready at hand. Men sent out in files, funneled into channels. Men with paper-thin bodies and gray faces and boneyard, blue-stained hands standing outside a warehouse where a man with a gold-headed cane looked for one who wasn't there.

"The Saxes are turning a scandal into a glory. That's making the family a law unto itself."

He had forgotten what friend of Jessica's, imbued with Solomon-like wisdom, had made that pronouncement. It didn't matter. That was how they'd had it figured, the stuffed shirts and the lorgnette crowd. He wondered sometimes what they had expected him to do.

"If you had a child by an Indian or a Hottentot it would be ours."

That hadn't fitted in with the herd laws, yet Jessica had only done what any real woman would have done, all the wild and delicate fecundity of her being going out to the lost and helpless! Jessica awake beside him, peaceful but alert, listening for the cough or the cry that meant a bad dream, hurrying into the nursery, one of her warm, soft, flannel robes pulled around her. Jessica beside the crib, leaning over to give the comfort that was needed in the secret night, in the lonely reaching of the heart. Jessica of the light, quick step so quickly turned to lead. Jessica whom nothing now would ever rouse from the place where the black box had settled on the bottom of an unplumbed black ocean.

374

Sometimes he was sorry he hadn't slugged that Bishop on the jaw. . . .

Time stood at his windows. Time slanted down the hill to the water in a million diamond panes of sparkling light and the salt air through which beat the great pulse of the fabled city and the turn of night and day and cloud and fog and the rhythm of ships passing and repassing. Anchylus came and went, his broad feet cased in polished leather, feet corned and calloused in his youth by the great roads of America, sinking softly into layered carpets.

Reuben tended to him. Dino waited outside, joking with the doorman. Room service in and out at all hours. A hand in politics. Throw the rascals out. Still the doughty smell of good cigars and the comfort of pipe tobacco. A finger in the pie. Matt Brody calling up for this or that. Grandchildren carrying on the seed of you, the newest one named after him. It could be worse, a hell of a lot worse, but there were times in the gray ash of night when he felt tired, a mountain of tiredness on him. He sat alone, a strong old man, kind, rhetorical, bad-tempered, spoiled, tough and lonely, growing a crust on ancient hurts, waiting for death, the Junkman, to knock on the door.

8 *The pickup had a homemade plywood cabin welded on with iron hoops and the cabin had curtains in the windows and a stovepipe raked back to match the twin upswept exhausts. The men standing beside the corrals watched as it came toward them, wobbling top-heavily on the rutted trail that led up from the black-top road.*

"What got you out so early, Coley?" Rancher Garvey said with heavy sarcasm.

Coley Fonce, the brand inspector, slid out from behind the wheel and lowered himself stiffly to the ground.

"Seems like every crutting outfit in the country's shipping today," he said. "I had to make the Lazy B first, five A.M. Wisht they'd give me somebody to he'p me, but I guess they won't."

"It's too durn bad, what they won't do for you," Garvey said, still annoyed at having been kept waiting. "Well, let's go."

Coley got up on the tally step and Garvey nodded to his Mexican, who pulled the gate latch and let half a dozen steers into the center

375

corral. A buckskin cowhorse had been waiting with more patience and dignity than any human present, back in a corner where the new sun made its first patch of green-brown shade; mounting, Garvey hazed the steers toward the loading chute. Either he moved in a little too fast or the animals had been made spooky by the long delay; they dodged repeatedly around the wing of the chute. The Mexican tried to help on foot and the driver of the semi from the slaughterhouse waited with the electric prod to boost them up the ramp if they ever got headed right but once more they refused to herd and Garvey sat on his horse and cursed, his face streaked with dust and sweat.

"Best way to load this bunch would be with a deer rifle," Coley said, and Garvey, "I git paid for live ones, not dead ones."

"If someone could prod them up I could hold them away from that wing," the driver said.

The suggestion made sense to Garvey.

"Maybe your wife could give us a hand, eh, Coley?"

"Why sure, Garv, I believe she will," the brand inspector said politely. "That is," he amended, "if she's awake."

Taking a few steps toward the cabin pickup, he called in a gentle, placating manner. "Baroness, honey, could you come out here for a minute?"

There was no answer, but the curtain in the nearside cabin window was no longer bunched where somebody was peeping around the edge of it and the cabin rocked a little showing there was life inside and not sleeping life either. Garvey backed the buckskin horse to get a better view and a sly, interested look came into his nail-colored eyes. The Mexican and the driver had something of the same expression— a knowing, expectant and derisive hopefulness, like spectators at a striptease. Only Coley Fonce remained proper in manner and bearing, broad and dandified in his slightly soiled but gala boots and his clean, expensive Stetson.

"We'd sure appreciate a moment of yore he'p out here, if you'd be willing, hon," he said.

Some reply, not quite distinguishable, but certainly female, came from the cabin, and Coley turned to his audience, quietly assuming the role of interpreter.

"She'll be right out," he said.

His statement was soon fulfilled. After another short delay the door of the cabin opened and a long-legged woman climbed out, her face heavy with sleep or drink or both and her thick, gray-streaked blond hair pulled up in a ponytail. Miscalculating the distance from the trailer step to the ground, she staggered but kept coming on toward

376

the fence, weaving a little, her eyes screwed up against the light and the full, hard-looking curve of her thighs bulging the dirty levis.

"Good morning, gentlemen, what seems to be the matter?" she said. "Can't the four of you load a few pisspoor runts like these without a woman's help?"

Garvey tipped his hat. "They're a little spooky, Baroness," he said, "that's all that's wrong with them."

"The hell it is," the woman said; "I suspect you spooked them just to see if I'd get out of bed."

Coley Fonce smiled in his deprecating, polite way, letting it be seen this was a joke. Nobody else seemed to think it was funny. The woman had an awful whisky breath on her. The driver got a whiff of it when she took the prod out of his hand. Nobody had to tell her what to do or where to go. She waited while the truckman moved to cover the exposed end of the wing, and the cattle, now completely encircled, closed in toward the chute, the buckskin horse shifting and weaving behind the laggards. Coley stood broad and rigid checking off the brands.

Suddenly the woman reached over the fence. She whacked the prod against the rump of the first steer, laughing as the electric charge hit him and he scrambled up the incline toward the semi. Soon that bunch was loaded and another was let in, the buckskin weaving like a boxer and the men on foot ky-yiing and the cattle kicking and shouldering and mounting each other but loading docilely now, filling the chute time after time and moving on into the semi, bellowing and wetting and grunting, the dust rising and the calves in the outside corral coughing and bawling and the sun mashing down, hotter every minute, in the hollow below the browning hills, under the bald-headed sky.